ISBN 978-1-5272-7855-4

Published by Cosmogonic Press
Printed by Micropress, Southwold, Suffolk, UK
In an edition of 750 copies

For more information see: www.sirjamesjeans.com

Address: 10 Adams Road, Cambridge CB3 9AD, UK

SIR JAMES JEANS

SCIENTIST, PHILOSOPHER AND MUSICIAN

Through Space and Time
in the first half of the 20th Century

An illustrated biography

by the late A.V. KOZENKO and C.V. JEANS

CONTENTS

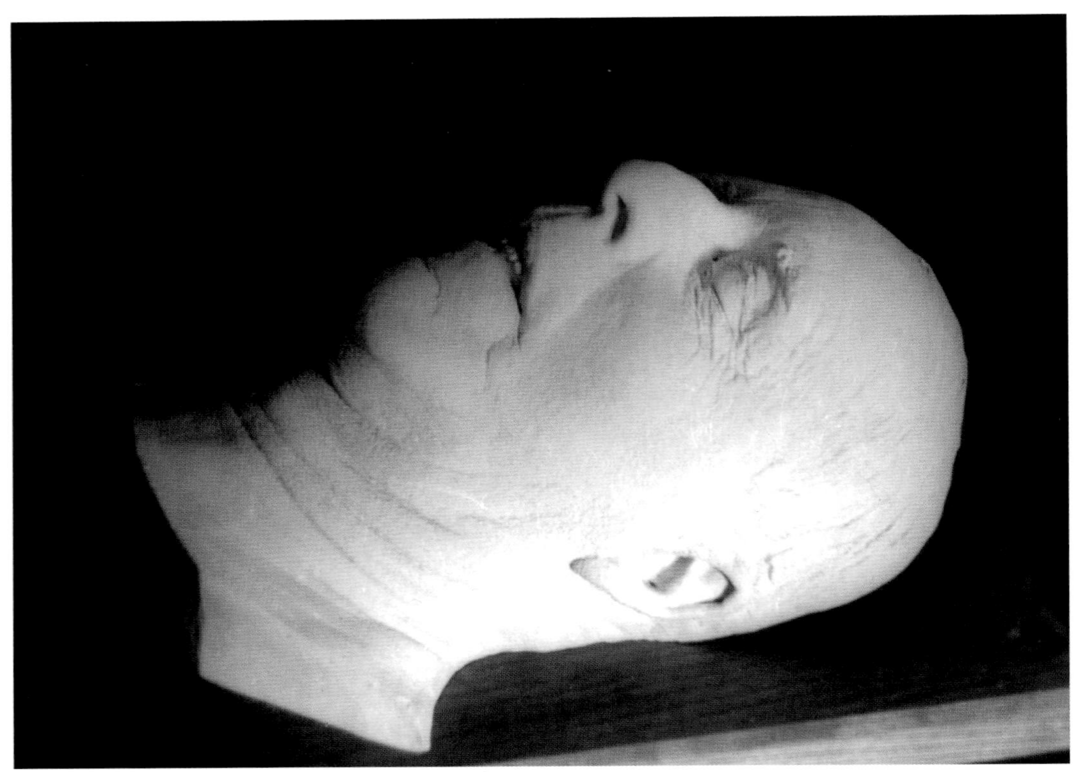

Death mask of James Hopwood Jeans donated to the Royal Society

PREFACE

On the centenary of his birth James Hopwood Jeans (1877–1946) was described as "a mathematician, astronomer, physicist, musician, a brilliant writer and lecturer one who could truly be described as a Renaissance man ... a giant in an age of gigantic developments in science and he had a great and honourable share in the making of that age".

He was also my father. What was he like, how did he live? These are questions that his young children have asked themselves during their lifetimes. There was also public curiosity about his personality with its air of distinction ... a certain magnificence ... that made him appear in some ways larger than life. This illustrated biography brings together the late A.V.Kozenko's recreation of my father's life "Сэр Джеймс Джинс: Ученый, философ, музыкант. Иллюстрированная биография" (*Sir James Jeans: Physicist, Philosopher, Musician*) published in Moscow in 2010 and the family papers and archival material held in the archives of Trinity College, Cambridge, under the care of Jonathan Smith and Adam Green. These records emphasise the important roles that his two wives played, first Charlotte Tiffany Mitchell (1876–1934) — a grand daughter of Charles Tiffany — and then Susi Hock (1911–1993) a young Austrian organist of international repute.

When my father died in 1946 I was six — the middle one of three children from Susi, his second wife — too young to have any clear memories. A familiarity of sorts came from living in and absorbing the atmosphere of Cleveland Lodge in Surrey — the rambling house with its ample grounds and magnificent views of Boxhill that my father and his first wife Charlotte had chosen to escape to from London and to have the peace of mind for their distinctive way of life. Two minutes walk away from its front door was Boxhill and Burford Bridge Station and my father could be in Central London in less than a hour to attend the numerous scientific and committee meetings during his time (1919–1929) as Physical Secretary of the Royal Society. There was his music room — the big music room as it was known to us children — little disturbed other than for our mother's annual festival concerts usually in late May or early June to coincide with the time when the rhododendrons in the garden were at their best. There was the bookcase with his various books carefully arranged with all their editions and translations, his double partners' desk with its drawers full of page proofs. In the corridor linking our mother's music room was a walk-in cupboard containing a series of enormous ledgers with all the newspaper cuttings recording the Public's reaction to our father's lectures, broadcasts, and books. The only thing that had really changed was his absence and the presence of his death mask lying peacefully on a table in the bay window overlooking the garden.

I never had any plans to be involved in a biography of my father. I knew the official biography (*Sir James Jeans. A biography by the late E.A.Milne* 1952) left a lot to be desired. After the death of my mother in 1993 the family papers came to my home in Cambridge and this brought me into close contact with the well known Russian physicist Alexander Vasilyevich Kozenko (1950–2015) and his wife Ludmila. Kozenko had a particular interest in the development of astronomy. Prior to *perestroika* he had already published accounts of the lives and scientific contributions of Eddington and Jeans, but in 1989, with an 'unofficial' invitation from my mother — and help from E.A.Gellner and the official stamp of the British Embassy in Moscow — he was able to come to England to examine the Jeans family papers both at my mother's home at Dorking while she was alive and later in Cambridge (see Appendix). From this research came the much fuller biography in Russian, "Сэр Джеймс Джинс: Ученый, философ, музыкант. Иллюстрированная биография.". The intention was for an English version to be published by Gordon and Breach but this never came about. In July 2013 Alexander Kozenko realised that he would soon be joining '*the majority*' as he put it — he was suffering from osteomyelofibrosis, the final stages of the erythremia — he asked if there was some way I could help find an English publisher. After a few futile attempts — biographies of scientists seemed to be out of fashion — I decided that there were reasons for this and by taking a novel approach and combining Kozenko's recreation of my father's life with my personal knowledge of three families — the Tiffanys, the Jeanses, and the Hocks — I hope to show that by making use of a more visual approach such a story could be of interest not just to scientists but the wider public as well.

The heart of the biography is the English translation of "Сэр Джеймс Джинс: Ученый, философ, музыкант. Иллюстрированная биография.", originally based upon a computer translation of the text provided by the author. The final transformation of this into the present text has benefited from the meticulous retranslation, editing and checking by Katerina Chernyakova, Ludmila Potapova, Shashikumar Chitre, Douglas Palmer and Keith Tritton. My role in this has been to guide this project, deal with the illustrations and provide occasional and illustrated commentary or '*asides*' making use of the abundant archival material housed largely in Trinity College, Cambridge, as well as objects that are either still within the greater Jeans family or their whereabouts are known — in order to illustrate different aspects of my parents' lives. Along the way there has been help from many institutes and people — relatives, friends, colleagues and strangers — who have gone out of their way to benefit this project. I thank them all.

ACKNOWLEDGEMENTS

The Masters and Fellows of Trinity College, Cambridge
The Master and Fellows of Darwin College, Cambridge
Royal Society
Royal Astronomical Society
Worshipful Company of Musicians
Whipple Museum, Cambridge
Royal Musical Association
British Institute of Organ Studies
Merchant Taylors Company
Merchant Taylors School
European Space Agency
University of Chicago
Yale University
Princeton University
California Institute of Technology

Paul Allitt
Nicolas Bell
Alfred Bingham
Alice Bondi
Nicholas Bradshaw
Vivien Brown
Johnathan Cable
Paul Campion
Robert Carter
Katerina Chernyakova
Shashikumar Chitre
Jeffrey Dean
Philip Diamond
John Dix
Ellen Embleton
Mary Fowler
Philip Gibbard
Sally Gilbert
Adam Green
William Griffin
Roger Griffin
Amanda Hopkinson
Adrian Jeans
Daniel Jeans
Friederike Jeans
Jennifer Jeans
Julia Jeans
Katharine Jeans
Michael Jeans
Adam Jermyn
Elizabeth Leedham-Green
Donald Lynden-Bell
Barbara Manighetti
Keith Moore
Russell Morris
Priyamvada Natarajan
Josh Noll
Guy Oldham
Jeremiah Ostriker
Sian Prosser
Anne Page
Ludmila Potapova
Martin Rees
Stephen Reed
Janice Rigby
Jonathan Smith
Philip Stickler
Nicholas Thistlewaite
Clair Treagus
Keith Tritton
Margaret Walker
Gillian Weir

Christopher Jeans
Cambridge 2020

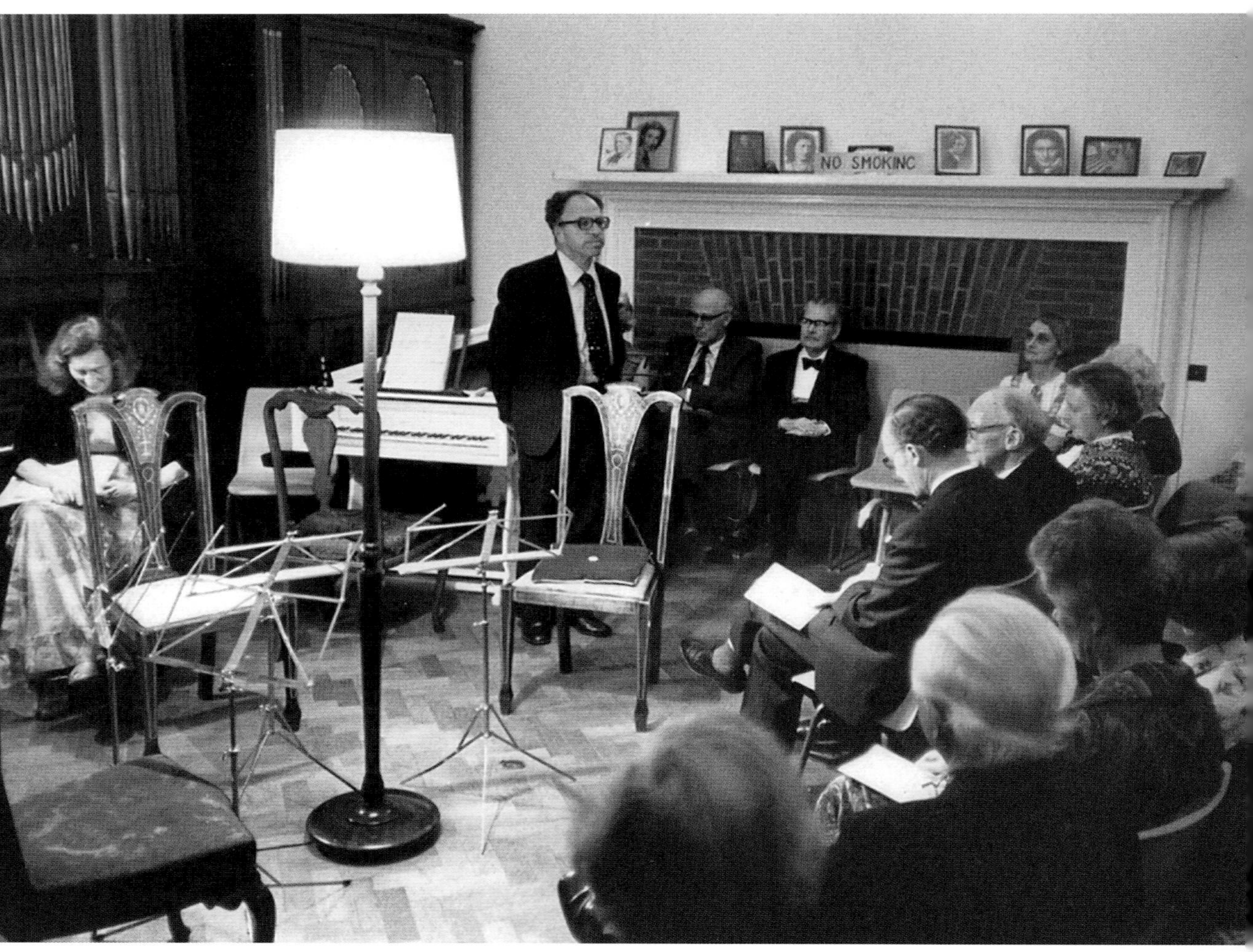

Hermann Bondi, the Austrian-born mathematician and cosmologist, giving the commemorative address at the concert celebrating the centenary of Sir James Jeans's birth on 11th September 1877. The concert was held in Jeans's music room. The wrought iron grill of the Hill, Norman & Beard organ is obscured by the two smaller instruments behind Susi Jeans (seated) — the "Manchester" Organ (early C19) to the left, the Samuel Green Organ (late C18) on the right.

INTRODUCTION

"a biography is of value only when it creates, or, certainly, recreates a character" John Galsworthy

In the autumn of the year 2000 a memorial plaque on the house in which the outstanding English scientist, James Jeans had lived and worked was unveiled, an honour accorded to only a few historical figures.

Jeans became famous in the 1920s and 1930s, not only to professional physical scientists and astronomers but also to a wide range of well-educated people in many different countries of the world. He was a leading scientist, the author of important works in the field of theoretical physics and astrophysics, and a talented popularizer of science. The range of his academic interests and his philosophical interpretation of scientific achievements, together with his style of writing, made Jeans's scientific works classic examples of writing in that genre.

In the history of science Jeans is regarded as one of the founders of theoretical astrophysics. He was one of the first skilled theoretical physicists who started working in the field of astronomy and applied the tools of theoretical physics to the investigation of heavenly objects. At the beginning of his academic career he worked on the kinetic theory of gases and radiation theory. He formulated the energy distribution in an equilibrium spectrum and then he proved it within the framework of the classical approach. This formula is referred to as the Rayleigh-Jeans law. Jeans is also the originator of the gravitational instability theory which is at the heart of modern cosmogony and cosmology. And his theory of atmospheric dissipation forms the foundation of planetary atmospheric physics.

As the years progressed Jeans became increasingly engaged in problems of astrophysics, writing fundamental works about stellar dynamics, the theory of stellar structure and evolution, and the theory of equilibrium figures for rotating structures. His tidal hypothesis for the formation of the planetary system brought Jeans his greatest fame — some of his theoretical results retain their value even today, although this hypothesis is not generally accepted.

As a Fellow of the Royal Society since 1906 and Secretary from 1919 till 1929 he contributed greatly to the development of science and industrial research in Great Britain. Participating in the first and second international thematic congresses of physicists, the Solvay Conferences, he encouraged and strengthened contacts between scientists of different countries.

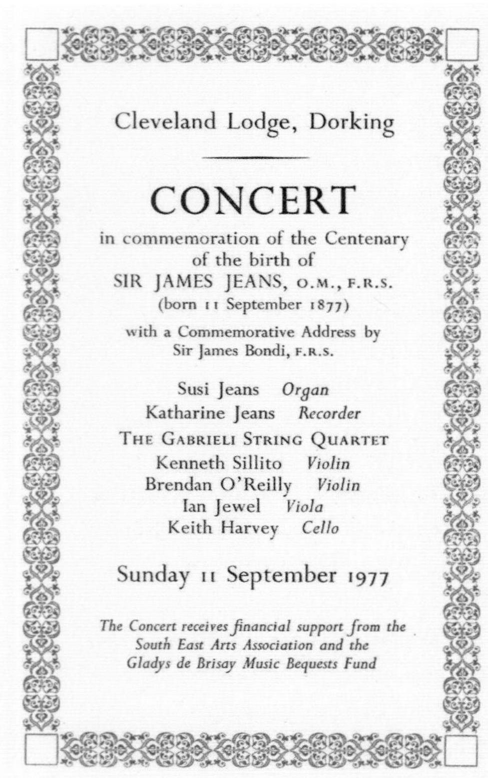

Cleveland Lodge, Dorking

CONCERT

in commemoration of the Centenary
of the birth of
SIR JAMES JEANS, O.M., F.R.S.
(born 11 September 1877)

with a Commemorative Address by
Sir James Bondi, F.R.S.

Susi Jeans *Organ*
Katharine Jeans *Recorder*
THE GABRIELI STRING QUARTET
Kenneth Sillito *Violin*
Brendan O'Reilly *Violin*
Ian Jewel *Viola*
Keith Harvey *Cello*

Sunday 11 September 1977

The Concert receives financial support from the South East Arts Association and the Gladys de Brisay Music Bequests Fund

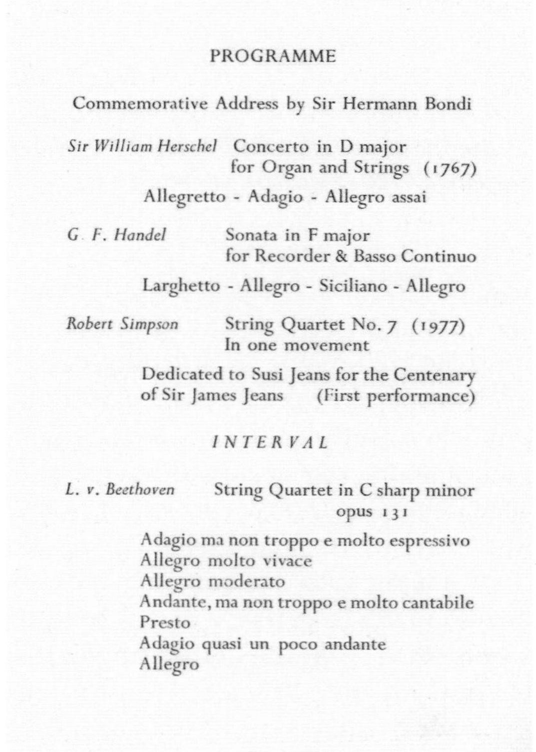

PROGRAMME

Commemorative Address by Sir Hermann Bondi

Sir William Herschel Concerto in D major
for Organ and Strings (1767)
Allegretto - Adagio - Allegro assai

G. F. Handel Sonata in F major
for Recorder & Basso Continuo
Larghetto - Allegro - Siciliano - Allegro

Robert Simpson String Quartet No. 7 (1977)
In one movement
Dedicated to Susi Jeans for the Centenary
of Sir James Jeans (First performance)

INTERVAL

L. v. Beethoven String Quartet in C sharp minor
opus 131
Adagio ma non troppo e molto espressivo
Allegro molto vivace
Allegro moderato
Andante, ma non troppo e molto cantabile
Presto
Adagio quasi un poco andante
Allegro

Programme of the concert given at Cleveland Lodge on 11th September 1977 to commemorate the birth of Sir James Jeans.

In 1977, to mark the 100th anniversary of his birth, a concert was held on his birthday — 11th September — in Cleveland Lodge, his former home. Organized by the scientist's widow Lady Jeans, it took place in his music-room with its big organ designed by Jeans himself. Many eminent British scientists attended. On October 14th in the same year, the Royal Astronomical Society celebrated the anniversary with a memorial meeting, which was opened by the President of the Society, Professor Sir Alan Cook. Professor William McCrea referred to Jeans as "a great pioneer of modern astrophysics" and reflected on the character of Jeans's work. "There is a story that after his brilliant undergraduate career, Jeans had called upon Sir Joseph Larmor to ask if he would care to offer any suggestion as to problems upon which Jeans might then start working. Legend has it that Larmor rounded upon him and said, 'What is the world coming to if a young man needs to be *told* what to work on?' .... If indeed, true, the experience could explain why Jeans was a lone worker for the rest of his days — so far as I know, he never collaborated with anyone." Remembering Jeans as a person, McCrea said: "In the idiom of our time, Jeans was a 'private man". From early youth, music was his chief relaxation. Most clearly his chief happiness was in his family and his home." [185, p. 163]. According to McCrea, Jeans suffered from shyness and uncertainty in communication with strangers, who sometimes considered him arrogant; in fact, he was a considerate, modest and generous person. McCrea quoted Sydney Chapman, who wrote in *The Dictionary of National Biography*, that Jeans was 'A shy and sensitive spirit'. Professor Martin Rees stressed the distinguished and unique role of Jeans's theory of gravitational instability in cosmogony and cosmology.

In the same year the famous Russian astrophysicist J. S. Shklovsky wrote: "We are very far from making light-hearted comment about the outstanding research works of the pioneers in cosmogony — Laplace, Poincaré, and especially Jeans, whose basic theory of gravitational instability pervades the whole of modern cosmogony … Every academic problem is solved in due time and the time for solving classic problems of cosmogony is upon us" [282, p. 100].

The Moscow astronomer Yu. N. Efremov states that "Jeans's work on gravitational fragmentation of diffuse material now remains in the core of the theory of stellar origins", [253, p. 373]. Efremov singled out two main approaches in the development of cosmogony: "The classical one is associated with the names of Einstein, Friedman, Lemaître, Hubble, Baade, Sandage, Zeldovitch and others. The other — referred to as heretical, radical or romantic — by Jeans, Dirac, Hoyle, Bondi and Gold, Ambartsumyan, Arno, Burbidge and others. Supporters of this 'heretical' approach come from different perspectives and do not always refer to each other, but they are all certain that observational data from extragalactic astronomy require generalization and modifications of existing physical laws for the explanation of a 'new physics'. The 'classicists' consider that the expansion of the Universe must have started from a density much higher than the nuclear one". [253, p. 391]. Of course this separation is only relative, and Efremov himself admits that Jeans is generally "a classic", and not "a romantic". Actually, Jeans was known for his consistent application of methods in theoretical physics to heavenly objects: he said the "ultimate aim is to weld cosmical physics onto terrestrial physics so as to form one all-embracing science".

The George Darwin lecture of 1975: "Does astronomy need new physics?," given by the Russian theoretical physicist V. L. Ginsburg (Nobel Laureate in 2003), was devoted to the same principal problem. Although Ginsburg relegated Jeans to the "radicals", he remarked on his outstanding role in astrophysics of the 20th century. He said that, ironically, those developments which Jeans thought needed "new" physical laws, found an explanation within the theory of gravitational instability developed by Jeans himself.

But recently the "romantic" approach has resurged. With observational evidence of the existence of dark matter (hidden mass) and the speeding-up of the cosmological expansion of the Universe as a result of dark energy — 'antigravity' — which contributes about 90% of the energy density of the Universe — it has become clear that we do not know the origins of the hidden mass or dark energy. It has also become clear that about 95 per cent of the whole mass of the Universe consists not of protons and neutrons, electrons and neutrinos, nor some other elementary particles now familiar to physics, but of **something** totally unfamiliar to modern science. It has a totally different origin, and even today we do not really know how to explore this **something**.

Perhaps Jeans's idea about "new" physical laws will be useful. Of course, these new physical theories will not replace the long-standing classical schemes of theoretical physics, but will be more far-reaching assimilations of new data and ideas dealing with extreme situations. Furthermore, energies much greater than those achieved in accelerators on Earth are required to verify modern theories of unified field and elementary particles. Therefore progress of micro-physics has become impossible without exploring the large-scale events in the Universe. We can see that the unification of these two branches of science — elementary particle theory and cosmology — is taking place. This union of the world of micro- and macro-physics, not originally foreseen, was not only predicted by but arose from Jeans's works.

Understanding the personality of such a scientist as Jeans provides an insight into the manner and style of one of the movers of scientific progress. The character of the researcher may have a significant and sometimes determinative influence on his work. Philosophical, religious and socio-political points of view of a thinker on such a scale are of substantial interest. In this biography the author has attempted not only to write about events of his personal life, but also to illustrate his development as a scientist, a philosopher and a popularizer of science.

GROWING UP IN THE 19th CENTURY

By the last quarter of the 19th century, the United Kingdom had reached the zenith of its power. Victorian prosperity owed much to the fact that for a whole century the country was not involved in major wars nor was it threatened by serious danger from outside. Protected by the biggest naval fleet in the world, the island solved its social-political problems in peace and safety.

The wealth accumulated in mid-Victorian times greatly softened the burden of social problems. This wealth was truly huge. In the 1870s the foreign trade of the United Kingdom surpassed the combined trade of France, Germany and Italy, and was three or four times higher than that of the United States of America. Thanks to the activities of the trade unions and the spreading of the cooperative movement, the national income started to be distributed more equally.

Trade unions began to play a political role in England and the electoral reform of 1867 brought suffrage to numerous classes of workers. In 1868 William Gladstone, from a family of Liverpool merchants, was elected leader of the Liberal Party. Although representatives of old families remained in the party, it increasingly represented the interests of the industrial bourgeoisie. It ruled English political life, it introduced the 'low tax, low spend' Gladstonian liberalism and implanted the liberal ideas of Bentham, Cobden, Mill and Spencer. After a four-year discussion in the press, Gladstone's government passed in 1871 the Trade Union Act making membership of trade unions legal for the first time.

Active leaders of the trade-unions — supported by the philosopher John Stuart Mill — made new demands. They objected to the so-called Manchester point of view that salary must be regulated by natural market forces of demand and supply. After 1871, those leaders started to encourage trade unions to vote against the Liberals. This resulted in the unexpected victory of the Conservatives in the 1874 election.

In the first year, Disraeli's government gave into all the demands of the trade unions. The Master and Servant Act 1867 was replaced by The Employers and Workmen Act 1875. Labour unions maintained their rights as legal entities, but all restrictions were eliminated and picketing, amongst other peaceful actions, was allowed. Such steps reduced social stress in Society and were successful tactics in the fight against the Liberals and their leader Gladstone.

When the Conservatives returned to power, their leader Benjamin Disraeli was 69. A popular writer, descendant from an episcopized well-to-do Jewish family, he had been an elected member of Parliament since 1837. He was an unusual Tory. Although he did not like the aristocracy — whose arrogance he had experienced in the first years of his political career — he stressed his admiration for the Monarchy and titles in every possible way. He always defended orthodox Anglicanism and English nationalism. Earlier the Conservative Party had represented the interests of landlords and employers, but under Disraeli it also supported the interests of the industrial middle class and the working class.

The Conservatives were most popular in England and were supported by the Anglican Church; the Liberals were popular in Wales, Scotland and Ireland. Parties were learning new techniques of canvassing — open-air meetings, hustings, illustrated posters etc.

As leader of the Conservatives Disraeli emphasized the three main principles of his politics called 'New Toryism': saving the national church, protecting the unity of the British state, improving the condition of the masses. He was the head of the Conservative Cabinet for six and a half years (1874–1880). In foreign policy, he had recommenced war in the colonies in order to protect the interests of the home country. In 1875–1876 he organized a ceremonial trip to India for the Prince of Wales, heir to the throne, after which Queen Victoria was declared Empress of India. From then on the term "British Empire' was officially used. In the same year, in recognition of his services, the Queen conferred a peerage on Disraeli with the title of Lord Beaconsfield.

After his death Disraeli was greatly admired as the regenerator of Toryism. He said: "I suppose, that now the Tory Party is occupying a more advantageous position than ever since the death of its greatest representatives, Pitt and Lord Grenville, it is free of the ties that were alien to its natural development ... Now we are leaving behind that period of fiscal tasks ... but there are other problems ... that will soon take the attention of the whole country: it is a question about prerogatives of the Constitutional Monarchy, a question of whether the aristocratic principle will be recognized in our Constitution, whether the House of Commons will comprise one of ranks of the Kingdom or will evolve into a disorderly crowd; whether the national Church will be saved". [226, p. 68–69]

Disraeli suggested that one of the basic tasks of the English Constitution was to ennoble talented and meritorious people, ignoring their origins. The historian G. Trevelyan wrote:

> Yet already "society was getting mixed", and men of mere wealth, like Sir George Midas in Du Maurier's *Punch* pictures, had been

prominent in London drawing-rooms for twenty years before the Queen died — the more prominent perhaps for being still somewhat exceptional. 'Society', in the older and stricter sense of the term, had still in Palmerston's day been a limited world, its entry closely guarded by certain Whig and Tory peeresses. But in the eighties 'society' had a vaguer meaning, perhaps covering the whole of the upper and professional classes, perhaps including all the well-dressed men and women, who crossed and recrossed each other in Hyde Park parades, or made conversation during the innumerable courses of a London dinner-party. Yet, as John Buchan truly records, these people maintained, at least in the capital, a certain aristocratic flavour and convention until the end of the century. They were different from the well-to-do bourgeois of the provinces, who still in Yorkshire and Lancashire preferred 'high teas' to dress dinners". [272, p. 588]

The English statesman and historian John Buchan (1875–1940), Governor-General of Canada (1935–1940) described in his memoirs London society of his youth on the eve of the South African Boer War of 1899:

"London at the turn of the century had not yet lost her Georgian air. Her ruling society was aristocratic till Queen Victoria's death and preserved the modes and rites of aristocracy. Her great houses had not disappeared to become blocks of flats. In the summer she was a true city of pleasure, every window box gay with flowers, her streets full of splendid equipages, the Park a show ground for fine horses and handsome men and women. The ritual went far down, for frock-coats and top-hats were the common wear not only for the West End, but about the Law Courts and in the City. On Sunday afternoons we dutifully paid a round of calls. Conversation was not the casual thing it has now become, but was something of an art, in which competence conferred prestige. Also Clubs were still in their hey-day, their waiting lists were lengthy, membership of the right ones was a stage in a career .... Looking back, that time seems to me unbelievably secure and self-satisfied. The world was friendly and well-bred as I remember it, without the vulgarity and the worship of wealth which appeared with the new century".
(John Buchan, *Memory Hold-the-Door*, 1940, pp. 92–4)

Righteousness, the strict adherence to moral and religious rules, penetrated all spheres and social strata of the Victorian era. Queen Victoria herself was an example of strict abidance by moral rules. The most popular characters were religious people such as the missionary David Livingstone

— the explorer of Africa — and the philanthropist General Gordon. Sunday, "the Lord's Day", was kept by families for worship and rest, disturbed only by attending a church service, bible reading and visiting relatives. This was particularly widespread in the upper and middle classes of society. In 1889, the Provost of King's College, Cambridge, wrote: "most of you come from homes, where family prayers are the custom … ' [272, p. 591]. This was in spite of the fact that academics in Oxford and Cambridge Universities had been freed in 1871 by The Universities Tests Act from swearing allegiance to the Church of England. By the end of the century the teaching staff of Oxford and Cambridge was already secular. They were allowed to marry, while still remaining a member of college. Academic subjects included not only theology, philosophy, philology, ancient history and mathematics, but also a wide range of natural sciences, modern and recent history. Finally, it led to a marvellous and rich flowering of scientific research in English universities.

Trevelyan has described the situation in the country and the political class of this period where intellectuals not only shared points of view of the political class, but formed this ruling class itself:

> "The liberal-minded and highly educated governing class of the 'seventies were more nearly affiliated to the universities than to the declining aristocracy or the rising plutocracy. Gladstone abolished patronage in all public offices and made competitive examination the normal entrance to the Civil Service. To select men for practical careers on the report of examiners had seemed an absurd proposal to Palmerston and the aristocratic politicians of the previous era. It was a compliment paid to the reputation of the Oxford and Cambridge system of examination for degrees, and it had the effect of making closer than ever the connection of university men with public life. Trained intellect was henceforth to be a young man's best passport, instead of social patronage or fashionable friends." [272, p. 594]

From the beginning of the second half of the 19th century university graduates started to play a considerable role in reforming British Society. The historian J. Roach referred to them as the "special class of educated people, which identified character of national mind on political, religious and cultural problems and who could be called the national intellectuals" [322, p. 134]. This led to the so-called 'Victorian consensus', held by the British elite at the end of the 19th century, allowing Great Britain to become the leading world power. This was a synthesis of national identity and religious behaviour. It was only possible because the intellectuals shared the views of the ruling class. It was not a blind conformism and dependence on 'the powers that be'. The independence of 'the intellectuals' was expressed not in "defence of indefinite overall interest, but in freedom to provide proper (usually professional) interest without ideological madness" [316]. The main principle was professionalism and competence in community service and social trust and this elevated the specialist, the representatives of "the intellectuals", above the ordinary people. Already in the middle of the 19th century one of the first representatives of this group a lawyer G. Thomson wrote: "These are the professionals, who are in the forefront of the great English middle class, establish character of its independence, identify moral standards and direct its mind." And further: "If they take a position in society, it happens only thanks to their activity, but not by reason of their origin, heritage, or wealth: their supremacy is a result of their recognition." [323, p. 16, 27, 68]

In 1880–1890 such public figures as Beatrice and Sydney Webb among the British intellectuals, were promoting the development of professionalism, including occupational education and further training. "They wanted to change the world in order to give importance to an expert and a skilled administrator as opposed to a slow politician and a selfish industrial worker." [304, p. 42]

These ideas of developing professionalism can be seen in the context of social reform. It became fashionable among the elite to live in working class areas, to form settlements there — Toynbee Hall in the East End of London was the most famous among them. The Liberal leader, D. Asquith, referred to them as a social laboratory.

The British intellectuals began to create night- and Sunday-schools for the poor, they organized public lectures. The Movement for Higher Education was strengthened. An emphasis was placed on moral, religious, ethical aspects in the problem of poverty. As Beatrice Webb said, "a new ferment of thinking and feeling, new realization of shame were working out." [326, p. 179]

She and many other English intellectuals gave their countrymen a sense of shame for the society which did not provide people with a good life. This "social shame" was not the same as personal sin or fault: "Ruskin and Morris were surrounded with beautiful things in their houses, D.S. Mill was not unfaithful to his comfortable life-style, and H.M. Hyndman was famous for his mode of dress, usual for members of the most fashionable clubs in West-End". [326, p. 180] These intellectuals were not on the fringe of English society, so they were able to reform it; Henry Hyndman was a barrister, privately schooled, a graduate of Trinity College, Cambridge; Sydney Webb was the Secretary of State for the Colonies and Dominion Affairs.

By the end of the Victorian era there was the conviction that a skilled person is a stabilizing element for social order. Together with such elements of Victorianism, such as the Crown, Parliament and the Church, power was personified also in outstanding rulers of the Empire, notable doctors, lawyers, and scientists. In 1886–1914 a fifth of the peers were professionals. In 1911 the income of representatives of the top professions was 4.7 times higher than the salary of semi-skilled workers, the majority among the employed.

In the 20th century the English intellectual aristocracy fulfilled not only the functions of research and education, but influenced the political world indirectly, moulding the social mind as well as more directly in Parliament and political clubs, both with personal contacts as well as in its role in the activity of influential organizations.

The elections of 1906 brought the Liberals back into power, and the subsequent passing of such laws as The Trade Disputes Act 1906, The Old-Age Pensions Act 1908, The Coal Mines Act 1908 that granted miners an 8 hour day and The National Insurance Act 1911 implementing illness, disability and unemployment insurance for the first time ever in the world. Spearheaded by Sydney and Beatrice Webb, the Left Liberals formed "a club for supporters" holding liberal policies. Experts of the highest standing joined: law — R.B. Haldane; economy — Sydney Webb; literature — H.G. Wells; science — Bertrand Russell.

So the tradition of the cooperation of political power and the intellectuals — concerning social reforms — were basically founded then.

~~ • ~~

James's father William Tulloch Jeans, born on the 1st of October 1847, belonged to that class of professionals. The surname Jeans itself is a French form of the names John and Johnson. His father, grandfather, and other relatives were involved with newspapers and William became a journalist. Being a native of Scotland, he was initially a town employee in Elgin for some time. The Jeans clan was represented in many other professions. Frank Jeans was a surgeon in the Liverpool Royal Infirmary, a lecturer at the University of Liverpool, and a Fellow of the Royal College of Surgeons. Two more Jeanses were well known artists. Philip Jean, born on the island of Jersey, became famous for his portraits and miniature paintings. The other Jeans, Charles Henry, worked as a limner in various magazines: many stamps of Great Britain were made based on his paintings, and his best pictures are now in the British Museum.

Possibly they all had a mutual forefather, Henry Jeanes, who was a vicar in Kensington and published some theological works in the 17th century.

James's father worked mostly in political journalism in parliament representing *The Globe* newspaper in the House of Commons. For a quarter of a century he worked in the press gallery of Westminster starting in the early 1870s. He was never a party member but supported the Liberal points of view.

James's mother: Martha Anne Jeans (née Hopwood: 22nd April 1843–26th August 1935).

James's father: William Tulloch Jeans (1st October 1847–25th February 1907).

William and Martha Jeans in their garden, pre 1907.

NEWSPAPERS AND THE JEANS CLAN

The Jeans clan had an association with newspapers and journalism that stretched from the mid 19th Century to the latter part of the 20th Century. Both James and his parliamentary correspondent father (William Tulloch Jeans) had journalism and the ability to communicate in their genes.

The first Jeans newspaper — The Elgin & Morayshire Courier — was established in 1845 in Elgin in NE Scotland by Robert Jeans, who was the brother of John, James's grandfather. Robert ran a printing business in Elgin and his younger brother Thomas was a printer compositor who may have been employed in the family business. William Jeans (born ca.1840) the eldest son of Robert was a parliamentary correspondent for the Dundee Advertiser; his son Herbert was chief editor of Reuters (Glasgow Herald of 3rd March 1934). A cousin Robert Stephen Jeans (ca.1843–?) was a newspaper owner living in London. And, three generations of Jeanses dominated the newspaper world of Liverpool. Alexander Gregor Jeans (1849–1924) arrived in Liverpool in the mid–19th century as the general manager of the Daily Post, he set up the Liverpool Echo in 1879. He was succeeded by his son Allan, and later by his grandson Alexander who became managing director and editor in chief of the Daily Post and the Liverpool Echo at the end of 1957. Alexander Jeans was president of the Newspaper Society in 1959 and served as both a chairman of the Press Association and a director of Reuters. He was knighted in 1967. He died in 1972 at the age of 59, and at his funeral he was described 'as a true servant of Merseyside, and a man of great integrity, respected by all who knew him'.

In 1876, at the age of 29, he married Martha Anne Hopwood, a very religious woman. She was a native of Stockport in Lancashire, which straddles the River Mersey south of Manchester. Martha came from an old Protestant family of craftsmen producing watches and other instruments. One of her forefathers was a churchman, heading an Independent community in Oliver Cromwell's time. His small chapel still exists. It is located at Marple, Cheshire, and was used as a school for two centuries. Records list the births in the Hopwood family:

James Hopwood, born April, 20th, 1814.
Hannah Hopwood, born December, 2nd, 1817.
Martha Hopwood, born July, 19th, 1840 at twenty minutes past five, morning.
Martha Anne Hopwood, born April, 22nd, 1843 at twenty five minutes to six, night.
Sarah Hopwood, born July, 21st, 1845 at half past one, afternoon.
John Hopwood, born May 29th, 1848 at twenty minutes past two, afternoon.
Mary Hopwood, born November 19th, 1852 at twenty minutes past six, morning.
Lucy Elizabeth Bartle Hopwood, born March 6th, 1856 at eleven o'clock at night.

William was notable for his latitude of thought and his Scottish blood infused him with special vitality. His colleagues from Fleet Street often asked him for help in difficult cases as he had an exceptional knowledge of the workings of Parliament. He never refused them.

He was not only a journalist but also expert in the field of economics and industrial development. He was interested in science and realized the necessity to explain it to the public, as the atmosphere of the Victorian age was steeped in science. He wrote two books: *Creators of the Age of Steel* (313a) and *Lives of The Electricians* (1887). The second book started the genre of scientists' biographies.

William Jeans starts his *Creators of the Age of Steel* with a quote of Richard Cobden (1804–1865) — one of the leaders of free-traders and their main ideologist — "Our wealth, commerce, and manufactures grow out of the skilled labour of men working in metals" Actually most people were not interested in problems of metallurgy, as they did not know either how it had contributed to industrial production or how it had bettered their lives. William Jeans tried a direct way of leading his readers into all these facts by simply describing the lives and achievements of the greatest innovators of metallurgy, such as Sir Henry Bessemer (1813–1898) who created the

Bessemer process of steel making, Sir William Siemens (1823–1883), the inventor of the regenerative furnace, Sir Joseph Whitworth (1803–1887), an engineer and inventor who created a standard system for cutting screw threads.

Writing about the activity of these famous engineers, William Jeans dealt also with more common problems in the development of science. He even discussed the *Dissertation on the Progress of Mathematical and Physical Science* by J.D. Forbes (1809–1868) — a Scottish physicist who studied the thermal conductivity of metals and discovered its dependence on temperature. Jeans applied Goethe's ideas that in a biography a person should be described within all the settings of his time. In addition to describing the lives and ancestors of these inventors, *The Creators of the Age of Steel* told its readers about the economic and social significance of their inventions.

The Times wrote:

> "To the average mind there is little romance associated with steel, and yet the record of its manufacture is probably charged with more genuine interest than attaches to any other branch of British industry ... That steel has had a remarkable history no one will doubt after reading this attractive volume by Mr. Jeans, who evidently writes from fulness and accuracy of knowledge. The reader will rise from its perusal not only interested in the personal struggles of the inventors dealt with, but also au fait with all the more important processes of steel manufacture ... The account of Sir Henry Bessemer's career is most entertaining ... Mr. Jeans's volume deserves a wide circulation."

But William felt that, much as he tried to write an interesting and popular book, it was not easy to read. *Lives of the Electricians* dealing with John Tyndall (1820–1893), Charles Wheatstone (1802–1875) and Samuel Finley Breese Morse (1791–1872) is much easier. It is obvious that William Jeans was an admirer of the famous English physicist and popularizer of science, John Tyndall, about whom he wrote: "... by his teaching and writing he has probably done more than any other man in England to kindle a love of science among the masses; and by his life he has set an example to students of science which cannot be too widely known or appreciated."

William Jeans died at the age of 59 on the 25th of February 1907. His wife Martha Anne Jeans outlived him by 28 years and died on the 26th of August 1935 at the age of 92.

~~ • ~~

James Hopwood Jeans was born on September 11th, 1877, in Ormskirk, near Southport in Lancashire. It was a big centre of trade in the low country between the estuaries of the Mersey and Ribble. It was already considered a suburb of Liverpool, which vied with London for being the premier trading port in the world.

When James was one and a half the family moved to Brighton on the Sussex coast. Memories of the sea were one of his strongest impressions. Through the eyes of the famous French geographer Élisée Reclus writing in the late 19th Century:

> "Brighton can neither boast of a beach presenting unusual facilities to bathers, nor is its climate very mild, nor the scenery of the surrounding county very attractive. It is indebted to its good fortune to the circumstances of having been built under the same meridian as London, and on a part of the south coast most readily accessible by train. Brighton is, in fact, a mere suburb of London. It has grown into a popular town though, owing to the favour extended to it by Londoners, and though having no other industries than its fisheries and the entertainment of visitors, it numbers 100,000 inhabitants, or 150,000 during the season, being in this respect the equal of many important manufacturing or commercial towns. Hundreds of merchants whose places of business are in London have chosen Brighton as their residence, and almost every morning they travel up to their offices and return thither in the afternoon. By degrees Brighton has come to be looked upon as the queen of watering places on the south coast of England, and its fine museums, in the curious Pavilion which George IV erected as a marine residence, unrivalled Aquarium, opened in 1872, schools, and other public institutions entitle it to rank amongst the foremost towns of England." [260, p. 98]

When James was nearly five, the family moved to London. They first lived on Tulse Hill, then Clapham Park as it was very convenient for the head of the family to be close to Parliament.

James was a highly precocious child with an exceptional memory. When he was three he could already tell the time and by four he could read. An aunt taught him reading and writing. He read everything he could get hold of and sometimes even read to his parents an editorial from *The Times*. James had two younger sisters Gertrude Mary (born 1st of February 1884) and Margaret Louise (born 1879). All his life he was especially close to Gertrude.

James's childhood was not a happy one. The atmosphere at home was very Victorian and Puritanical. His mother with her strong belief and devotion taught him to pray before and after breakfast, dinner and supper and at bed

James's sister: Margaret Louise Jeans (circa 1879–1968) as a young woman.

James's sister: Gertrude Mary Jeans (1st February 1884–June 1974) as a young woman.

James Hopwood Jeans 2 years and 2 months old.

James, the young gentleman, with his pocket watch and his two sisters, Margaret (centre) and Gertrude (standing) ~1886.

time. The family went regularly to church on Sundays. For the other family members religion was just a part of their everyday life, as was common in Victorian England. For James it was not so easy to accept this, although religion was beyond doubt for him until the end of his life, yet he never had an anthropomorphic view of God.

Already in childhood he was uncomfortable about Christian myths on the origin of the world and of other natural events. He preferred to develop his own interests. Getting older, he was more and more engaged in technical matters and science. He took long walks around London alone and cycled to the nearest villages.

London was then the most populous city on Earth.

E. Reclus noted:

"London, unlike Paris, in this respect, has no collective personality. It is not, strictly speaking, a town at all, possessed of a well-defined individuality, and differing in any marked way from the towns in any other parts of Britain. Its growth has been too rapid to enable it to develop a well-defined character of its own. Like a plant whose sap rises too quickly, it has not displayed the firmness of contour and special physiognomy which are the characteristics of organisms of slower growth. London, very unlike Paris and most of the great cities of the continent, has not grown around a kernel, but is an agglomeration of distinct towns, amongst which the City of London, Westminster, and Greenwich were the most considerable. The vast metropolis is the outcome of a combination of numerous towns and villages placed in continuity to each other. This mode of growth prevented London from acquiring a distinctive personality. It is above all an assemblage of distinct worlds — warehouses, banks, factories, princely dwellings and villas — each world having its proper physiognomy and history." [260, p. 131]

At the end of the 19th century there were not many buildings from before the 17th century in London as the result of the Great Fire (1666) which destroyed six-sevenths of its buildings. Exceptions are the Tower and a few minor houses, the Norman Church of Saint Bartholomew, the Round Church of the Templars built between 1185 and 1240, and St. John's Gate which belonged to the hospital of the Knights of St. John.

The capital of the Empire was a political and cultural centre. The British Museum, one of the richest in the world, was famous for its unique collections and its library with more than half a million books and manuscripts. Scholars from all countries worked in the reading room of the Museum. The National Gallery on Trafalgar Square, many other galleries and museums, theatres and libraries were accessible for the general public. This is the environment that Jeans grew up in and his father always encouraged the boy's intellectual development, whereas his mother had a rather narrow view of the world. His father's influence apparently prevailed.

His father was then writing a book about scientists and James also tried to write about things that he was interested in. The earliest of his surviving childhood works is a small book with a blue cover, dated January 19th, 1885, which is already the 4th of a series (the first three are missing). It contains a variety of reference data, for example, the population of the United Kingdom, of individual counties and London, calendar, the reign of kings and queens, as well as time intervals with a count of seconds in an hour, a day, a month, and a year. This shows that, when he was only 7, James could already deal with seven-digit and higher numbers. The book also contains numerous childish drawings. Jeans was fond of working with numbers and remembered them very easily. When he was seven, he amused himself by multiplying the licence numbers of cabs. Reading his father's books, he came across a table of logarithms. Although he could not understand what they were for, he easily remembered the first twenty values. In the Jeans family they remembered an instant, when his mother had forgotten her train ticket but James could provide its number to the ticket collector.

During the long Church services, which he had to attend, Jeans thought much about perpetual motion and about a machine capable of infinite movement, but he also listened to music with pleasure. He appeared to have perfect pitch, and he started piano lessons, again thanks to one of his aunts. By the time he was 12 he already played the organ. His favourite composer was J.S. Bach.

But watches enthused him most of all. Childish drawings of his show clocks of all shapes and sizes, sometimes he even drew a small shop with rows full of watches. In that era the sitting rooms of most houses had massive long-case clocks, and clocks on the mantelpiece, the tables or the walls. When his father gave him a pocket watch in 1886, James wrote a very small book of twelve pages in a light blue cover, "CLOCKS BY J. JEANS". It was beautifully illustrated and the text contained the main principles of clock mechanism and provided detailed descriptions of their construction and some other information including prices. These childhood interests show Jeans's love of intellectual pursuits.

There was the problem of choosing a school suitable for his natural abilities. Schools in England varied greatly, some were founded by rich individuals, others by the Church and worshipful companies such as Merchant Taylors. By the last quarter of the nineteenth century many primary schools were state-funded however almost no secondary ones were.

The little book "CLOCKS BY J. JEANS" dated 1886.

Drawings by the young James Jeans (~1886): A shop window full of clocks and watches.

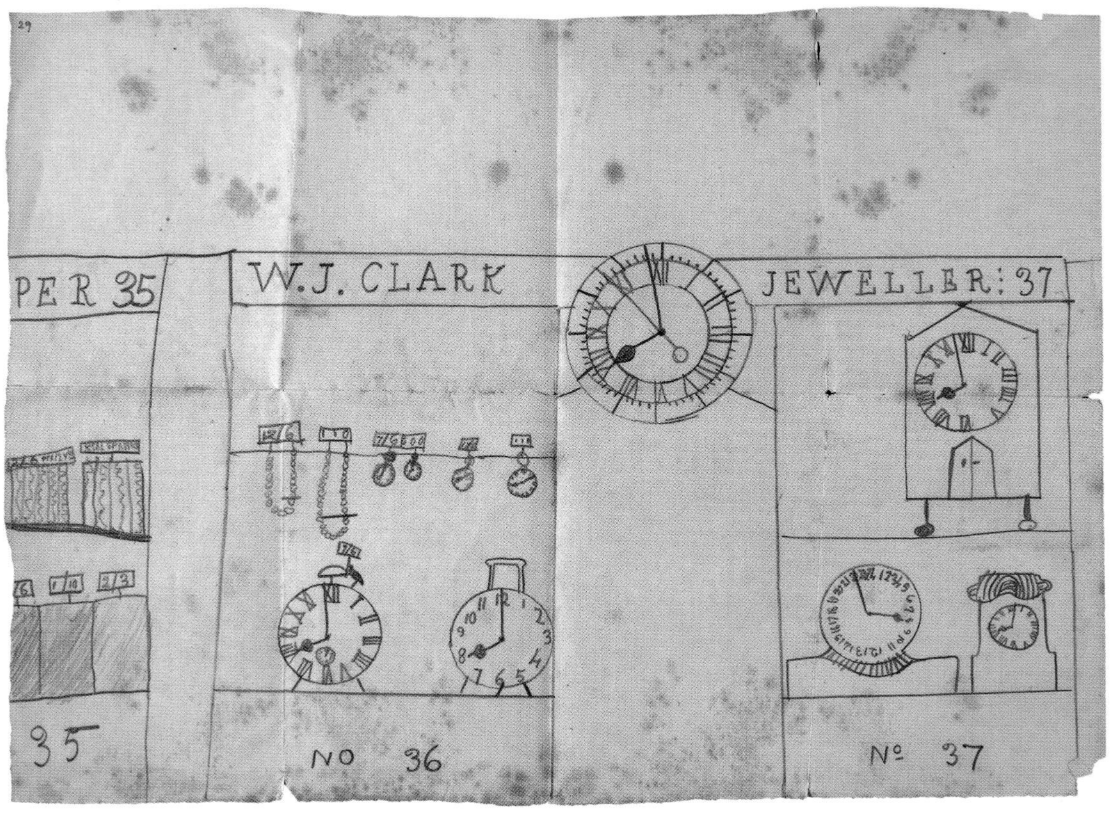

Corporal punishment was common and teachers often used canes or other implements for 'educational purposes'. In exclusive schools, rules could be more stringent, and were particularly difficult for newcomers as they suffered already under the separation from their usual home environment. According to the tradition of 'Fagging', supported by the authorities, the youngest were obliged to fulfill the orders of the seniors, and in some public schools the monitors had the right to impose corporal punishment.

In his 1861 essay about education, Herbert Spencer pointed to the deleterious influence of such educational institutions on the whole nation. Children became accustomed to a system of despotism, the domination by physical force and, ultimately, to adopting ideas of social status even of a lower level than the existing one. Such practices were maintained intentionally in the schools — without learning to obey, it's impossible to learn to command. The pupils of those institutions primarily replenished the ranks of the English political class. It is opportune that, for the sons of wealthy families — not from the aristocracy — Eton, Harrow, Winchester and a few other 'public schools' were the only places where they had the opportunity to make contact with future influential people. A circle of 'old classmates' of higher social standing was considered to be worthy of any investment.

James's primary schooling was at Wilson's School, Camberwell, London, an ancient Grammar School founded in 1615, rebuilt and reopened in 1883.

In September 1890 James entered the Merchant Taylors' School, a highly esteemed and long established day-school for children of the middle class, without aristocratic traditions, but with a high standard of teaching. Jeans's father was probably not keen to pay the fees for an exclusive school such as Eton or Harrow.

The School was founded by the Worshipful Company of Merchant Taylors in 1561 and was located in a manor house called the Manor of the Rose in the parish of St. Lawrence Pountney in the City of London. In 1866 a new and adjacent City site was purchased from the Governors of the London Charterhouse which had been vacated by Charterhouse School when it moved out of London in 1872 to Godalming in Surrey. This had originally been the site of a Carthusian monastery founded in 1371, confiscated by Henry VIII in 1537 with the Prior, John Houghton, being hanged, drawn and quartered, with his severed hands impaled upon its gates to "encourage the others to obey". Nine of the ten remaining monks starved to death in the nearby Newgate Prison, the last one was executed three years later at Tower Hill. The new Merchant Taylors' School was rebuilt on this site and was completed in 1875 and it was to this that Jeans went.

The school was about five miles from home. The family lived then at Clapham Park in a new prosperous district south of the Thames, and James had to walk to school through working class areas with factories, docks, slaughter houses, cattle markets, leather and fat-rendering plants.

Élisée Reclus described these areas:

> "The very poorest quarters of London have immediate contact with that wealthy City, which not many years hence will count only employees and housekeepers among its resident population. The labyrinth of streets around the Tower and the Docks is dreaded by the stranger, and not often entered by the Londoner residing in more favoured districts. The mud is carried from the streets into the passages of the houses; the walls are bespattered with filth; tatters hang in the windows; a fetid or rancid odour fills the atmosphere; while most of the men and women you meet in the streets have sunken eyes and emaciated limbs. The soiled garments which they wear have originally belonged to the fine ladies and gentlemen of the West-end; they have changed hands ten times since their original owners parted with them, and finish as rags upon the bodies of the inhabitants of Shadwell and Wapping. Certain narrow streets in Rotherhithe, Bermondsey, and Lambeth, to the south of the Thames, are likewise the seat of misery, and it is with a feeling of relief we emerge from them, and obtain a sight of the Thames, of some wide thoroughfare, or of a public park." [260, p. 134–135]

It is clear how Jeans's mood must have changed, as he went to the Thames — after all, the main goal of architecture is to improve a person's mood with those man-made developments which form the best areas of cities.

Crossing the Thames, Reclus describes the bridges and their setting:

"Eight of them are met with between Westminster Palace and the Pool, or Port of London, a distance of less than 2 miles by the river, and three of these vibrate almost incessantly beneath the weight of passing railway trains. Until quite recently it was impossible to admire these bridges without embarking in a steamer; but the Thames has been "regulated" for a considerable portion of its course, and superb quays have taken the place of fetid banks of mud, left dry by each succeeding tide. The Victoria Embankment now stretches for 6640 feet from Westminster to Blackfriars Bridge. Its river walls, of solid granite, rise 40 feet above low water, and rest upon a foundation descending to a depth of from 16 to 40 feet. Public gardens and rows of trees occupy a considerable part of it, and gladdened the eyes which formerly turned away with disgust from wretched hovels and narrow alleys, washed by the turgid waters of the Thames. Upon this embankment stands "Cleopatra's Needle" one of the forty-two obelisks known to exist in the world. It was taken from Alexandria." [265, p. 142–3]

By now Jeans, walking towards the City, could smell the ink and hear the roar of giant printing presses, which were shaking the foundations of the printing offices. He crossed Fleet Street — frequently visited by his father — and mingled with the London crowd in the business centre of the City, so well described by Reclus:

"In order to gain some idea of the immense multitude of London it is by no means necessary that we should be present on one of those occasions when a public procession through the streets attract its multitudes, or take part in the festivities inseparably connected with public holidays. It is quite sufficient to visit some of the leading thoroughfares of the City, such as Cheapside, Ludgate Hill, Cannon Street, or Lombard Street, during business hours. Carriages, omnibuses, and vehicles of every description appear at first sight to be mixed up in extricable confusion. But after a while we perceive that within this moving chaos there are two well-marked currents though flowing in opposite directions, carefully avoiding each other. Beneath the crowd passing along on the tops of the omnibuses and in carriages there moves another crowd, which glides between the wheels, dives beneath the horses' heads, and flows in contrary streams along

> the pathways. Now and then may be heard the dull rumble which announces the arrival of a train; the railway station sends forth its crowd of passengers, and these are quickly lost amongst the greater crowd pouring through the street ....
>
> The Metropolitan railways, carried along high viaducts above the houses or running through tunnels and deep cuttings beneath them, are great passenger highways in no way inferior to the streets of the City, and far more important than the Thames. The number of passengers that arrive daily at the railway stations of London cannot be less than a million." [260, p. 128–30]

Sometimes, however, he travelled by train, often with a close friend, William Palin Elderton. Jeans's life-long shyness and slightly abrupt manner of speaking limited the number of his friends at school. But Elderton liked the inquisitive James, and he took him as he was. Later he said that he enjoyed the ease with which Jeans explained difficult mathematical problems. His abilities and interest in mathematics and physics became very obvious at school. He enjoyed installing the wiring for lighting and a bell at the front door of his home. He loved playing with small battery driven toys. He even set up a little laboratory in his room, where he conducted simple physical experiments and tried to understand why it was impossible to create an 'eternal engine'. His childhood dream was to become an engineer.

Merchant Taylors' School provided a good general secondary education with a practical emphasis. Some of those who studied there with Jeans became subsequently part of the English establishment; for instance, his friend William Palin Elderton, the famous actuary and statistician, Head of the Equitable Life Assurance Society; Cyril Norwood, President of St. John's College, Oxford; Major Greenwood, the eminent epidemiologist and statistician; and Herbert Creedy, Permanent Under-Secretary of State for War.

The headmaster was Dr William Baker, who had founded the Modern Side but preserved the seniority of the Classics. The Classical Side had eight senior students who oversaw the junior class and eight tutors, the Modern only four of each. Jeans reached the lower sixth on the Classical Side in 1893 and then moved over to the Modern Side. At Easter 1894 he was at the top of the upper sixth Modern and two years later he was 2nd Modern monitor and first in mathematics. In November 1895 he won an entrance [major] scholarship at Trinity College, Cambridge.

At Merchant Taylors' Jeans came under the influence of three mathematics teachers: the Rev. S.T.H. Saunders, S.O. Roberts, and C.W. Payne. The first became vicar of a city church and at the age of ninety-one could still remember Jeans's quiet industry — 'a schoolboy', he said, 'who never got up to mischief'. Roberts, who had been the Eighth Wrangler

Oilette
Charles E. Flower
Pensioners Court,
The Charterhouse, London.

Hall
Oilette

in 1880, was too quick for many of the boys but provided Jeans with a real stimulus towards mathematical study; Payne was a sympathetic and generally more popular teacher. The three of them, as Sir William Elderton remembers, 'made a good team.' [193, p. 3].

Morton Palmer, who graduated from Jesus College, Cambridge, later becoming a private practitioner at Worthing, sat at the same desk with Jeans in Saunders' classes. He remembered Jeans's favourite pose: sitting cross-legged, leaning his elbow on his knee and resting his chin in his hand. He kept this habit throughout his life.

W.E. Bowers, later the Secretary of the Imperial Continental Gas Association, was in Jeans's opinion, one of the most talented of his classmates. He helped Jeans with his German and Jeans, in turn, helped him with mathematics. Classmates remembered how Jeans could not bear that something remained unclear and needed explanation, but he was interested not only in science. Bowers related how Jeans took on small female roles in the school play at the graduation celebration in 1894. But most of all he was impressed with his organ playing in the school chapel.

Above: Pensioners Court
Below: Charterhouse

James's secondary schooling (1890–96) was at the Merchant Taylors' School based in the Charterhouse, City of London. These contemporary coloured postcards from Charlotte Jeans's collection show various aspects of the school.

CAMBRIDGE 1896–1905

Jeans went up to Trinity College in October 1896 with a Parkin Scholarship from his school as well as his entrance [major] scholarship. He read mathematics. A.W. Verrall was his tutor, and his director of studies was G.T. Walker (later Sir Gilbert — Director-General of Indian Observatories [1904–1924], Professor of Meteorology at the Imperial College of Science. In 1889 Walker had graduated with the highest honours as Senior Wrangler from Trinity). Other teachers were: J.W.L. Glaisher, W.W. Rouse Ball, A.N. Whitehead, R.A. Herman and E.T. Whittaker. They were talented scientists and excellent teachers.

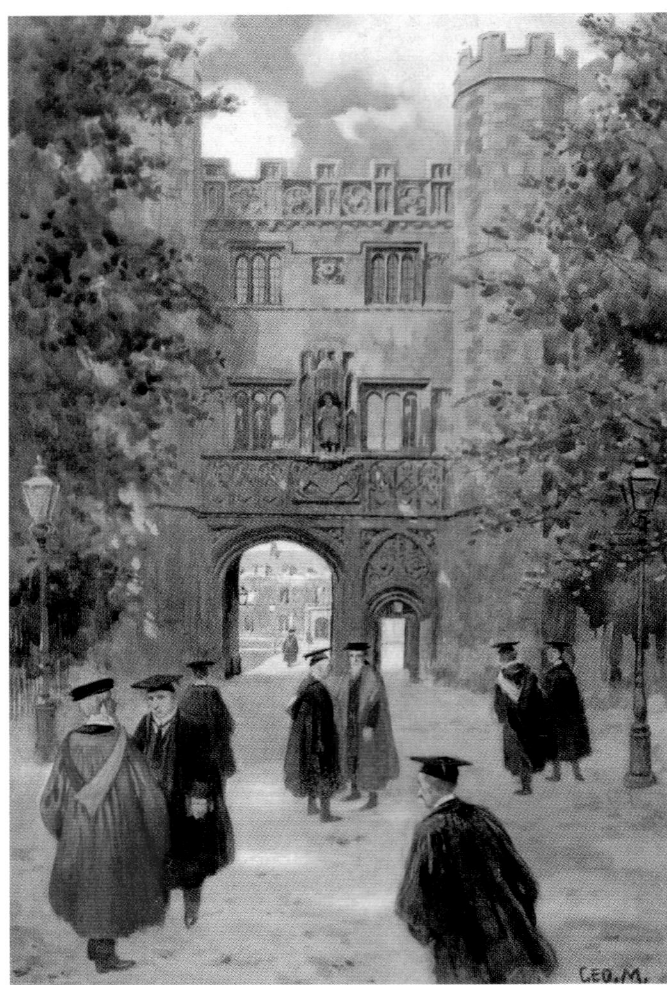

The Gateway to Trinity College 1908 (from a drawing by George Morrow).

J. H. Jeans ~21 years.

E.T. Whittaker, later in 1906 became the Royal Astronomer of Ireland, and then as Sir Edmund Whittaker, became Professor of Mathematics at Edinburgh University. A.N. Whitehead was not only a mathematician, but also a philosopher, world famous through his book *The Foundations of Mathematics* written together with Bertrand Russell. As a philosopher, he held a professorship in London and later in Harvard (USA). In his lectures he put forward the concept that "space-time" itself did not exist. "It is abstract, and its explanation requires specifying what it abstracted out" [274, p. 123]. But even more important, perhaps, was that Whitehead first noted that "observation(s) are selection". [274, p. 74]

Jeans decided to apply to Cambridge because the universities of Oxford and Cambridge were the oldest and most prestigious in the UK. With the high standard of teaching and outstanding achievements, Cambridge was considered better in mathematics and natural sciences. The creator of classical physics, Isaac Newton, graduated from the University of Cambridge in 1665 and was the Lucasian Professor of Mathematics (1669–1701). Another great physicist, James Clerk Maxwell, the creator of the theory of the electromagnetic field, also graduated from this University and in 1877 became its first Professor of Experimental Physics.

Cambridge lies along the River Cam, the southern tributary of the Ouse, in rather bland, flat countryside. The buildings of the ancient colleges were attractive and some even monumental. Kings College Chapel, dominating the whole city with its great height and four towers at its corners, was a remarkable monument to the perpendicular architecture of the 15th century. Trinity College was the richest and largest in the University. The University library housed about a quarter of a million volumes. There was one of the Europe's best geological museums and at the Observatory, under the direction of John Couch Adams and then later Sir Robert Ball, intensive astronomical observations were made. The oldest College, Peterhouse, was founded in 1284, thirty-five years after the establishment of the first college in Oxford.

Mediaeval traditions and rituals were preserved in everyday life. Fellows and students dined together in Hall, dressed in black gowns; solemn ceremonies awarded academic degrees; the system of supervision still exists, where students meet their tutors or supervisors, individually or in groups of two or three, discussing particular subjects or their work in an informal atmosphere.

A Professor in an English University had to give only a small number of lectures, which left a significant amount of time for research. Then and still today, fundamental scientific research is mainly conducted in University laboratories.

TEACHERS AT CAMBRIDGE

Arthur Woollgar Verall (1851–1912)
Oil painting by Frederic Yates

Alfred North Whitehead (1861–1947)
pencil portrait by Paul Drury 1928,
© Trinity College Cambridge

Gilbert Thomas Walker (1868–1958)
© Trinity College Cambridge

Edmund Taylor Whitaker (1873–1956)
© Trinity College Cambridge

Walter William Rouse Ball (1850–1925)
© Trinity College Cambridge

James Whitbread Lee Glaisher (1848–1928)
pencil portrait by Francis Dodd 1927,
© Trinity College Cambridge

Godfrey Harold Hardy (1877–1947)

But along with the advantages of personal learning, there were also drawbacks of the traditional Cambridge honours examinations, forcing students to prepare for it by learning a vast amount of inconsequential material and practice in solving artificial tasks.

At the entrance exams Jeans and his Cambridge companion G.H. Hardy, who later became a world-famous mathematician, distinguished themselves. Walker realized their exceptional abilities, and on the 29th of September 1896 invited them to take the first part of the mathematical honours examination in two years instead of three, so that they could save a year for more serious work preparing for the second part of the examination. He warned them he could not guarantee that they would rise above the fifteenth place in the list, but he vouched they would never regret it. Having agreed, they began to work with R.R. Webb, the most famous tutor of the time. Both the Director of Studies, Walker, and the two students showed considerable courage with this decision.

In March 1897 Jeans was elected to an ordinary major scholarship at Trinity. Already at the end of the first year Jeans had disagreements with Webb, and Walker took him on, with excellent results. In the first part of the examination in 1898 Jeans came second, together with J.F. Cameron, who later became Master of Gonville and Caius College, R. Hudson was placed first, and Hardy took the fourth place. After the places became known, Jeans wrote to his friend William Elderton, that Hudson was fairly easily head of the field and had deservedly topped the list because he could work seven or eight hours a day, while all the others could manage no more than six hours.

And indeed, to get the Bachelor of Arts degree Jeans and Hardy had to sit a 'special exam' in mathematics in 1899, which qualified them for the ordinary, but not the honours degree. The disadvantages of the existing examination system for gifted students became more visible, and in 1910, it was modified, not without the influence of the already famous mathematician, Hardy. [242]

J. Talbot.
C. H. Clague
F. W. Dobbs.
George M Booth.
B E Holloway
G. W. Young
C. Martin Jones
A. L. Reckitt
J. R. P. Sclater.
A. M. Mackay.
Hugh J Sheringham

QUERY CLUB AT TRINITY

Query clubs were a socialist-liberal mutual support organisations for working people. The Trinity-based club to which Jeans belonged may be the earliest recorded in Britain. The reason for Jeans's absence from either photograph is not known.

Left: The Trinity Query Club: list of names and their college admission dates — begin at the centre.

Francis Wellesley Dobbs (adm. Trinity, 29 June 1895)
Geoffrey Winthrop Young (adm. Trinity, 29 June 1895)
Felix Martin Levi (adm. Trinity, 29 June 1895)
Charles Martin Jones (adm. Trinity, 1 Oct 1895)
Basil Edward Holloway (adm. Trinity, 1 Oct 1895)
Christopher Andrew Wordsworth (adm. Clare, 5 Jan 1895)
John Talbot (adm. Trinity, 29 June 1895)
Cyril Kingston Clague (adm. Trinity, 29 June 1895)
John Williams Pickles Hayton (adm. Trinity, 29 June 1895)
Edward Hilton Young (adm. Trinity, 25 June 1897)
Godfrey Harold Hardy (adm. Trinity, 30 June 1896)
George Macaulay Booth (adm. Trinity, 1 Oct 1896)
Francis Herman Lucas (adm. Trinity, 1 Oct 1896)
Albert Leopold Reckitt (adm. Trinity, 1 Oct 1895)
John Robert Paterson Sclater (adm. Emmanuel, 18 Sept 1895)
Alexander Morrice Mackay (adm. Trinity, 1 Oct 1895)
Hugh Tempest Sheringham (adm. Trinity, 1 Oct 1895)

The Query Club at tea.

Jeans got great pleasure from the arts, especially music, often performing in student concerts. He was an excellent pianist and organist and had a grand piano in his room, taking lessons from Kathleen Bruckshaw, a well-known pianist.

He was Secretary of the 'Query Club': One of the members, from the well-known Rothschild banking family, was successfully prepared by Jeans for the preliminary examination for a Bachelor degree. He thanked him with a tie-pin set with diamonds in the form of a question mark.

The life of the Cambridge student of the late 19th century was almost luxurious. A student, as a rule, had no fewer than two rooms, a bedroom and a living room, used also as a study. There were servants to light the fire in the morning, clean the rooms and boil the kettle for breakfast. Later, a servant cleaned the big bath tub and filled it. In the afternoon she returned to clean the fireplace and keep the fire burning, especially in the cold season. There were shoe shiners, who dealt with the shoes left outside the students' rooms.

Everything was done to make student life more comfortable, so nothing would distract them from work, except entertainment, which meant joining some of the many students' clubs and participating in sports. It was predominantly a male society. Higher education statistics for 1897, showed that in the University of Cambridge there were 19 colleges, 125 teachers and 2929 students, and only two colleges specifically for women: Newnham College and Girton College, with respectively 166 and 108 female students. For that, or perhaps other reasons, romance did not awake in Jeans's soul during his University studies, or if it did we know nothing about it.

Jeans was not much interested in social problems as he lived far away from them. Life at the University was quite cloistered and it was little concerned about the tumultuous events going on in the world. For instance, in 1899 the Anglo-Boer war started and demanded from England enormous effort until its end in 1902, but in Cambridge it was hardly noticed.

John Galsworthy, describing the views of pupils in aristocratic public schools and colleges of the time, said: "We almost all were reactionaries ..." [273, p. 10]. Jeans supported the liberal views of the sociologist and economist John Stuart Mill. Mill discussed the idea of freedom within the concept of utilitarianism, stating that freedom would give a rational selfish person the opportunity to fully look after his own interests, which would be of use for society. Freedom of speech, thought, press, and association are of highest value and are the purpose of a developing human society, according to Mill.

No doubt, working at the Cavendish Laboratory in 1899 contributed to developing Jeans's physical intuition. It was the heyday of the laboratory under J.J. Thomson, who in 1897 discovered the electron; he also conducted active research into the conductivity of gases, and began to be interested in

X-rays and radioactivity. Thomson was the third Cavendish Professor, the successor of Maxwell and Rayleigh, as head of the Cavendish Laboratory, which had opened on June 16, 1874. "Thomson delighted me ..." Rutherford wrote in 1895 to his bride Mary Newton and five years later Niels Bohr said: "I saw a really great man ...".

From 1895 onwards, research programmes for talented young scientists from around the world were established in Cambridge. An international spirit among physicists developed, so characteristic for the great discoveries in the first third of the twentieth century. On a quiet street, Free School Lane, Cambridge, a New Zealander (Rutherford), a Scot (Wilson), a Frenchman (Langevin), and others — who became famous scientists and builders of new physics — "trained in the Cavendish Laboratory". Brian Pippard wrote: "By 1898, it had been very hard to find any trace of the former purely quantitative approach; searching for natural laws started outside of mathematical predictability" [249, p. 25]. Jeans with his formal mathematical mind succeeded to get into the spirit of physical science, which enabled him later to evaluate critically its future developments.

Jeans's preparation for Part II of the mathematical Tripos was interrupted with tuberculosis of his knee. He left Cambridge after Easter term, 1899.

J. H. Jeans in the tuberculosis sanatorium (Ringwood or Mundesley) during 1899–1903.

Jeans was curiously uncared for as a boy in spite of the quite comfortable circumstances of his parents. From the age of 14 he cost his parents practically nothing at all because of scholarships he had won. Apparently there was the choice of either walking to Merchants Taylors' School from his home in Clapham Park and having funds to have lunch at school or going by train but without a proper lunch. This early neglect led to his being the victim of bovine tuberculosis soon after he took his BA in Cambridge. Although he made a remarkable recovery he was never robust thereafter. It left him with a weak knee, the loss of his teeth, and probably the early oncoming of heart problems in 1917 . This austere Victorian upbringing may be reflected in the care he took with financial and professional matters in all his dealings, whether on household matters, the Royal Society, the Royal Astronomical Society, Madam Curie Hospital on the death of Charlotte, or the staff at Cleveland Lodge.

First he was treated in a sanatorium in Ringwood, Hampshire, and later in Mundesley, Norfolk, where he finally recovered after three years.

In spite of this setback Jeans never stopped working. While there he wrote his first monograph *The Dynamical Theory of Gases* [11], published in 1904, when he was just 27 years old. It was reprinted several times and served as a classic textbook for students and researchers for decades.

He didn't lose touch with Cambridge, judging by his extensive correspondence with many members of Trinity College and other friends like G. H. Hardy, R. Laurence, R. Parry and some others who kept him informed of the University's news, reported on new scientific achievements, and warmly shared their personal experiences. That helped Jeans not to feel isolated from the academic world.

He returned to Cambridge for the completion of Part II of the Tripos in 1900 and took second place with honours. Hardy was first. Soon after, Jeans was awarded an Isaac Newton scholarship for astronomy and optics. In 1901 he got the Smith's Prize, at the same time as Hardy, for his paper '*The Distribution of Molecular Energy*' [2] and they both were declared Smith prizemen 'of unspecified relative merit'. Jeans's subject of research — the central problem of energy distribution in a dynamical system defined with many parameters — was of great importance and was published in the Philosophical Transactions of the Royal Society in 1901.

F. W. Morton Palmer

Jeans was elected a Fellow of Trinity College in October 1901 at the same time as his old school friend the historian Ronald Laurence. In a letter to another class-mate, Morton Palmer, Jeans wrote: "I am very glad that Laurence was elected on the same day with me, after a long period of time we are back together" [193, p. 6]. Hardy had also been elected to a prize fellowship at Trinity College in the previous year and he used to say that he considered his election as the most important event in his life. For Jeans, his election meant he could continue treatment of his knee without financial worries.

In 1903 Jeans received his M.A. and in the following year was appointed University Lecturer in

Mathematics. He occupied that post until his departure to Princeton in 1905. During 1903 Jeans became the President of the Nabla Squared Club, which he had founded together with Professor P.V. Bivan, J.F. Cameron and other applied mathematicians, A. Eddington joined a little later. These were years of intensive pedagogical and scientific activities.

The beginning of Jeans's scientific activity coincided with the start of a new century. The funeral of Queen Victoria in winter 1901 symbolized a farewell to the past century:

> "In '37, when she came to the throne, "Superior Dosset" was still building houses to make London hideous; and James, a stripling of twenty-six, just laying the foundations of his practice in the Law. Coaches still ran; men wore stocks, shaved their upper lips, ate oysters out of barrels; "tigers" swung behind cabriolets; women said, "Là!" and owned no property; there were manners in the land, and pigsties for the poor; unhappy devils were hanged for little crimes, and Dickens had but just begun to write. Well-nigh two generations had slipped by — of steamboats, railways, telegraphs, bicycles, electric light, telephones, and now the motor-car — of such accumulated wealth, that eight per cent, had become three, ..." [214, p. 275].

All those achievements in industry would have been impossible without the achievements in the field of heat and electrical engineering. In turn, they had influenced the development of physics during that time.

In the second half of the 19th century the internal combustion engine and steam turbine were added to steam machines. And after the discovery of the Siemens principle of the dynamo an Englishman, William Ladd, built the first dynamo suitable for current generation in 1867. Various types of electric motors started to be widely used in industry. For the industrial development of the electric-bulb it was necessary to create a good vacuum, and this need led to new techniques. Without these, it would have been impossible to develop the electronic theory. At the time, J.J. Thomson wrote:

> "If science helps industry, industry helps science in turn. One example is the fact that the need for a high vacuum for electrical and electronic lamps meant that obtaining a high vacuum became commercially viable; as a result, a physicist had at his disposal pumps of sufficient power that could maintain a vacuum even in a vessel containing a continuously flowing stream of the particles being studied. This is extremely important when studying charged particles and electrons" [269, p. 109–10].

The needs of industry and the internal logic of scientific development led to particularly intensive research into the theory of heat and electrodynamics. In the theory of heat, the development of thermodynamics related directly to heat engineering, and the creation of the kinetic theory of gases led to the emergence of a new field — statistical physics. In electrodynamics it was the creation of the electromagnetic field theory as well as the beginning of the electron theory.

Milne suggested [193] that Jeans started his study of physics with two books popular in the late 19th century — *Popular Lectures on Scientific Subjects* by H. Helmholtz, published in 1893, and *Fragments of Science* by J. Tyndall (1892).

Those works mainly covered the first law of thermodynamics — the law of conservation of energy and the story of its discovery, from J. Mayer and J. Joule up to the research of Helmholtz. They also dealt with the concept of equilibrium radiation and the history of its origin. It must be said that, although the law of conservation of energy led to an understanding of the universal connection between the phenomena, Helmholtz reduced all the physical forms of motion to mechanical movement. Electromagnetic phenomena, including optical, were considered as manifestations of mechanical wave-like motion in a pervasive environment, called ether. In the encyclopedia of industrial science "Industry and Technology" — well-known in the 19th century — Professor Arthur Wilke interpreted that question as: 'Another clever English physicist, Maxwell, developing Faraday's ideas mathematically in a theoretical way, realized that light and electricity were in close kinship, but the first to prove this relationship was the German researcher Heinrich Hertz'. And further: 'The great English physicist Faraday in 1845 opened a kind of connection between light and magnetism. As the reader, of course, knows, modern physics considers light as vibrations of luminiferous ether, perpendicular to the direction of a light ray'. [255, p. 602].

Physicists at that time assumed that understanding the connection between electricity and light could give a key to a deeper penetration into the secrets of nature. There were two concepts: Some preferred interaction of 'tangible particles', others saw a 'tremendous receptacle of the natural forces and energies' in a weightless ether. The general situation was described by Einstein: "Let us now turn to physics, just what it was at that time. Although in some areas it flourished, dogmatic stagnation dominated the fundamentals. At the beginning (if it was) God created Newton's laws of motion together with necessary masses and forces. That was all there was; the rest had to come through deduction, as a result of working out appropriate mathematical methods" [287, p. 265].

Despite the fact that natural radioactivity, X-rays and the electron had already been experimentally discovered, the confidence in the completeness of physical science was so strong that Lord Kelvin in his speech at the Royal Institution in London in April 1900 assured scientists that physics had entered into a calm harbour, with the most significant issues solved. Similarly when Planck suggested to his teacher F. Yolli his intention to engage in theoretical physics, Yolli replied, "Young man, why do you want to ruin your life, because theoretical physics has been mostly completed, differential equations resolved, it remains to consider some particular cases of the modified boundary and initial conditions. Is this hopeless case really worthy of being studied?" [244, p. 90]. However Kelvin mentioned two 'clouds' on the clear sky of science. One was the inability to determine the exact law of the spectral distribution of the energy density of the equilibrium radiation and the other the impossibility to explain the experiment of A. Michelson using classical concepts. In an attempt to understand those phenomena two tracks were followed and these led to the quantum theory and the theory of relativity — the foundations of modern physics.

Jeans's early works strengthened the first track. His first scientific work *The Striated Electric Discharge* [1] was published in 1900, when he was still studying in Cambridge and dealt with the theoretical explanation of the optical behavior of discharges in vacuum tubes. Complex stratified glow was first observed by J. Abria in 1848, and then studied by H. Geissler and J. Hittorff in Germany, and also by W. Crookes in England more than half a century later (incidentally, the evacuated glass tubes with solder electrodes were called 'Crookes tubes'). They studied the behaviour of glowing discharges depending on a variety of factors such as the nature of the gas, the geometry of the electrodes and the pressure. Spurred by the discovery of X-rays by W. Röntgen in 1895, J.J. Thomson became interested in that field. Earlier in 1893, he had considered cathode rays as a phenomenon similar to electrolysis. And in 1897, whilst measuring the deviation of the cathode rays in electric and magnetic fields, he discovered a particle, in which the ratio *e/m* (*e* the charge *m*, the mass) was three orders of magnitude larger than the ion of hydrogen produced by electrolysis.

Joseph John Thompson inspecting Crookes Tubes, Cavendish Laboratory, Cambridge.

That ratio did not change depending on the electrode material or type of gas. He wanted to call it a 'corpuscle', Kelvin wanted to call it an 'electrion', but the term 'electron'— earlier given by G. Stoney — was chosen, thanks to H. Lorentz.

It was Thomson who suggested to Jeans a theoretical study of discharge in a Crookes tube, so he worked in the Cavendish laboratory for about a year. His results were published in two parts in March 1900 and in May 1901 and both were communicated by J.J. Thomson to the Royal Society. They showed that Thomson's theory of electric conductivity of gases by ions explained the stratified nature of the illumination and other observable effects during a discharge in a Crookes tube. Jeans's brilliant mathematical talent provided the analytical solutions of highly complex equations that Thomson had solved only by graphical or numerical methods. Jeans also provided a physical interpretation of his analysis. Showing deep physical intuition, he introduced in the second part of his work the assumption that the speed of negative ions (electrons) was much greater than that of the positive ones. Summing up his work, Jeans wrote at the end of the second part: 'The results were obtained with strong mathematical methods' [1, p. 529].

Jeans's paper *The Distribution of Molecular Energy* published in 1901 [2] was devoted to energy distribution in a dynamic system with a large number of parameters. It gives a rigorous proof of the law on the equipartition of energy in the kinetic theory of gases and expresses the idea that: 'the condition of a gas can be considered as dependent on the core temperature and also some auxiliary temperature ..., each of which corresponds to one (or possibly more), degrees of freedom of molecules.' Milne pointed out that this idea was often used in subsequent theoretical studies of the atmospheres of the sun and stars.

During 1903 and 1904 Jeans published five papers related to the kinetic theory of gases: *The Kinetic Theory of Gases Developed From a New Standpoint* [9] (1903), *On the Vibration Set Up by Molecular Collisions* [10] (1903), *The Kinetic Theory of Gases* [12] (1904), *The Determination of the Size of Molecules From the Kinetic Theory of Gases* [14] (1904), and *The persistence of Molecular Velocities in the Kinetic Theory of Gases* [15] (1904). These contributed to his monograph *The Dynamical Theory of Gases* [11] published in 1904 by the Cambridge University Press. In it he established the Maxwell equations for the distribution of velocities of molecules, considered vibrations of molecules, discussed methods of defining the sizes of molecules and their effect on the viscosity of gases, also heat conductivity and the diffusion coefficient of gases, Boyle's law and the volume occupied by a substance in the solid and liquid states. Part of this work was discussed at the meeting of the British Association on August 23rd, 1904, with particular regard to the effective diameters of gas molecules — and Jeans's calculation of approximately 2.7×10^{-8} cm for the average diameter of air molecules is close to the present accepted value. He never restricted himself to purely theoretical considerations, and always tried to produce numerical results to compare them with the experimental data.

By the beginning of the 20th century the electromagnetic nature of light was generally accepted and radioactivity was discovered. Jeans had an early interest in their nature. His first work on the theory of radiation *The Mechanism of Radiation* [4], published by the Physical Society in 1901, contained a number of interesting hypotheses. Jeans believed that radiation in gas was generated by a large number of vibrators. To explain a linear spectrum of elements, he supposed that radiation was produced with "vibrators, that did not depend on the location of ions in an atom" [4], it was quite an ingenious solution for the time when a correct model of an atom did not yet exist. Jeans tried to estimate the size of atoms and came to the conclusion that their radius was about $n^{1/3}10^{-9}$ cm, where n is the atomic weight. He also attempted to give an explanation of the Zeeman effect, which, of course, could not succeed and was a purely formal scheme for that period of time.

In 1904, his brief article *A Suggested Explanation of Radioactivity* [13] appeared. Although the work was incorrect in general, we must remember that the nature of α-particles was not established and Jeans used the concept of ether, but still Jeans's guess, that natural radioactivity was not the result of external causes but was a property of matter, was later confirmed.

The development of the classical theory of equilibrium radiation occupied a central place in Jeans's physical research. It was first studied by Pierre Prevost, who in 1809 found that radiation of a heated object was not dependent on the environment. The proper theoretical understanding of this problem, according to the laws of thermodynamics, was provided by Kirchhoff between 1859 and 1861. He established the basic law of heat radiation and introduced the concept of an absolutely black body as an object which neither reflects nor transmits radiation falling on it, but absorbs it fully. The emitted radiation has a universal character, i.e. the same for all black bodies with equal temperature. Using the laws of thermodynamics Kirchhoff showed that for all bodies emitting and absorbing thermal radiation, the ratio of emission $E(\nu)$ and absorptivity $A(\nu)$ of the same things is a universal function of frequency and temperature $f(\nu, T)$.

Kirchhoff did not present the explicit form of the function $f(\nu, T)$, but only noted that it tended to zero at low temperatures for the visible region of a spectrum and it was different from zero for longer wavelengths. It was necessary to determine the form of this function experimentally, by studying the distribution of radiation energy in a spectrum of a black body, as the universal function is related with a simple ratio to the energy density of the equilibrium radiation $\rho(\nu, T)$:

$f(\nu, T) = (c/4\pi)\rho(\nu, T)$
where c is the velocity of light.

As Kirchhoff wrote, physics had an "enormously important task to find the function $f(\nu, T)$".

The first step in that direction was made by J. Stefan in 1879 in the work *On the Relationship between Thermal Radiation and Temperature*, which defined power M, emitted by a heated surface:

$$M(T) = \pi \int f(\nu, T)d\nu$$

Analyzing experiments of J. Tyndall, P. Dulong and A. Petit, P. Prevost and others, Stefan deduced a law — $M(T) = aT^4$, showing that the total intensity of equilibrium radiation at the temperature T was proportional to T^4. Theoretical substantiation of that ratio was given in 1884 by Boltzmann in *The derivation of Stefan's Law concerning the dependence of the thermal radiation on the temperature, on the basis of the electromagnetic theory of light*. Boltzmann based his theory on the fact that radiation had not only energies but also created pressure. With isotropic radiation, for example, $p = \bar{\rho}/3$, where p is pressure, — $\bar{\rho}$ average density of radiation.

The next step was taken by Wien, who proposed in 1896 a formula for the distribution of energy in the spectrum of equilibrium radiation. It was based on the ratio, established in 1893, according to which the specific intensity I of black-body radiation:

$$I_{\lambda,T} = \lambda^{-5}F(\lambda T) \text{ or } I_{\nu,T} = \nu^3 F(\nu/T)$$

These formulas resulted in Wien's displacement law $\lambda_{max}T$=const. However, certain thermodynamic considerations were enough to determine the type of the function F. Therefore Wien considered a group of independent molecules — oscillators — in a closed mirror cavity. In thermodynamic equilibrium the distribution of energy is established, corresponding to blackbody radiation. Using the Maxwell distribution, taking into account the displacement law and the Stefan-Boltzmann Law, Wien came to the desired ratio.

$I_{\lambda,T} = a\lambda^{-5}\exp(-b/\lambda T)$, where a and b are constants.

For some time Wien's law seemed to explain adequately the experimental data. However, studies over a wide range of wavelengths revealed a discrepancy between the theoretical and experimental curves in the long-wave region of the spectrum, and this stimulated new theoretical research.

The year 1900 marked the publication of Rayleigh's paper *Remarks upon the Law of Complete Radiation* [321]. Based on his investigations of the oscillations of an enclosed air mass, he considered vibrations of the ether to be analogous to vibrations in air, representing radiation located in a closed cavity in the form of a set of standing monochromatic waves and attributing to each wave two degrees of freedom. Rayleigh applied the law of equipartition of energy according to the number of degrees of freedom. Then in the case of thermodynamic equilibrium each monochromatic wave has average energy $\bar{\varepsilon}$, equal to kT, where k is the Boltzmann constant. Based on this condition, Rayleigh easily got: $I_{\lambda,T} = c_1\lambda^{-4}T$

However, to avoid an infinite value for the total energy of the radiation, he intuitively introduced an exponential factor and the formula became $c_1\lambda^{-4}T\exp(-c_2/\lambda T)\,d\lambda$, where c_1 and c_2 are some constants [321].

In October of the same year, at the meeting of the Physical Society in Berlin, German physicist Max Planck proposed a new formula for the distribution of energy obtained by a semi empirical method.

$$I_{\lambda,T} = \frac{8\pi c}{\lambda^5}\frac{h}{\exp\left(\frac{hc}{k\lambda T}\right)-1}$$

or

$$I_{\nu,T} = \frac{8\pi\nu^2}{c^3}\frac{h\nu}{\exp\left(\frac{h\nu}{kT}\right)-1}$$

where h is the Planck constant; k is the Boltzmann constant.

This formula provided complete agreement with the experimental data at all frequencies. Indeed, for $h\nu \ll kT$ it gives the Rayleigh law, and in the opposite case $h\nu \gg kT$ — gives Wien's formula. Planck had difficulties in providing a strict theoretical substantiation of the proposed ratio, however he managed to do it in December 1900. Theoretical consideration inevitably led him to the conclusion that energy was distributed between oscillators not arbitrarily, but in finite proportions i.e. quanta, multiples of $h\nu$. The recognition of the discreteness of energy goes beyond classical physics. So Planck himself and the whole scientific world viewed that assumption only as a working hypothesis, which could later be explained on the basis of a classical approach.

Further development of science showed that it was not just a working hypothesis, but a brilliant discovery of one of the basic laws of Nature. That year marks the birth of quantum physics, and Planck is rightly considered its founder.

In the early 1900s, this hypothesis was only looked upon as an exotic assumption and scientists searched for ways to solve problems, while remaining within the framework of the classical concepts, and Jeans was no exception. Although his efforts were unsuccessful, it cannot be said that they were absolutely useless because ultimately they led to the recognition of quantum ideas. The intensity of black body radiation was deduced by Jeans using different methods. In 1905, he showed that Rayleigh's law could be obtained by using common methods of classical statistics applied to waves in the ether in a closed cavity [17]. He simulated radiation in a mirror cavity system of standing waves where the energy of radiation could be represented as a sum of energies of non-interacting harmonic oscillators. The energy density of the standing waves is equal to the total of the average energy of all oscillators, applying normal vibrations of the same frequencies:

$$\rho(\nu,T) = \frac{8\pi\nu^2}{c^3}\,\varepsilon$$

Jeans applied the classical equation $\varepsilon = kT$ to express the average energy of the oscillator and obtained the dependence of the intensity of the equilibrium radiation on temperature

$$I(\nu,T) = \frac{8\pi kT}{c^3}\,\nu^2 s \quad \text{or} \quad I(\lambda,T) = 8\pi kT\lambda^{-4}$$

This ratio is now known in physics as the Rayleigh-Jeans law. When calculating the average energy of fluctuations Jeans used the theorem of the equipartition of energy. Previously he had already dealt with the justification of this theorem. A substantial part of his *Dynamical theory of gases* was devoted to a review of this theorem in various cases.

However, as one can see, the Rayleigh-Jeans law is not applicable for the whole spectrum, because when integrating over all frequencies it leads to an infinitely large energy density at $\nu \to \infty$.

That fact would have led to the situation where sources of energy, closed in a cavity, would have radiated until all thermal energy was transformed into electromagnetic radiation, but the temperature would not have fallen to absolute zero. We now know that this is the consequence of the non-applicability of the classical Boltzmann statistics with its continuous distribution function to radiation.

In this example, physics first encountered the inadequacy of the classical approach. The situation was not clear. Jeans insisted on the validity of his ratio for all frequencies, without an exponential multiplier, which had been arbitrarily, but prudently introduced by Rayleigh. Strictly, in the classical sense, Jeans's conclusion had no place for an exponential multiplier. The semi-empirical exponential factor of Rayleigh prevented the appearance of infinite values of total energy radiation, or as it was called by P. Ehrenfest, 'ultraviolet catastrophe'. In 1905 the problem became apparent when Jeans raised the question of the necessity of implementing a ratio for all wavelengths, based on the laws of classical physics [21]. Focusing on that point, he eventually contributed to the recognition of Planck's theory. Jeans's merit was that he showed that a classical wave theory of electromagnetic radiation was described only by the Rayleigh-Jeans law. In the early 1900s Planck, and other authors, used Rayleigh's ratio of intensity of radiation only in a long-wave area. But the paradox of developing science led to the situation, when Jeans [18], already knowing about Planck's theory and its discrete quanta of energy considered it necessary to limit transitions to the continuous distribution. For that it had to be supposed that $h=0$, when the Planck formula becomes the Rayleigh-Jeans law. Thus, Jeans firmly adopted the classical point of view.

Thinking about the state of physics in the early twentieth century, Jeans could not but realize the crises. Almost half a century later L.D. Landau very accurately characterized the state of physics at that time: "Planck introduced, if it may be said, irrationality in physics. He did it extremely reluctantly, being forced to, because he saw no other choice. However this illogical situation lasted twenty-seven years, during which the foundations of physics were, essentially, contrary to elementary logic. It became possible to restore consistency only later". [244, p. 97]. So the problems of physical science then current did not give Jeans the opportunity to form a reliable mathematical model of the phenomena to which he could apply his refined methods, which were the strongest aspect of his research. However he could apply them to astronomical problems.

Jeans's interest was inspired by the lectures of George Howard Darwin (Plumian Professor of Astronomy and Experimental Philosophy, at Cambridge) who came from the family that provided the world with the famous physician and poet, Erasmus Darwin (1731–1802) and Charles Robert Darwin (1809–1882), the great scientist, author of the theory of the origin of species. George Darwin (1845–1912) was the second son of Charles Darwin. He graduated from Trinity College, Cambridge in 1868, and since 1873 taught there, devoting himself to research on theoretical questions in astronomy. He considered the origin of double stars on the basis of the theory of equilibrium figures of rotating liquid mass; he suggested a resonance theory of the origin of the moon and applied harmonic analysis for studying tides, etc. His success in developing astronomy was greatly

George Howard Darwin (1845–1912) Plumian Professor of Astronomy and Experimental Philosophy at Cambridge (1883–1912).

Hugh Frank Newall (1857–1944) Professor of Astrophysics at Cambridge (1909–1928). He greatly facilitated the development of astronomy at Cambridge.

appreciated, and in 1899 he was elected President of the Royal Astronomical Society. George Darwin had the gift of engaging his listeners in science and inculcating a love of astronomy. He was the author of several popular works on astronomy. In the introduction to one of them he wrote:

> "The Problems of the origin and history of the Solar and other celestial systems have little to do with our life on Earth, but they cannot but interest anyone who even in some degree has a scientific mind" [217, p. 13].

Jeans could not but get interested, particularly about Darwin's hypothesis on the origin of the Moon:

"Can we imagine that as the rotation of the primitive Earth gradually slowed due to friction by solar tides, the period of these tides was more and more consistent with the natural period of oscillation and that, therefore, the solar tides were getting higher and higher? In this case, fluctuations could finally become so large that, combined with the rapid rotation they shook the planet, until it broke in pieces, and enormous wreckage, separating from the planet, later became our Moon. There is nothing that would prove the validity of the theory of the formation of the Moon, and I say that this is only a very loose assumption that it is impossible to verify" [217, p. 197].

This last claim must have seemed like a direct challenge both to Jeans with his refined mathematical methods and to the theory about the shape of celestial bodies which was already quite advanced after almost three centuries of scientific discussion.

The theory originates from Newton's research on the shape of the Earth, in which he showed that rotation should lead to a flattening. The Earth, as well as all large bodies in the Universe, has a spherical shape, which is determined by self-gravitation. Indeed, it is the force of gravity which holds separate fragments of heavenly bodies together. Mathematically it can be shown that the force of gravity is directed toward the centre of the attracting body and that is why it is characterized by a spherical shape. The latter is only possible in the absence of rotation. And, of course, for large bodies we can neglect the strength of the matter from which they are made, in comparison with pressure at their centre when the behaviour of matter is the same as that of a liquid.

Under the influence of centrifugal forces, a rotating mass will take the form of a ball slightly compressed at the poles. A strict mathematical representation of the shapes of rotating bodies is possible for the case of an incompressible fluid. For such a fluid the shape is called the ellipsoid of rotation.

A Scottish mathematician Colin Maclaurin in 1742, summarized Newton's result in the case of rapid rotation and introduced the concept of equipotential surfaces. With increasing angular velocity of rotation of a body of an incompressible fluid up to the value corresponding to $\omega^2/\pi G\rho=0.4493$, the compression reaches a limit corresponding to an eccentricity of 0.93. With greater speeds, spheroidal figures of equilibrium will not exist. However, before reaching the critical value ω the configuration of rotation becomes unstable. This occurs when the value ω corresponds to $\omega^2/\pi G\rho=0.37424$ with an eccentricity of 0.81267. At this so-called point of bifurcation the sequence of Maclaurin's spheroids 'branches' into a sequence of Jacobi ellipsoids (all the axes of the ellipsoid are different), which were discovered by Carl Gustave Jacobi in 1834. The last Maclaurin spheroid is the first Jacobi ellipsoid but with its two equatorial axes of equal length. Much later, in 1885, Henri Poincaré showed that at the point of bifurcation, stability moves to the Jacobi ellipsoid.

Poincaré showed that the further development of Jacobi's ellipsoids would reach another point of bifurcation, from which another series of equilibrium configurations originates, the so-called pear-shaped figures. At this point of bifurcation, Jacobi's ellipsoids lose their stability, and the question arises as to whether this pear series is stable?

Poincaré did not deal with this issue. George Darwin, based however, on not quite strict calculations, believed that pear-shaped figures were stable.

Almost at the same time a prominent Russian mathematician Aleksandr Mikhailovich Lyapunov, came to the opposite conclusion.

Jeans, trying to solve this problem, considered the complex question of the stability of rotating self-gravitating equilibrium configurations in a simplified but specific two-dimensional case in which the three-dimensional body is a cylinder. The two-dimensionality of this form would allow the use of the theory of functions of complex variables. Jeans solved the equilibrium equation in the case of rotation with different angular velocity ω. Thus, he obtained a series of equilibrium configurations. With increasing angular velocity ω, the two-dimensional counterpart of a series of Maclaurin's spheroids is replaced by a series of analogous Jacobi ellipsoids, and then pear-shaped figures. This good match between the results of two- and three-dimensional cases allowed Jeans to extend the analogy to high values of ω for which there were no results in the three-dimensional case.

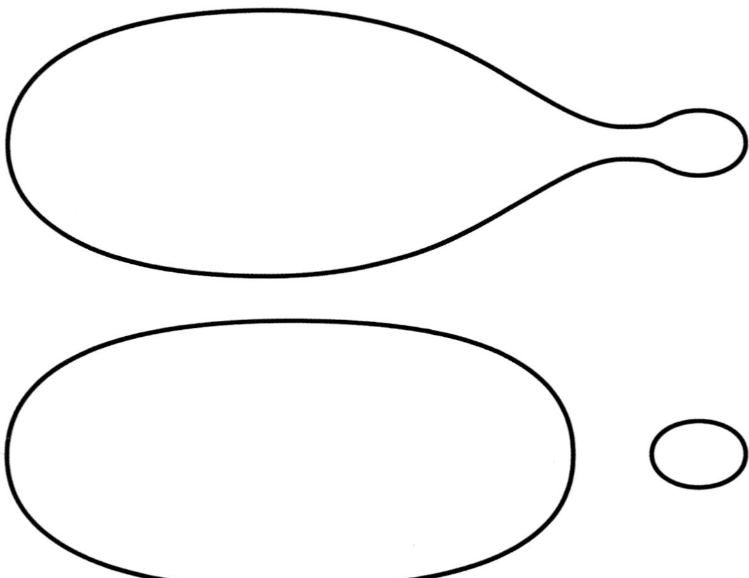

Fig. 1. Pear-shaped configuration by J. Jeans

The two-dimensional series ended with its division into two separate ellipsoidal configurations when $\omega^2/2\pi\rho=0.455$ (Fig. 1). This was an important result on the stability of pear-shaped figures of equilibrium although Jeans did not recognize it at the time. This was because his calculations, contained an unfortunate numerical error, which he himself discovered in 1916.

While studying in Cambridge, Jeans considered a wider, much more crucial issue, i.e. how did the structure of our Universe arise? Of course, in the early twentieth century prior to the creation of relativistic and quantum physics, Jeans could search for a solution to that issue only in the framework of classical physics. This is how he would have approached the question as to how stars and planets were formed from some primary cosmic material, dust and gas.

Jeans knew that Isaac Newton, who discovered the laws of gravity, had already understood the instability of matter when it was uniformly distributed in space. Indeed, in a letter to Richard Bentley in 1692 he pointed out that in the case of the distribution of matter in a finite space it would move to the middle and form one spherical mass; in the case of infinite space it could not come together as one mass, but would form an infinite number of masses scattered throughout space. Newton even suggested that the Sun and the fixed stars could have been formed in this way, but with only qualitative reasoning.

Jeans clearly understood that mathematics could provide quantitative results. He defined the problem of the stability of uniformly distributed matter and solved it using the theory of small perturbations. He obtained an expression for the linear size of the perturbation above which instability develops and the corresponding mass disturbance; these are now referred to respectively, as the 'Jeans wavelength' and the 'Jeans mass'. Those values were dependent on the density of the medium and the speed of propagation of sound. This is natural because the solution was obtained when considering a perturbation in which two forces start operating on an element: gravity (due to the change in density) and pressure (due to the density gradient). For this he solved Euler and Poisson's system of equations of continuity.

Here's how Jeans later described his approach in the 4th edition of "*The Universe around us*":

GRAVITATIONAL INSTABILITY

It is natural to enquire whether the forces which now keep a star together may not also have been responsible for its falling together in the first instance. This leads us to study the aggregating power of gravitation in some detail.

Five years after Newton had published his law of gravitation, Bentley, later Master of Trinity College, wrote to him, raising the question of whether the newly discovered force of gravitation would not account for the aggregation of matter into stars, and we find Newton replying, in a letter of date December 10, 1692:

> It seems to me, that if the matter of our sun and planets, and all the matter of the universe, were evenly scattered throughout all the heavens, and every particle had an innate gravity towards all the rest,

> and the whole space throughout which this matter was scattered, was finite, the matter on the outside of this space would by its gravity tend towards all the matter on the inside, and by consequence fall down into the middle of the whole space, and there compose one great spherical mass. But if the matter were evenly disposed throughout an infinite space, it could never convene into one mass; but some of it would convene into one mass and some into another, so as to make an infinite number of great masses, scattered great distances from one to another throughout all that infinite space. And thus might the sun and fixed stars be formed, supposing the matter were of a lucid nature.

Exact mathematical investigation not only confirms Newton's conjecture in general terms, but also provides a method for calculating what size of aggregates would be formed under the action of gravitation.

THE FORMATION OF CONDENSATION.

You stand in the middle of a room and clap your hands. In common language you are making a noise; the physicist, in his professional capacity, would say you are creating waves of sound. As your hands approach one another, they expel the intervening molecules of air. These stampede out, colliding with the molecules of outer layers of air, which are in turn driven away to collide with still more remote layers; the disturbance originally created by the motion of your hands is carried on in the form of a wave. Although the individual molecules have an average speed of 500 yards a second, the zig-zag quality of their motions reduces the speed of the disturbance, as we have already seen, to about 370 yards a second–the ordinary velocity of sound. As the disturbance reaches any point, the number of molecules there becomes abnormally high, for the stampeding molecules add to the normal quota of molecules at the point. This of course produces an excess of pressure. It is this excess pressure acting on my ear-drum that transmits a sensation to my brain, so that I hear the noise of you clapping your hands.

This excess of pressure cannot of course persist for long, so that the excess of molecules which produces it must rapidly dissipate. It is thus that the wave passes on. Yet there is one factor which militates against its dissipation. Each molecule exerts a gravitation pull on all its neighbours, so that where there is an excess of molecules, there is also an excess of gravitational force. In an ordinary sound wave this is of absolutely inappreciable amount, yet such as it is, it provides a tiny force tending to hold the molecules back, and preventing them scattering as freely as they otherwise would do. When the same phenomenon occurs on the astronomical scale, the corresponding forces may become of overwhelming importance.

Let us speak of the gas in any region of space where the number of molecules is above the average of the surrounding space, as a "condensation." Then it can be proved that, if a condensation is of sufficient extent, the excess of gravitational force may be sufficient to inhibit scattering altogether. In such a case, the condensation may continually grow through attracting molecules into it from outside, whose molecular speeds are then inadequate to carry them away again.

Whether this happens or not will depend of course on the speed of molecular motion in the gas, as well as on the size of the condensation. But it will not depend at all on the extent to which the process of condensation has proceeded. On doubling the extent to which condensation has proceeded, we double the excess number of molecules in any condensation. In so doing, we double the gravitational pull tending to increase the condensation, but we also double the excess pressure which tends to dissipate it; we merely double the weights on each side of the balance, so that the balance still swings in the same direction. If once conditions are favourable to its growth, a condensation goes on growing automatically until there are no further molecules left for it to absorb.

The further a condensation extends in space, the more favourable conditions are to its continued growth. Other things being equal, a condensation two million miles in diameter will exert twice as much gravitational force on its outermost molecules as a condensation one million miles in diameter, but the excess pressures are the same in the two cases. Thus, the larger a condensation is the more likely it is to go on growing, and by passing in imagination to larger and larger condensations we must in time come to condensations of such a size that they are bound to keep on growing. Nature's law here is one of unrestricted competition. Nothing succeeds like success, and so we find that condensations which are big to start with have the capacity of increasing still farther, while those which are small merely dissipate away.

Suppose now that an enormous mass of uniform gas extends through space for millions of millions of miles in every direction. Any disturbance which destroys its uniformity may be regarded as setting up condensations of every conceivable size.

This may not seem obvious at first; it may be thought that a disturbance which only affected a small area of gas would only produce a condensation of small extent. Such an argument overlooks the way in which the gravitational pull of a small body acts throughout the universe. The moon raises tides on the distant earth, and also tides, although incomparably less in amount, on the most distant of stars. Each time the child throws its toy out of its baby-carriage, it disturbs the motion of every star in the universe. So long as gravitation acts, no disturbance can be confined to any area less than the whole of space. The more violent the disturbance which creates them, the more intense the condensations will be to begin with, but even the smallest disturbance must set up condensations, although these may be of extremely feeble intensity. And we have seen that the fate of a condensation is not determined by its intensity but by its size. No matter how feeble their original intensity may have been, the big condensations go on growing, the small ones disappear. In time nothing is left but a collection of big condensations. The mathematical analysis already referred to shows that there is a definite minimum weight such that all condensations below this weight merely dissipate away into space. This minimum weight is such that if approximately a tenth of this weight of gas were isolated in space, and all the rest of the gas annihilated, the molecules would just and only just fail to escape from its surface.

We may say that the original uniformly distributed mass of gas was "unstable" because any disturbance, however slight, causes it to change its configuration entirely; it had the dynamical attributes of a stick balanced on its point, or of a soap-bubble which is just ready to burst.

PRIMAEVAL CHAOS.

These general theoretical results may now be applied to any mass of gas we please. Let us begin by applying them to Newton's hypothetical "matter evenly disposed throughout an infinite space". We return in imagination to a time when all the substance of the present stars and nebulae was spread uniformly throughout space; in brief, we start from the primaeval chaos from which most scientific theories of cosmogony have started.

We have already seen that if all the substance of the present universe — nebulae, stars, stray matter and everything else — were uniformly scattered through space, there would be something like 10^{-28} grams of matter to the cubic centimetre, so that this is the kind of density we must assign to the hypothetical primaeval nebula. It is almost inconceivably low. In ordinary air, at a density of one eight-hundredth that of water, the average distance between adjoining molecules is about an eight-millionth part of an inch; in the primaeval gas we are now considering, the corresponding distance is nearly a yard. If the amount of air which occupies the space of a pinhead in our atmosphere were reduced to this density, it would occupy a hundred million cubic miles — a cube 460 miles each way. The contrast again leads back to the theme of the extreme emptiness of space.

We must, however, not forget that the universe appears to be expanding very rapidly, and changing its mean density of matter in space. The mean density of the primaeval chaos may have been greater or less than now according as space has increased or decreased its volume in the meantime.

Assuming the Friedmann-Lemaître cosmology, Eddington has estimated that the mean density of matter in the original Einstein space must have been about 10^{-27}.

We proceed to inquire what is the minimum weight of condensation that would persist in a primaeval gas of such densities.

Calculation shows that if ordinary air were attenuated to a density of 10^{-28}, so that its molecules were about a yard apart, no condensation could persist and continue to grow unless it had at least 640,000 times the mass of the sun; any smaller weight of gas would exert so slight a gravitational pull on its outermost molecules, that their normal molecular speeds of 500 yards a second would lead to the prompt dissipation of the whole condensation.

Hence if such a gas were spread uniformly in space, and disturbed in any way, all incipient condensations whose mass was less than that of 640,000 suns would be smoothed out, and the gas would ultimately break up in larger condensations each having 640,000 times the mass of the sun or more.

We can carry out similar calculations with reference to other assumed molecular velocities. The following table shows the weights of condensations which would be formed in primaeval masses of chaotic gas of this same density 10^{-28}, with the molecules moving at different speeds:

Speed (km/sec.)	Where found	Minimum mass of condensation
500	Air in room	640,000 suns
2,000	Hydrogen at 0°C	40 million suns
27,000	?	100,000 " "
120,000	Free electron at 0°C	9,000,000 " "

If we make similar calculations for a density of 10^{-27} grams per cubic centimetre, the masses prove to be only about one-third of those tabulated above.

All known stars have weights comparable with that of the sun. Thus if, as Newton conjectured, the stars first came into being as condensations of this kind, then the entries in this table ought to be comparable with unity. Newton's conjecture, in the form in which we have just considered it, is clearly untenable, since the calculated weights are of the order of millions of times that of the sun. If there ever existed a primaeval chaos of the kind we are now considering, it would not condense into stars, but into enormously more massive condensations, each having the weight of millions of stars.' [163, p. 213–18].

It must be said that, despite the undoubted correctness of the deduction, Jeans understood the invalidity of his assumption that the unperturbed state is a stationary gas, evenly distributed in space. It appeared due to the fact that an infinite uniform distribution of matter has no certain gravitational potential, and a finite space distribution, as indicated by Newton, should collapse.

Anyway, Jeans realized that gravitational instability was the basis of processes leading to the structure of our world, and at some stage, even to the complex development of this structure, thus providing the possibility of evolutionary processes which have directed the events that have made our world the way it is now. We ourselves, being cognitive subjects, are to some extent also the products of these processes.

At this stage of his life, Jeans did not want to be distracted by philosophical reflections. He was more interested in concrete results. His report *The Stability of a Spherical Nebula* outlining the theory of gravitational instability was sent to the Royal Society and published in 1902 [7].

Building on these results, Jeans considered the problem of oscillations and the stability of rotating gravitating bodies. He managed to show that for a spherically symmetric self-gravitating mass stability depended on its radius, the average density and average compression modulus. It became clear to him that the assessment of the stability of real objects was complicated by the ignorance of the compressibility of their material and the distribution of the density. Nevertheless Jeans managed to apply and develop theoretical approaches to the classical nebular hypothesis of the origin of our planetary system.

He wondered about the application of similar approaches to the study of stresses and vibrations in the Earth. Jeans had priority in the development of a technique of determination of the so-called Lamé parameters. These characterized the elastic properties of the material of the planet by measuring the time of propagation of seismic waves caused by earthquakes. He outlined the results of those researches in his work *On the vibrations and stability of gravitating planets*, which was published in the Proceedings of the Royal Society in 1903 [8]. The Secretary of the Royal Society, Joseph Larmor, informed Jeans about a positive assessment of his work in a letter dated 20th March 1903.

Despite the growing recognition of the scientific achievements of Jeans and his natural desire to improve his academic status, there were no suitable professorial vacancies in Cambridge. Periodically, they came up in other universities and in the autumn of 1904, his candidacy was put forward for the vacant position as head of the Department of Mathematics in the University of Aberdeen, Scotland. He was able to obtain recommendations from academics and scientists known throughout the world.

The Master of Trinity College, H.M. Butler wrote 'he is regarded as one of the most brilliant and original of our young mathematicians. His character is of the highest, his manners are most agreeable, and he has won the warm regard of us all.' [193, p. 11].

The Professor of Astronomy, G.H. Darwin testified: 'I did not see anything of Mr Jeans during his career as an undergraduate at Trinity College, but a very remarkable essay by him was submitted to me as one of the examiners for the Fellowship at Trinity College. The paper showed much originality and a very unusual power of dealing with a mathematical problem of great difficulty. The subject was especially interesting to me, and we had several long discussions of it after the fellowship examination. I ultimately had the pleasure of presenting the paper to the Royal Society for publication in the Philosophical Transactions. At a later date I presented two other papers by him to the Royal Society, and I consider that the investigations contained in these papers form important contributions to science.' [193, p. 12].

And the Cavendish Professor of Physics, J.J. Thomson affirmed: 'I have read many of Mr Jeans's papers, especially those dealing with electrical subjects, and with the kinetic theory of gases, and have been greatly struck by the originality and power displayed in them. I know of no one among the younger mathematicians who has done abler or more important work in the application of mathematics to the explanation of natural phenomena. I think that any University would be fortunate if they could secure the services of Mr Jeans, whose papers have shown him to be a mathematician of the very highest order.' [193, p. 12].

Henry Montagu Butler (1833–1918) Master of Trinity College, Cambridge.

But Jeans was not successful, and H.M. MacDonald was elected to the Aberdeen chair. Soon, however, Jeans was offered a new vacancy.

In the summer of 1905 he was in South Africa as Secretary of section A (Physics and Mathematics) for the meeting of the British Association for the Advancement of Science (founded in 1831) being held at Cape Town. Almost immediately after the opening of the conference, he received a telegram inviting him to take a position as Professor of Applied Mathematics at Princeton University, New Jersey. Without hesitation Jeans accepted, leaving his work at the British Association, and immediately returned to England to prepare for his move to America.

There was nothing to keep him in England. He had no home or family. Jeans was full of ambitious aspirations, and at Cambridge vacant professorships were infrequent. He did not have the patience to wait and other universities in the UK were too provincial and he decided to seek his scientific future overseas.

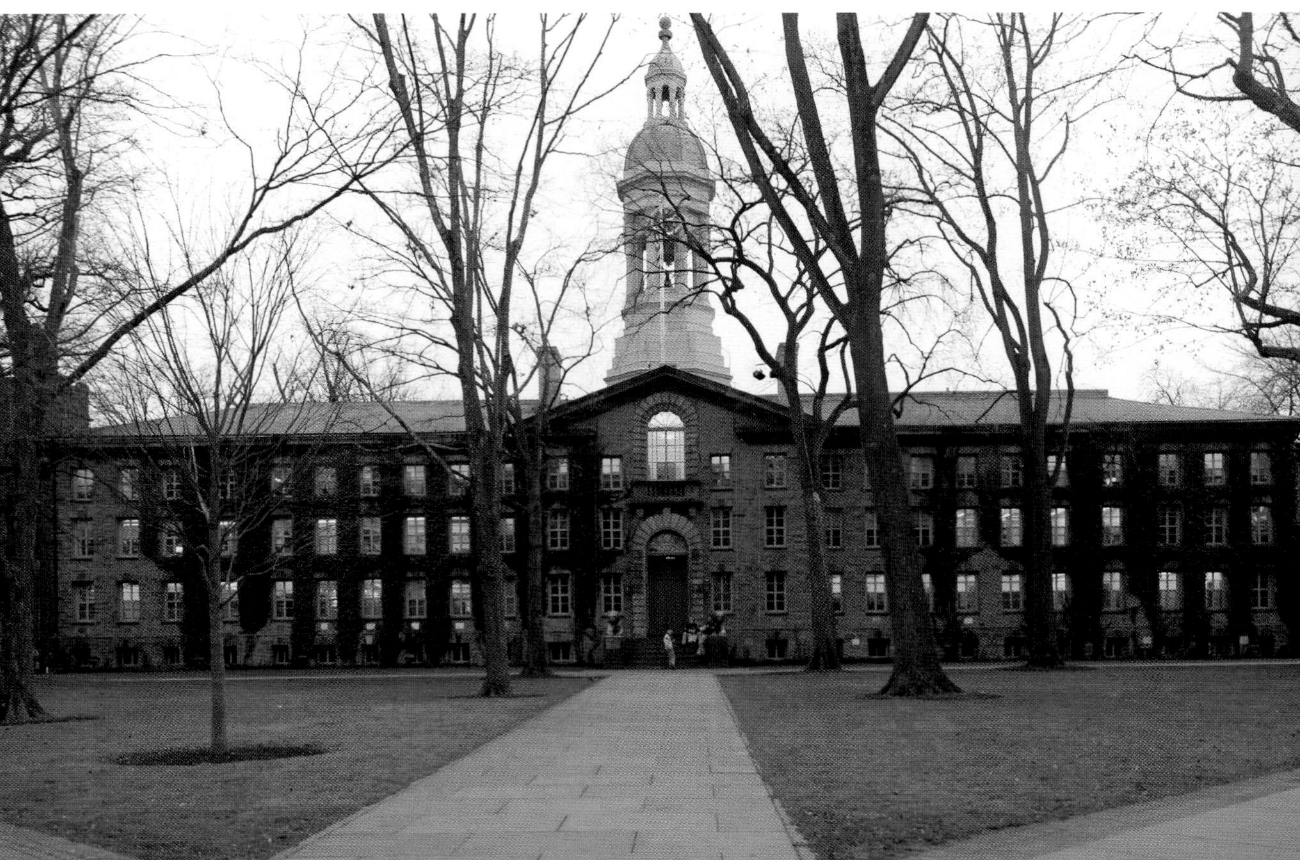

Nassau Hall, built in 1756, is the oldest building of Princeton University, New Jersey, US

PRINCETON AND MARRIAGE TO CHARLOTTE MITCHELL 1905–1909

Woodrow Wilson, the President of Princeton University, who actively participated in the organization of its expansion and strengthening, invited Jeans to take the Chair of Applied Mathematics in 1905. Wilson went on to win the Presidential election of 1912, as a candidate of the Democratic Party, and become the President of the USA.

New York met Jeans with the Statue of Liberty, skyscrapers, honking of horns, bustle of people and glaring lights of advertisements. But Princeton, a small University town, green and quiet, not far from the ocean, was more like 'good old England'.

G. B. Fine, friend and assistant to Wilson, possessed extraordinary intuition in recognizing promising young scientists. It was he who recommended Wilson to invite Jeans. And in 1905, three other scientists began teaching in Princeton: Owen Willans Richardson, who received later a Nobel prize for the discovery of the dependence of the current density of thermonic emission on the cathode temperature; mathematician George David Birkhoff, who had developed a general theory of dynamical systems and proved the theorem of ergodicity; and astronomer Henry Norris Russell, who drew the first spectrum luminosity chart for the stars, made the first reliable estimates of the content of chemical elements in the Universe, and did other outstanding work in astrophysics.

Arriving in Princeton as a well-known scientist, Jeans gave advanced lectures mainly to the most capable students in the senior courses. Soon after his arrival Jeans was elected a Fellow of the Royal Society of London. That recognition at home came to him when he was only 28 years old. On that occasion, witty students responded with a humorous song that they performed at an impromptu gathering on the steps of Nassau Hall together with other students' songs:

Here's to Jimmy Hopwood Jeans
He tries to make us Math-machines
A young and brilliant F.R.S.
That's going some, we all confess.

Jeans did not devote all his time just to teaching and research. In spite of his shyness, he felt lonely. It is therefore not surprising that Jeans befriended another newcomer to Princeton who was also invited by Woodrow Wilson in September 1905 — Hiram Bingham — 'preceptor in history, politics

J. H. Jeans (~1906–07, Hollinger & Co, New York).

Hiram and Alfreda Bingham and three sons (~1905). Alfreda was Charlotte Mitchell's elder sister.

HIRAM BINGHAM

Hiram Bingham (1875–1956), Jeans's colleague at Princeton, had strong academic and political ambitions. Married to Alfreda, sister to Charly, Jeans's future wife, he benefited from his parents-in-law inherited Tiffany wealth and support — including building for their extensive family of seven sons a 35 room mansion. He pursued his interest in Latin American Studies particularly at Princeton and Yale, and was responsible for the 'discovery' of Machu Picchu, the famous Inca centre high in the Peruvian Andes.

Learning to fly at the age of 42, he played a role in the aviation section of the US Signal Corps and Air Service during the World War I. Bingham was chief of the air personal division of the Army and, as a lieutenant colonel, commanding the largest American flying school in France, at Issoudun. His public career started in 1922 in Connecticut as Lieutenant Governor, Governor and then as the Republican senator (The Flying Senator) for the state from 1926 to 1933. A return to public life in 1951 at the height of McCarthyism was regarded as an effort by the Truman Administration to counter charges that the Administration, including the Loyalty Review Board, was soft on Communists in 1951, as it required a finding that "reasonable grounds" existed to believe a person disloyal before he could be dismissed. Bingham was chairman of the loyalty programme and was responsible for introducing a much lighter burden of proof — "reasonable doubt" — on the Government. The board issued some of the most newsworthy and controversial findings including reviewing and reversing favourable findings by departmental loyalty boards. Bingham remained chairman until President Eisenhower abolished the panel and substituted a new Government security programme in 1953.

and economics'. Bingham had received his doctorate at Harvard University shortly before. His field was the history of the Spanish colonies. He gathered material for a political biography of Simón Bolívar, the liberator of South America. Striving to achieve real success, and the thirst for fame, brought together these two young men. Jeans soon became a frequent guest in the big mansion of the Binghams on Washington Road. There he met his future wife, Charlotte Tiffany Mitchell, Bingham's sister-in-law. She was a shy but attractive girl, with a poetic talent, and belonged to a well-known family in the United States.

Her maternal grandfather, Charles Lewis Tiffany, was a founder and the President of Tiffany & Co, the world-famous jewellery firm. He was born in Connecticut in 1812, into the family of a prosperous manufacturer of fabrics. They belonged to the descendants of the first settlers in America. It is known that a squire Humphrey Tiffany settled in Massachusetts in about 1660. Charles Lewis Tiffany acquired business skills working in his father's textile factory, managing the main store in Connecticut and making purchasing trips to New York. In 1837, at the age of twenty, he was lent $1000 by his father, and together with his companion John B. Jung opened a small jewellery store on Broadway, opposite the City Hall Park. Times were bad: few people had money to spare, many had been ruined by the panic on the stock market that year, and New York still had scars from two great fires of two years previously.

Although the revenue for the first day was only $4.98 Charles Tiffany was said to be born for trade. He sold bronze statuettes, Japanese water colours, Chinese umbrellas, Venetian glass and boxes of cigars. He had the gift to predict future tastes, and he recognised the general public's wish for novelty.

Initially, the store's products could be seen as high-quality imitations of real jewellery. However, from 1841 Tiffany and Jung started buying jewellery in Europe. Their shop was the only one in New York which traded real jewels and had a permanent representative abroad.

Big success came in 1848, when John Jung did his annual procurement in Paris. Frightened by the revolution, the aristocracy sold their family jewels at half-price. Soon Charles Tiffany became known as the king of diamonds.

Two years later Tiffany opened a branch in Paris and quickly overtook his New York competitors. He bought fabulous treasures from the Hungarian Prince Esterhazy and from Marie Antoinette and sold them piece by piece. Throughout the second half of the 19th century empires fell and monarchs were deposed. Tiffany bought their jewels and sold them to millionaires. He focused, however, not only on super-rich people, but also on ordinary members of the middle classes. After his companion John Jung resigned, he was the sole director of the company Tiffany & Co. In 1877 a diamond weighing 128.51 carats was found in South Africa and named after Tiffany.

Alfred Mitchell (1832–1911), his wife Annie Olivia Tiffany Mitchell (1844–1937) and their two daughters (Alfreda 1874–1967; Charlotte Tiffany 1877–1934), 27th April 1891.

Charles Tiffany married Harriet, John Jung's sister. They had four children: two sons, Lewis Comfort and Barnett, and two daughters, Annie and Louise. The elder son, Lewis Comfort Tiffany, born on the 18th of February 1848, became an outstanding artist and modern designer. He participated in the leadership of the family firm. When Charles Lewis Tiffany died in 1902 at the age of 90, his family inherited almost $10,000,000 — in those days an incredibly large amount — each child inheriting a quarter of it.

The eldest daughter Annie, born in 1844, married Alfred Mitchell in 1872. He was born in 1832. At the time of the wedding he was no longer a young man. There is a letter dated 1870 to Annie from her friend Mae Goddard, who introduced them to one another. Alfred Mitchell was a cousin of Mae's mother. He was almost a family member of the Goddards — Mae called him 'Uncle Alf'. Alfred fell in love with Annie and started courting her. Annie herself told Mae about her growing sense of attachment to Alfred despite the age difference. Mae, who considered 'Uncle Alf' as an elder brother, wrote to Annie that she would be happy if they married.

Alfred Mitchell was a descendant of one of the first families of the colonial 'aristocracy'. His father — also Alfred — a vicar, died before young Alfred's birth. A rich relative, William Williams from New London, became his guardian. He too was a godly man and sponsored American missionaries abroad.

When his ward reached the age of majority (21) and received a modest inheritance left him by his mother, Williams sent him to Honolulu, Hawaii. He hoped the young man would try his luck in the profitable business of supplying whaling ships, many of which belonged to Williams' family and were laid up in the harbour of Honolulu between the Arctic and Antarctic seasons. Williams gave Alfred a letter of introduction to Samuel Damon, the pastor of the sailors' Church in Honolulu.

Damon was one of those missionaries whose primary objective was not the salvation of the souls of aboriginals but ministry to the congregation of crews of whaling ships. It is interesting to notice the coincidence: for several years before Mitchell's arrival, the head of the mission was Hiram Bingham, whose grandson, also named Hiram Bingham, became the husband of Alfred Mitchell's elder daughter, Alfreda.

The Reverend Mr. Damon introduced Alfred Mitchell to the business community of the Hawaiian Islands. Alfred was not a natural businessman, rather a quiet young man with literary inclinations. If he had any ambition, perhaps it was to become a famous writer, as his older brother Donald was. His capital was spent, and he had to leave the island and enter military service. After the Civil War it was very difficult for him as an officer to find a useful profession. Alfred decided to engage in politics, using the easily-won votes of Negroes in Charleston in South Carolina.

At first, Alfred and his new wife moved there to live. But that business didn't interest Mitchell, and he preferred to leave it; moreover, his wife's income allowed them to live without working. They liked to travel. Mitchell wanted to show Annie the place where he had lived in his youth, and he took her on a nostalgic trip to Hawaii. They looked a respectable couple — a handsome gentleman with a delicate young lady.

After three years they had a daughter. Most likely Annie wanted a son and had hoped to name him in honour of her husband, and therefore named her daughter Alfreda. She wanted the second child to be named after her father Charles Tiffany, but again it was a girl. She named her Charlotte.

Charles Mitchell disliked the cold winters of his native New England. So he travelled to southern countries with his wife and two daughters, encouraging them to learn foreign languages and music. He believed that to be the basis of female education, but for women to acquire any real profession, he believed, was not only unnecessary but undesirable.

After building a magnificent villa in Jamaica — a marble and concrete palace overlooking the Caribbean at the entrance to the harbour of Port Antonio — the Mitchells started to live there for half the year, and the remaining half, mainly the summer, in New London.

Charlotte* was a determined and independent woman, who wanted to get a real education. When she was 17 she rebelled against her eccentric father and his narrow views about women's education. Enlisting the support of her father's cousin — headmistress of a school for girls — she got permission from him to enter Bryn Mawr College, which was among the first institutes

*** Charlotte never liked her own name, her preference was Charly. As a young girl, not wishing to offend her parents who had given her such a bizarre name, she played with changing it to its Italian equivalent — 'Carlina'.**

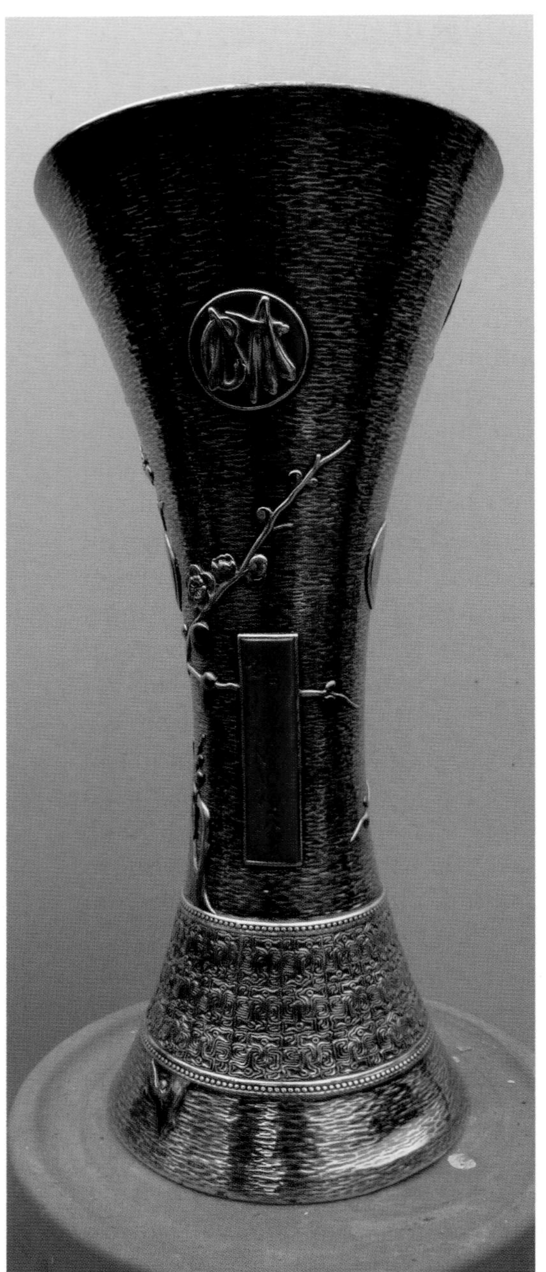

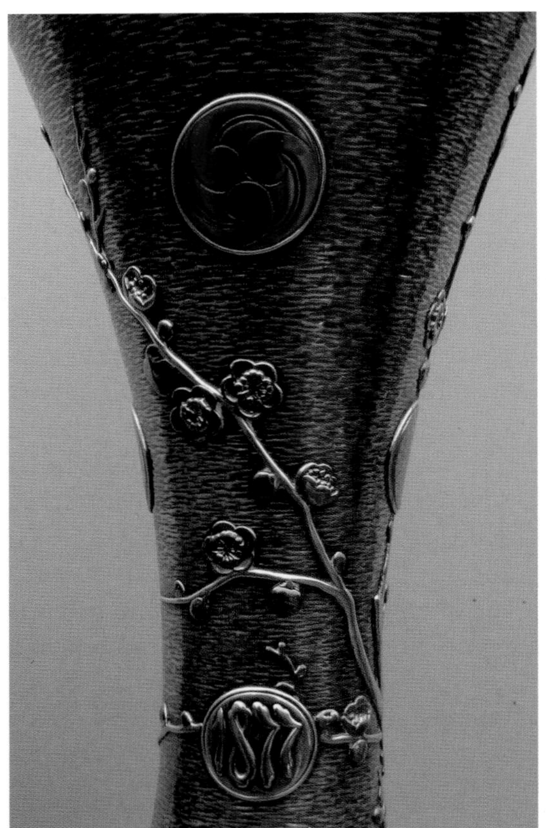

CHARLOTTE'S CHRISENING VASE

The Tiffany silver vase by Edward Moore celebrating the birth of Charlotte Tiffany Mitchell in 1877. Height 260 mm.

Right:
Alfreda and Charlotte Mitchell (date unknown).

offering higher education for women. As she had not completed secondary education, she had to study hard and take private lessons to enter the College at the end of 1894. The following four years were spent in the stimulating atmosphere of the college and the women's rights movement.

Shortly before the end of her student years Charlotte wrote to her mother:

> "I have been having a most exciting week. Thursday evening we went to Miss President Thomas's reception, and as the young ladies in this college are not very easy on such occasions, Juliet and I had to furnish all the conversation. I evidently made a very good impression on Miss Thomas for I was invited yesterday to lunch with her which is a great triumph for me, or in fact for anyone, as only a very few are ever granted that honour. I met there Mr. and Mrs. Sidney Webb, who are two of the most prominent social and political workers in London, both of them very well known for their books and work as members of the Fabian Society. They spoke this morning on the methods of social and political work and its great necessity in America, and fired us all with much enthusiasm."

Then, recalling her father's connection with Hawaii, she asked him whether he could provide the Webbs with letters of introduction, as they planned to visit the island. Her father must have written a caustic reply, because in her next letter to her mother she wrote "Please do not show this letter to Papa", and it was full of bitterness.

First of all, she thanked her mother for some addresses in Honolulu. "I think cards will do as well as letters, especially as I hardly know the Webbs. Of course the Honolulu people will not be foolish enough to sneer at people that have an exceedingly high position in London. I hope I may never be myself so narrow-minded as to call this place a "crank-mill", nor so out of touch with youth and change that I shall have no comprehension of the advance from one century or one generation to another."

In the letter she continued to talk about her fear of returning home after the completion of her education, where she would have "no occupation and no end in view or object for which to live". "I do not like" — she wrote — "to look forward to a life of continual laziness and inactivity. I don't like to think that I am bound down to nothing for the rest of time."

After finishing her education she had eight troubled and not very happy years living at her parents', or travelling with them. Her father, as she wrote, had "absolutely no regard for anything that is really me or any sympathy with youth and ambitions". Then her parents allowed her to go to Europe, accompanied by an elderly cousin as a chaperon. It seemed impossible to

HOME IN NEW LONDON
The Mitchell family home, Pequot Avenue, New London, Connecticut, USA.
The original section purchased in 1870 and considerably added to over the years. Now part of Mitchell College. This was the home that Charlotte and Alfreda knew, for their parents it was more of a summer house whereas winters were spent either in Folly Point in Jamaica or travelling.

find a job, but even if she were looking for one, what career could she follow except, perhaps, a literary one? Charlotte found an outlet for her inclination for literature, writing poems, poems about loneliness and death, the sea and the beauty of the iceberg "with gems of rainbow spun", later collected and published posthumously by Jeans.

In 1906, she wrote "The Star-Gazer": a poetic story about melancholy and two stars in a collision. A poem called "To a Scientist" begins with the line "From far and humbly let me worship thee". And when she met Jeans, she fell in love with him.

He seemed to her a young English Professor, intelligent, witty, courteous, of attractive appearance and charm, always carefully groomed in a light grey suit with matching waistcoat and blue or grey ties reflecting his grey-blue eyes. In America — as a tribute to its democratic tradition — Jeans did not wear a high-standing collar, fastened in a special manner with a broad tie

THE CAMP
After Charlotte graduated from Bryn Maur in 1899 she accompanied her parents on their visit to Japan. Her father was particularly taken by traditional Japanese architecture — resulting in an extensive single floored teahouse, the Camp. This was built in 1905 on the Connecticut Estate, it had seven bedrooms and extensive servants' quarters without hot water or electricity. Whereas Charlotte's discerning eye had been attracted by the style, form and colours of the ceramics, prints and ornaments of the East that in her married life she used and decorated her homes in Cambridge and Dorking.

and a pearl clasp such as he wore in Cambridge. But now a turned-down collar and a three-piece suit did not make him less elegant. Jeans quickly noticed Charlotte — a beautiful, modestly dressed girl with bushy hair and with a thoughtful and somewhat sad look. He recognised her loneliness, perhaps because he himself felt lonely in America. For Jeans it became clear that she was bored and dissatisfied with the role of women in her social setting. Jeans became interested in Charlotte, conversations became more relaxed. Soon his interest and fascination grew into deeper feelings. Realising that he loved her, she felt happy. She wrote a number of sonnets, modestly entitled "Old Fashioned Love". Charlotte was no longer alone. In this young man — they were both 28 years old — whom she called "My Beloved Lord", she found the answer to her aspirations: "Thy fame my fame". "Woman's fate" did not trouble her any more.

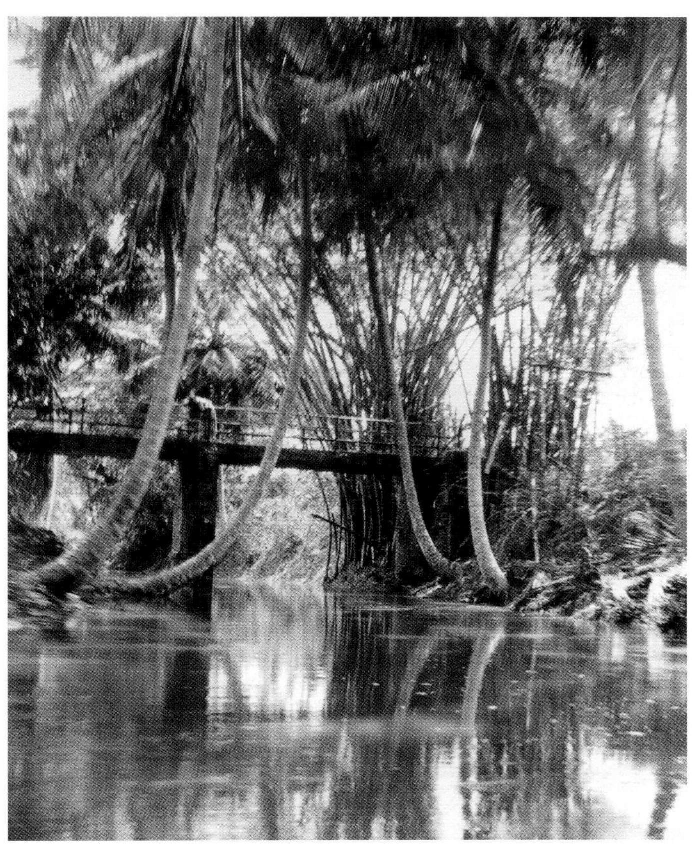

FOLLY POINT
Folly Point, the large mansion designed by Chapman & Fraser of Boston, US, and built (1904–5) for Alfred and Annie Mitchell overlooking the Caribbean at Port Antonio, Jamaica.

Views of the mountains behind Port Antonio from Folly Point.

The setting of Folly Point.

Wilder parts of the garden at Folly Point, Port Antonio, Jamaica.

The two-storey atrium at Folly Point overlooking the Caribbean.

Another topic of her poems was the bitterness of love. "Our hands have clung together during rain" as it is written in one of the sonnets. And when she wrote that they will "sleep together and forever, side by side", then she was thinking more about a grave than a marriage-bed.

James and Charlotte had met in the house of her older married sister Alfreda, where professors, scientists and musicians were entertained. Alfreda herself studied and played the violin; her contemporary and friend Susan Metcalfe sang with Pablo Casals and later married him.

In childhood Charlotte and her sister were always together, but when Charlotte went to college, she wrote: "I don't like her. Freda is not ambitious. She had no such desires such as I have, naturally she does not fret then against circumstances". Except for one winter, when her parents had settled her in an apartment in New York with an elderly cousin as chaperon, Alfreda almost never left the house nor travelled without her parents until her marriage. Charlotte called her sister 'Id', and in one undated letter written to her sister on her engagement to Hiram Bingham in 1900, she shows some hostility and her own associated guilt.

> "Dear Id —
> Your letter heaped coals of fire on my head, for it seemed so absurd for you to be accusing yourself of being a selfish sister when it has always been I who was the selfish and you the sweet and generous one. As for my nature being nobler than yours, that is an absurdity; only it is a very different one. I feel that I have been very disagreeable to everyone ever since I left college and in fact much longer that that — not because I did not appreciate my surroundings, but because of my disagreeable disposition, I suppose."

She continued her letter by saying how she was glad for their happiness, and that she always liked Hiram. After Freda married and settled in Cambridge, Massachusetts, and became a mother, the two sisters saw little of one another.

It is not known when James and Charlotte first met. Charlotte spent the end of the winter of 1905–06 in New York with 'Aunt Julia', the elderly cousin, who had supported her wish to attend college. While the Mitchells lived in their new Caribbean mansion in Jamaica, Aunt Julia wrote to them — as early as January 1906 — about the courtship with a brilliant young Englishman.

She again began to see more of her sister, who lived with her family in the big mansion given by the parents. In March she said to Alfreda that she wanted to move to Princeton. "Her ways disturb me", Alfreda wrote in her diary. Tensions arose between the sisters. Alfreda was already pregnant with her fourth child and Charlotte, almost thirty, was not yet married. All the same, when Charlotte and James went on walks alone, Alfreda commented: "A little too!".

Summer came. The Mitchells returned to their house in New London. Hiram was not satisfied with his position at Princeton and tried to find a better appointment at Yale.

In the same summer Charlotte wanted to live separately from her family and moved to Salem, fifty miles from New London, where her father bought her an old farm-house once the home of his great-grandfather. There, the story is told, James showed up one day, having taken the train from Princeton to New Haven, then the shore line trolley to East Lyme, then walked nine miles over Grassy Hill to Salem, only to find Miss Mitchell not at home. Propriety won out in a battle with ardour. James left his card, trudged back the nine miles to the trolley, and so by train back to Princeton. However, with the beginning of the University term the Binghams returned to the big house on Mercer Heights in Princeton, bought for them by the Mitchells. Alfreda lived there with her four children, nannies, and staff, but Hiram got leave of absence for health reasons — he had a difficult appendectomy earlier in the year. Until June of the following year he travelled to Venezuela and Colombia in the footsteps of Bolívar's army.

Charlotte spent the autumn with her parents in Jamaica and winter with Aunt Julia in New York, but Princeton was only an hour away by train, and Alfreda could not withhold her hospitality. Courtship continued. Charlotte was not in very good health, suffering from some nameless infection and she was taking heavy doses of a dangerous drug. But in December they got engaged.

James was known to close friends as 'Fred' — as he signed his letters to them — at least until he became Sir James. But in a letter to Mr. Alfred Mitchell, in which he asked for the hand of his daughter, he signed simply "Yours, J.H. Jeans". The letter was sent from Princeton University to Port Antonio, Jamaica, to a person whom he had never met and whose daughter Charlotte he had known for nearly a year.

> Princeton, New Jersey
> December 27th, 1906
> Dear Mr. Mitchell:
> In view of what I am going to ask, I very much wish I was better known to you. To be brief, I have asked your daughter to be my wife, she, to my great happiness, has consented, and I now write to ask for your approval.
>
> Before I can ask this I ought to explain to you something of who and what I am. My present position is that of a Professor at Princeton

— you may also wish to know why I left my own country — England — and what my circumstances were there. I believe my family to be of good origin, although I can give no convincing proof of this, even to myself — I mistrust, as you probably would also do, the genealogical researches of the family itself. My father, who is just retiring from his profession, is a Parliamentary Journalist — he has not been very successful in life — and behind this statement you will be able to read all that is implied to a man of no private means, by want of success. The rest of his family, although not hopelessly obscure, have never achieved real success or distinction, although his only brother, J.S. Jeans, is tolerably prominent in London — you will be able to find a list of his activities in the English "Who's Who" if you care.

My reason for leaving England was not want of success. Again I will refer you to "Who's Who" for my English career — but a belief that I should have better opportunities here. One of the main interests of my life — the main interest until the beginning of recent events — has been the advancement of my own branch of science, and I hope to do more here than I could at home. Perhaps — as I feel somewhat on my defensive — you will forgive me for saying that I believe I am regarded as in the front rank in this country (as indeed I was in England — I am at the present moment the youngest man who has held a Fellowship in the Royal Society for many years) — and I believe that whatever position is possible inside my profession I ought with favorable circumstances to be able to attain it. I wish you to see that I have a right to be regarded seriously in this respect. I intensely dislike writing about myself at all, but you naturally expect me to do so, and I think I have a right to tell you of the good as well as the bad.

You will say the main question remains unanswered — "Is the fellow a gentleman, and can he be trusted?" To this I will not attempt an answer, I know you will trust your daughter's judgment. I will only assure you that I love her with my whole nature, through and through, and without reserve, and that I have the supreme happiness of knowing that she loves me. I believe I can make her life happy, I need hardly say that I shall try to do so.

After this explanation, may I repeat my request, will you accept me as your son-in-law?

With sincerest regards to Mrs. Mitchell and yourself,
Yours,
J.H. Jeans

Charlotte Mitchell at Ausable, New York, US, August 1907.

James Jeans at Ausable, New York, US, August 1907.

Obviously, the young man asking for Charlotte's hand was uncertain about the answer. No doubt Charlotte had told James that her father would give his consent. Mr. Mitchell came from the colonial 'aristocracy' and wanted his son-in-law to come from a good family, too. He was already an old man in poor health when he received Jeans's letter. In the collection of Jeans's letters in the United States, there is another one addressed to Mr. Mitchell, thanking him for his reluctant consent. Mr. Mitchell died four years later, never having been reconciled with his English son-in-law, nor with the other then needy young man who married his eldest daughter. It is doubtful that he would have accepted them, even if he had known that one of them would become Sir James, and the other would be a U.S. Senator.

Around the same time, Aunt Julia wrote the following to Mrs. Mitchell, from New York:

> "Jeans has arrived. Charly came from Princeton yesterday and he came with her, and they are both in a state of cooing bliss. He deliberately kissed her before me and led me to congratulate him — cool as a cucumber. I rub my eyes and look again to see the critical and scoffing Charly very very much in love, and not only unashamed

> but proud of it. She never looked so pretty or seemed so well as she does now. I think she has found a cure for all her ills and is a very happy woman. She is utterly and entirely bound up on Jeans. I cannot get used to it, sure as I have been of it ever since last winter. Love has beautified him too, he looks better than I ever saw him, is well dressed and well mannered."

In other letters Aunt Julia admitted she was getting "quite fond of J.J. myself, though he is quite unlike anybody we have had in the family. I think him very honest and straightforward, ambitious in his work, undeniably clever and entirely modest. He is heels over head in love — and so is Charly". Her doctor was astonished at the great gain she had made in health. "So much for the curative power of love."

The official announcement of the engagement was made and the wedding planned, although the Mitchells in Jamaica were still doubtful about his "origin and breed". The couple continued to meet in the Binghams' home, although the unfortunate sister Alfreda felt that her husband had forgotten his own family. She felt depressed with winter illnesses; she and the children found it hard to see Charlotte so healthy and happy. In March — after several rows with Charlotte — Alfreda ran to her parents in Jamaica, leaving two children with nannies at home.

However, Charlotte's chronic disease diagnosed as congenital syphilis got worse, and her doctor insisted on postponing the marriage. That brought on deep depression and nervous prostration. During the six weeks from April 16th to May 25th, 1907, Jeans wrote to Charlotte's mother thirteen letters describing the symptoms of her illness, the doctors' opinions, hopes and fears about Charlotte, and his own recommendations for improvement of her health. His scientific activity at that time was almost halted, as he tried to be with Charlotte supporting her. Her parents, at least her father, thought that her suffering was caused by James's visits, but he continued to visit her, and Charlotte confirmed to her Aunt Julia that she feels relieved only when he is near her, even saying nothing.

Changes in medical treatment lessened the acute phase of the mental and emotional crisis, and after a few months Charlotte recovered sufficiently to plan a new date for the marriage. However, that difficult period was not forgotten. Mrs. Mitchell, who preserved Jeans's letters until the very end of her life, undoubtedly became his close friend, and those letters show his deep respect for her. Jeans was consistent in his emotional attachments. Having lived almost three decades together, he and Charlotte remained a dedicated couple until her death in 1934.

They wanted a modest wedding. The united Mitchells and Binghams were represented only by Aunt Julia and two cousins. The local priest led a

MUMFORD HOUSE, SALEM, CONNECTICUT, US.
Part of the Salem estate of 2,000 acres that Alfred brought together between 1900 and 1903. The house, originally belonging to Alfred Mitchell's grandparents, was given to Charlotte by her father before her marriage to James. Their simple wedding ceremony took place here in November 1907.

simple ceremony in the living room in the family farmhouse in Salem. It was on September the 11th, 1907 — the day of Jeans's 30th birthday, Charlotte was eight months older — she was born on January the 22nd, 1877.

Apparently, the Mitchells were very concerned that both their daughters' spouses were slightly younger than their wives. In both cases, their weddings took place when the men reached the age of their brides. Alfreda married Hiram Bingham on the 20th of November 1900, the day after he reached the age of 25; she was already 25 — seven months older. Charlotte married James on the day he reached her age.

Four days later Jeans wrote from Princeton to his mother-in-law, thanking her for "the best wife, most dear …".

The Mitchells took care to protect their daughter from the burden of housework as she was still weak from her illness. Their son-in-law Hiram had accepted a position at Yale and moved with his family to New Haven.

So their house in Princeton was offered to the Jeanses. There their happy family life started. But restless, romantically inclined Charlotte probably did not help to improve the mood of her husband, who himself was subject to frequent changes of mood and dissatisfaction.

Perhaps you can feel the mood of their lives in one of the sonnets written by Charlotte during the first year of marriage:

"When I look down the avenue of years
That stretch before us, on the unknown way
I see two aged forms! Lovers are they
And life-long friends tried by life's smiles and tears;
On their calm brows a radiance appears
Of mellow joy, although their heads are grey.
How sweet, my friend, not, lonely in decay,
Thus to grow old together down the years!
Oh loved with all the strength and tenderness
Of a passionate heart — fear not, not then
Shalt thou be loved less fervently than now!
Although age fades the hearts of other men,
Ours shall keep young! Kisses shall still caress,
And love be throned upon, thy silvered brow." [307, p. 63]

Charlotte's letters to her mother were less concerned with feelings but more devoted to domestic issues. They can be read as a detailed diary.

The first year in Princeton passed quietly as Charlotte's health improved only slowly. Life became brighter after two months of touring England and moving into their own house at 80 Stockton Street, Princeton. There they started to be sociable — having dinner parties — well-trained servants providing a comfortable life style. In January 1909 they spent their vacation in Bermuda, often riding around the island by bicycle.

Jeans's years in America could not be called very productive in scientific terms. Preparation of the new curricula and lectures at the University took much time. Also the romantic events in the personal life of the young scientist did not permit his total immersion in the world of scientific problems.

However, already in 1905 Jeans published an article about the variable star Algol in the leading American periodical 'The Astrophysical Journal' [20]. The next year he published in Boston his famous textbook on theoretical mechanics [27], for many years a useful guide for undergraduates and postgraduates. He did not lose contact with the leading physicists of that era. On 1st of February 1906 Jeans received a letter from Lord Kelvin.

"Dear Jeans,
I hear today from the Cambridge University Press that you wish to use a certain diagram from my Electrostatics & Magnetism, and I have written to them saying, certainly yes ...".

On the basis of his lectures Jeans published in 1908 the book *The Mathematical Theory of Electricity and Magnetism* [28], which was a comprehensive introduction to Maxwell's theory. As stated in the Preface to its first edition:

> "There is a certain well-defined range in Electromagnetic Theory, which every student of physics may be expected to have covered, with more or less thoroughness, before proceeding to the study of special branches of developments of the subject. The present book is intended to give the mathematical theory of this range of electromagnetism, together with the mathematical analysis required in its treatment.
> The range is very approximately that of Maxwell's original Treatise, but the present book is in many respects more elementary than that of Maxwell. Maxwell's Treatise was written for the fully-equipped mathematician: the present book is written more especially for the student, and for the physicist of limited mathematical attainments."

The second edition of 1911 was published in three parts: *Electrostatics and Current Electricity*, *Magnetism*, and *Electromagnetism*. According to Jeans, the first part is simply the development of the ancient notions about amber, the second is the development of ideas about the property of magnetite. Those parts are independent. They are united in the third part, devoted to the teaching of electromagnetism, developed by M. Faraday and J. Maxwell. Explaining the theory, Jeans uses modern mathematical apparatus: Green's theorem, the theory of potential functions, Legendre functions, complex variables and conformal transformations. The monograph is large, because it does not use vector methods, but the style is easy for a beginner to understand. It contains a lot of interesting examples and exercises, which make it particularly useful.

During his Princeton period Jeans also published a number of scientific articles on the dynamical theory of gases, the theory of radiation and also on the sustainability of submarines, which suggests that applied problems, also, were not alien to him.

Some of Jeans's other works of that period deal with specific problems of molecular theory. He was involved with the electron theory of metals. In 1909 he published *The Motion of Electrons in Solids* [31] in two parts; the first *Electric conductivity, Kirchhoff's law and radiation of great waves-length* was published simultaneously with Lorentz's monograph *Theory of Electrons and Its Application to the Phenomena of Light and Heat Radiation*. Jeans largely comes to the same conclusions. He improves the theory, developed by P. Drude, according to which metals contain a huge number of free electrons participating in the thermal motion. In the absence of an external electric field, owing to the chaotic nature of the electrons' movement, transfer of electricity does not happen. If there is a potential difference, the electrons are subject to a force in a certain direction and there is an electric current. Drude's theory essentially develops the view of W. Weber, who in 1862 considered that an electric current is the result of the ordered motion of charged particles. Jeans justifies the Drude formula for the electrical conductivity

$$\delta = e^2 Nl/mu$$

where e, m, u, l are the charge, mass, velocity and mean free path length of the electron, respectively, and N is the number of electrons per unit volume.

In that work Jeans also showed that Kirchhoff's law was a direct consequence of the electron theory of matter. The second part *Radiation of all wave-lengths in a perfectly reflecting enclosure. Natural radiation. Dependence of natural radiation on the law of force* [31] was published later in 1909 and took into account Lorentz's monograph. It considered radiation of a moving electron. In the quantitative analysis the Lorentz expansion was modified by an exponential multiplier. Of course, Jeans understood perfectly well the limitations of his approach, but a strict solution of the problems of the theory of gases, liquids and solids was possible only on the basis of quantum concepts.

We do not dwell in detail on these works, because they are now only of historical interest. However, Jeans's work on the theory of radiation contributed to the formation of quantum theory.

In 1909 Einstein wrote in *On the present status of the radiation problem* (Zum gegenwärtigen Stand des Strahlungsproblems):

> "Jeans's interpretation can be disputed on the grounds that it might not be permissible to apply the general results of statistical mechanics to cavities filled with radiation". And further: "There can be no doubt, in my opinion, that our current theoretical views inevitably lead to the law propounded by Mr Jeans. But with no less certainty we can say that the formula [Jeans's Formula. — A.K.] is not compatible with the facts. Why, after all, do solids emit visible light only above a fixed, rather sharply defined temperature? Why are ultraviolet rays not swarming

Lady Jeans Sees Mitchell College Laboratory Named for Her Husband

In her first visit to the laboratory subsequently to be named in honor of her late husband, she was forced to climb a wooden ladder, skirts flying, step over tools and lumber and keep out of the workmen's way.

Yesterday, four years and three days later, Lady Susi Jeans saw the finished product—the Sir James Jeans Memorial Physics Laboratory in the science-engineering building at Mitchell College.

This time President Robert C. Weller escorted her up the spiral staircase and into an elaborately furnished room complete with the mechanical trappings of the typical college laboratory.

The room was empty yesterday during the first day of the college's Easter recess, a marked change from the typical school day when it is occupied and in use from 8 a. m. to 11 p. m.

On the wall hung a picture of Sir James, who died in 1946, and a bronze plaque proclaiming, "He gave the world a new vision of the mysterious universe."

An Original Benefactor

The world-famous astronomer, physicist and cosmologist, related by marriage to the Bingham family and heir to the Alfred Mitchell estate, was one of the original benefactors of the college, donating his share of the estate to the establishing of New London Junior College.

Much of the equipment in the laboratory named for Sir James, Lady Jeans, herself, was instrumental in providing.

An organist of international repute, she presented a benefit concert in 1961 in St. James' Episcopal Church. Proceeds of this financially successful performance were donated toward the purchase of scientific equipment.

Yesterday's visit to the college was of the whirlwind variety. She and her hostess, Mrs. Hiram Bingham, were able to stay only long enough to view the laboratory and pose for a few snapshots.

Reason for the rush was Lady Jeans' demanding schedule. She is now on an American tour, first since 1961. Engagements in the east include stops at Yale and Dartmouth. She had only recently come north from Florida and was on her way to Hamden to hear records she has made to accompany her musical performances.

The eminent scientist's widow now includes a measure of scientific discourse with her organ recitals, finding the two most compatible and well received.

The tall, youthful, friendly native of Austria is now a British resident and has been since her marriage to Sir James.

VISITS LABORATORY—Mrs. Hiram Bingham, left, and Lady Susi Jeans under a plaque at Mitchell College memorializing the late Sir James Jeans, eminent British astronomer, physicist and cosmologist.

MITCHELL COLLEGE
New London, Connecticut, USA. James Jeans gave his share of the Alfred Mitchell Estate, inherited through his first marriage to Charlotte Mitchell, towards establishing the New London Junior College. Rose Bingham and Susi Jeans pose beneath the plaque recording this donation.

everywhere, if they are indeed constantly being produced at ordinary temperatures? How is it possible to store highly sensitive photographic plates in cassettes for a long time if they constantly produce short-wave rays?" [287, p. 166–7].

In the same paper Einstein discusses the positive sides of Jeans's approach, in his dimensional analysis, and notes its "extreme importance". Jeans largely contributed to Planck's theory, so its correctness could gain recognition; and already in 1916, Einstein could write: "Today we know that no approach based on classical mechanics and electrodynamics will give the correct formula for radiation, whereas the classical theory provides us with Rayleigh's formula [in Jeans's formulation. — A.K.]" [287, p. 393]. This is demonstrated in Jeans's work. Already in the article [23] submitted in 1906 from Princeton, Jeans came to the conclusion that the theory of radiation in its classic form is not valid for thermodynamics. In 1909, he used the Planck formula and Lorentz's approximation [30].

But Jeans was not able to abandon the classical physical paradigm. Perhaps he could not even imagine such a possibility. He placed too much emphasis on the quantitative side of physics: experimental measurements and their quantitative description — standard physical methodology. The results of experiments of fundamental importance are often essentially qualitative in nature, and Jeans could not take this step. The time for quantum theory had not come yet. Jeans was not one of the creators of the new physics. He belonged to an older generation whereas the creators of the new quantum mechanics were a quarter of a century younger. Therefore, at the beginning of the century, in America, Jeans could not correctly evaluate his place in physical sciences. This led him to become considerably dissatisfied with his contribution to science. It had an effect on his overall emotional state. He expected more from himself. Besides, Jeans was unhappy with his life in America. He did not feel at home in Princeton. He did not like the American way of life. His teaching responsibilities became a chore to him. The Mitchells established a trust fund for their daughter Charlotte with an annual income, which would allow Jeans to give up his meagrely paid University duties.

They decided to take that step in 1908 after their lawyer had informed them that their sons-in-law — researcher, historian Hiram Bingham and cosmologist Fellow of the Royal Society James Jeans — could never make enough money to support their families.

The capital for the trust fund consisted of 50% of Charlotte's parents' shares in Tiffany & Co. Charlotte's mother, Annie Tiffany Mitchell, had inherited them from her father. The new provision determined that Alfreda would receive 60% of the net income and Charlotte 40%. [291, p. 191]

Since it was at Cambridge that Jeans had for the first time obtained professional recognition, so it seemed to him the most desirable destination for his future scientific research. At the beginning of 1909 Charlotte wrote to her mother that they were considering moving to England: "Conditions are for many reasons very trying for Fred, and as for me, although it will be very difficult, since it has to come, I would rather have it come quickly". Jeans no longer needed a paid teaching position. In July, he and Charlotte had already crossed the Atlantic, and she wrote that they had no clear plans for their future life in England, but it was very likely that they would settle in Cambridge.

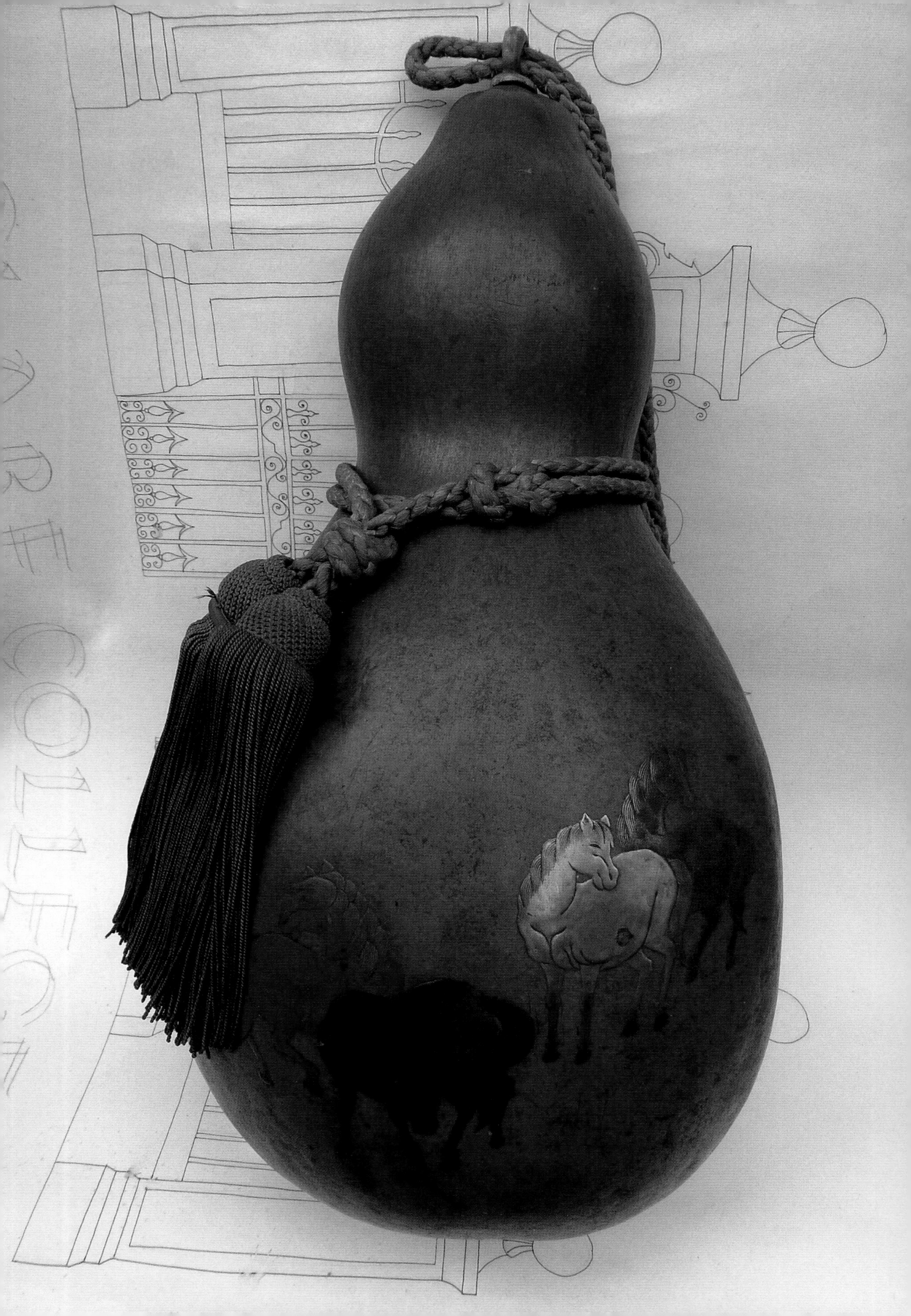

CAMBRIDGE AND DORKING 1909–1919

After a month of looking for a suitable place to live, James and Charlotte Jeans finally bought 'Woodlands' a house in Chaucer Road, in the suburbs of Cambridge. They moved there in September 1909. Then they spent the first weekend in Cornwall, which remained their favourite holiday destination. They liked the cliffs, rocks and hills, covered with heather and gorse. There was the sound of surf and the moist and salty sea air. The main town of the southern slope of Cornwall, Penzance, is picturesquely situated on the shore of the semi-circular Mounts Bay, between the Land's End and Lizard Head peninsular. Near Penzance, directly opposite the charming village of Marazion is the almost perfect pyramid of Saint Michael's Mount with its bell tower of the ancient Abbey rising above the sea. The romantic views, mild climate and its more southern flora: the attractiveness of the place is very evident.

In 1910, Jeans was appointed Stokes Lecturer in Applied Mathematics in Cambridge. That position was not too burdensome and so in March 1910 he and his wife were able to go to Jamaica to visit her parents. The difficulties with Charlotte's father had not changed, but he died a year later. Relationships with her mother were better. Almost a year later Jeans signed letters to her "With love, devoted to you, Fred".

Charlotte wrote to her mother more frequently than her husband, drawing a picture of a calm and boring life. She did not know how to be happy and was almost painfully shy and resentful of any intrusion into their private world. Charlotte wanted to live in the country and wrote about the fruitless search for a house away from the centre of Cambridge. Those letters made no mention of Jeans's teaching or his research.

But it was his work that saved him from melancholy. It gave his life a certain tension, the passion that made him forget about himself. His fascination with science was a real passion. He did not do it for the sake of earning a living as he was financially secure.

Jeans taught in Cambridge and was engaged in scientific work on the theory of radiation, the movement of electrons and the structure of the atom. In 1910 he published: *On the analysis of the radiation from electron orbits* [33] and *On non-Newtonian mechanical systems, and Planck's theory of radiation*

GOURD WITH HORSES
This Japanese decorated gourd from the 19th Century may have been one of Charlotte's finds when she was travelling with her parents in the Far East in 1899.

THE CAMBRIDGE HOME

In September 1909 James and Charlotte Jeans purchased 'Woodlands' a substantial detached house at 2 Chaucer Road in west Cambridge. It was bought for £2,520 from a Mrs Redfern. The Jeanses left Cambridge in 1912 selling the house to a Mr Appach for £2,425. Formal photographs of the interior reproduced here were probably sent to Mrs Annie Mitchell, Charlotte's mother in the United States. Much of the furniture, ornaments and pictures found their place in Cleveland Lodge where they finally settled in 1918. Some of the colourful porcelain and the ornamented gourd from Japan can be seen in the dining room.

Woodlands, 2 Chaucer Road, Cambridge.

Entrance hall, Woodlands, Cambridge (1909–1912).

Charlotte's study, Woodlands, Cambridge (1909–1912).

Dining room, Woodlands, Cambridge (1909–1912).

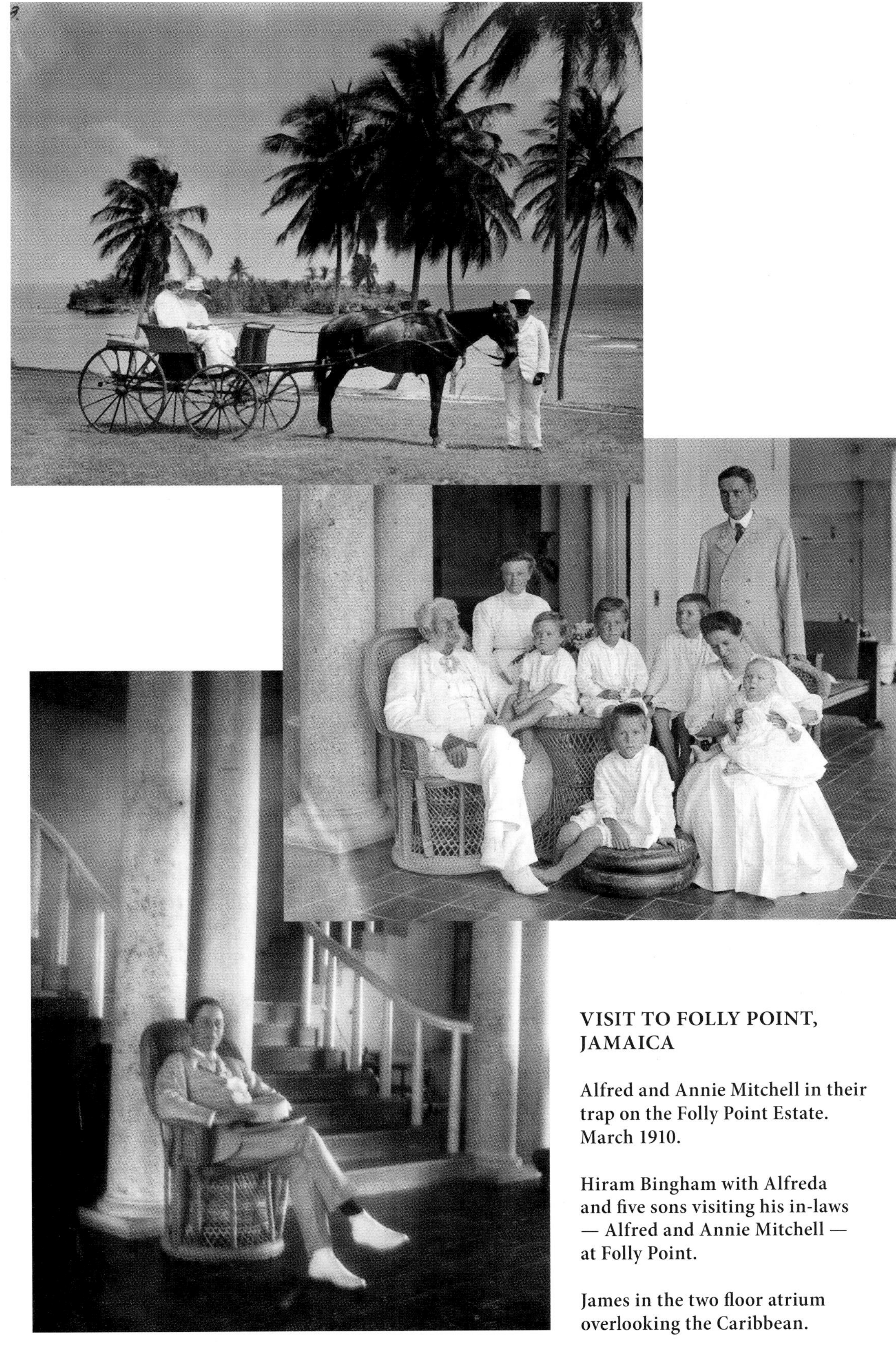

VISIT TO FOLLY POINT, JAMAICA

Alfred and Annie Mitchell in their trap on the Folly Point Estate. March 1910.

Hiram Bingham with Alfreda and five sons visiting his in-laws — Alfred and Annie Mitchell — at Folly Point.

James in the two floor atrium overlooking the Caribbean.

Ernest Solvay and the 23 physicists who attended the first Solvay Conference in November 1911. The conference was concerned with the theory of radiation and quanta.

NOHRL
HOSTELET
HERZEN JEANS RUTHERFORD
WIEN EINSTEIN LANGEVIN
RRIN Mme CURIE POINCARÉ KAMERLINGH ONNES

Jean Stas, Bruxelles.

Studio portrait of J. H. Jeans (Palmer Clarke, Cambridge). This appears in the book of individual portraits given to each participant of the 1st Solvay Conference.

Studio portrait of Charlotte Jeans (Palmer Clarke, Cambridge) ~1910–11.

[34] in which he demonstrated that his own theory did not match the experimental data and concluded that Planck's Law is correct. His working hypothesis, that the mechanisms of radiation and absorption are the same, is interesting. It was a successful guess, because these mechanisms had not yet been discovered and a model of the atom did not yet exist. His authority in that area was such that he was invited to the first Solvay Congress, among the 23 most prominent physicists of the world.

The idea of an international physical congress came from the famous physicist and chemist Walther Nernst, Professor at Berlin University. A rich Belgian industrialist, Ernest G.J. Solvay, provided financial support. Employed in his uncle's chemical factory, Solvay invented a method of producing soda and then established several factories that brought him great wealth. By the end of his life he was the owner of a vast industry, two banks and 38 castles and estates [205, p. 329]. He felt special affinity for pure science and scientists involved in fundamental problems.

Brussels was chosen as the venue of the Congress. Solvay asked Hendrik Lorentz to head the organizing committee. The Secretary of the Congress was Maurice de Broglie, the elder brother of the subsequently famous Louis

Postcard sent by James to Charlotte pointing out the Hotel Metropole in La Place de Brouckère, Bruxelles where the 1st Solvay Conference was held.

de Broglie. Participants for the Congress were selected by Hendrik Lorentz, Max Planck and Walther Nernst who also decided on its programme. The most distinguished physicists of the world were sent invitations and were offered reimbursement of all costs and fees up to a thousand francs.

The Congress was held from the 30th October to the 3rd November 1911 and was entirely devoted to radiation and quanta. In his opening remarks Lorentz said: "… we have the feeling that we are at a dead end; the old theories are becoming less able to pierce the darkness that surrounds us on all sides" [243, p. 88].

Twelve reports were presented. Of particular interest to the meeting were the following: Hendrik Lorentz's *Sur l'application au rayonnement du théorème de l'equipartition de l'energie* [Application of the theorem on the equipartition of energy to radiation], Max Planck's *La loi du rayonnement noir et l'hypothèse des quantités elementaires d'action.* [*Die Gesetze der Wärmmestrahlung und die Hypothese der elementaren Wirtungsquanten*] [The law of thermal radiation and the hypothesis of the elementary quantum of action], Arnold Sommerfeld's *Application de la théorie de l'élément d'action aux phénomènes moléculaires non périodiques.* [Application of the theory of quantum action to non-periodic molecular processes in physics], Albert Einstein's *L'état actuel du problem des chaleurs spécifiques* [On the current state of the problem of specific heats].

In Lorentz's contribution 18 issues were considered: 1) the nature of the problem; 2) Kirchhoff's law and the theorem of equipartition of energy; 3) the Rayleigh-Jeans Law, and 4) its experimental verification; 5) methods of statistical physics; 6) the canonical variables and statistical mechanics; 7) application of the Hamilton principle for electromagnetic systems; 8) introduction of a system of coordinates; 9) the expression for the potential and kinetic energies; 10) canonical equations for electromagnetic systems; 11) the general application of the equipartition theorem; 12) the mean kinetic energy of the electron; 13) the exception of short waves; 14) doubts about the Jeans hypothesis; 15) the constants in the laws of radiation; 16) difficulties encountered in understanding the discrete structure of the energy of radiation; 17) the question of fluctuations in the electromagnetic field and the analogy with Brownian motion; 18) the case of free electrons.

Some questions could not be answered within the framework of classical concepts. If metals contain particles with vibrations of a certain frequency, why are these oscillators at rest below a certain temperature? If, instead of oscillators, we take chaotic motion, leading to a certain state which can be decomposed into harmonic components, why do high-frequency components disappear at low energies? To answer these questions we must assume a principle that would allow the transition of energy of high-frequency vibrations of the ether to the substance, but would prohibit the reverse transition. In that case, one could avoid the conversion of energy to the ether, which has an infinite number of degrees of freedom.

The Rayleigh–Jeans formula comes about by assuming that the theorem of equipartition of energy over the degrees of freedom of a mechanical system follows from Hamilton's equations and that this also applies to radiation. However, several issues must be considered:

1) Are Hamilton's equations applicable to black body radiation?
2) The validity of deducing the theorem of equipartition of energy from Hamilton's equations;
3) Is a statistical mechanical description applicable to radiation?
4) The method by which the Rayleigh–Jeans formula was derived.

Despite the inapplicability of the equations at relativistic speeds as remarked by Paul Langevin, the first issue was considered irrelevant. The second and third hypotheses, were considered (with the support of Einstein) to be correct. But the fourth point, the question of the validity of the method of derivation of the Rayleigh–Jeans formula from classical premises, is not possible to sustain. Opening the discussion of his report, Lorentz said: "Later, I realized that all of the mechanisms that you can think of, would lead to the Rayleigh formula, unless their nature is such that the Hamilton's equations did not apply". [243, p. 101–2]

The results of the experimental testing of Planck's theory were discussed by Emil Warburg and Heinrich Rubens. Planck in his report described the status of the problem and agreed with the conclusion of Lorentz that all the classical approaches led to the Rayleigh–Jeans ratio. Planck considered a possible physical nature of the constant h (the quantum of action). All development of a theory depends on whether h is the only mechanism of emission and absorption of, or distribution of, electromagnetic radiation in a vacuum, as had been suggested by Einstein in 1905. Neither Planck nor other members of the Congress could accept Einstein's point of view; the time for the recognition of photons had not come. Even Planck 'backed off'; he offered 'the second variant' theory, where emission was discrete, but absorption was continuous. To clarify the physical meaning of h, Planck believed it necessary to define a dynamic law for the vibrations of an oscillator, changing the equation of the electron theory, so that h could be introduced. But a classical model did not meet that condition, and led to the Rayleigh–Jeans ratio. Planck examined in detail the model of the atom proposed in 1910 by Arthur Haas, in which for the first time an attempt was made to associate the quantum nature of radiation with the structure of the atom. This was a variation of the model of Thomson's atom, in which electrons oscillate near the centre of a positively charged sphere. The maximum energy $h\nu$ was reached at the moment when the amplitude of oscillation was equal to the radius of the sphere. At larger distances, oscillations are terminated because the electron goes beyond the sphere, and at smaller energy they change continuously.

In the discussion of Planck's report, Einstein remarked that if one has not been given the physical definition of the probability of the state, one could not construct a theory based on the Boltzmann ratio between entropy and probability. Lorentz supported Einstein in that position, but spoke against his photons.

The focus of the Congress was Planck's theory. Naturally, Jeans's participation was very useful as his work had shown that the classical methods were inapplicable for the analysis of problems of radiation. But he had to find some way out of the situation. He had made efforts to resolve that contradiction, based on the classical approach, and championed the correctness of both his deductions and the final result.

Jeans suggested considering the establishment of a thermodynamic equilibrium between the radiation and walls of the cavity that would require an infinitely long time. To save his formula, he suggested that in

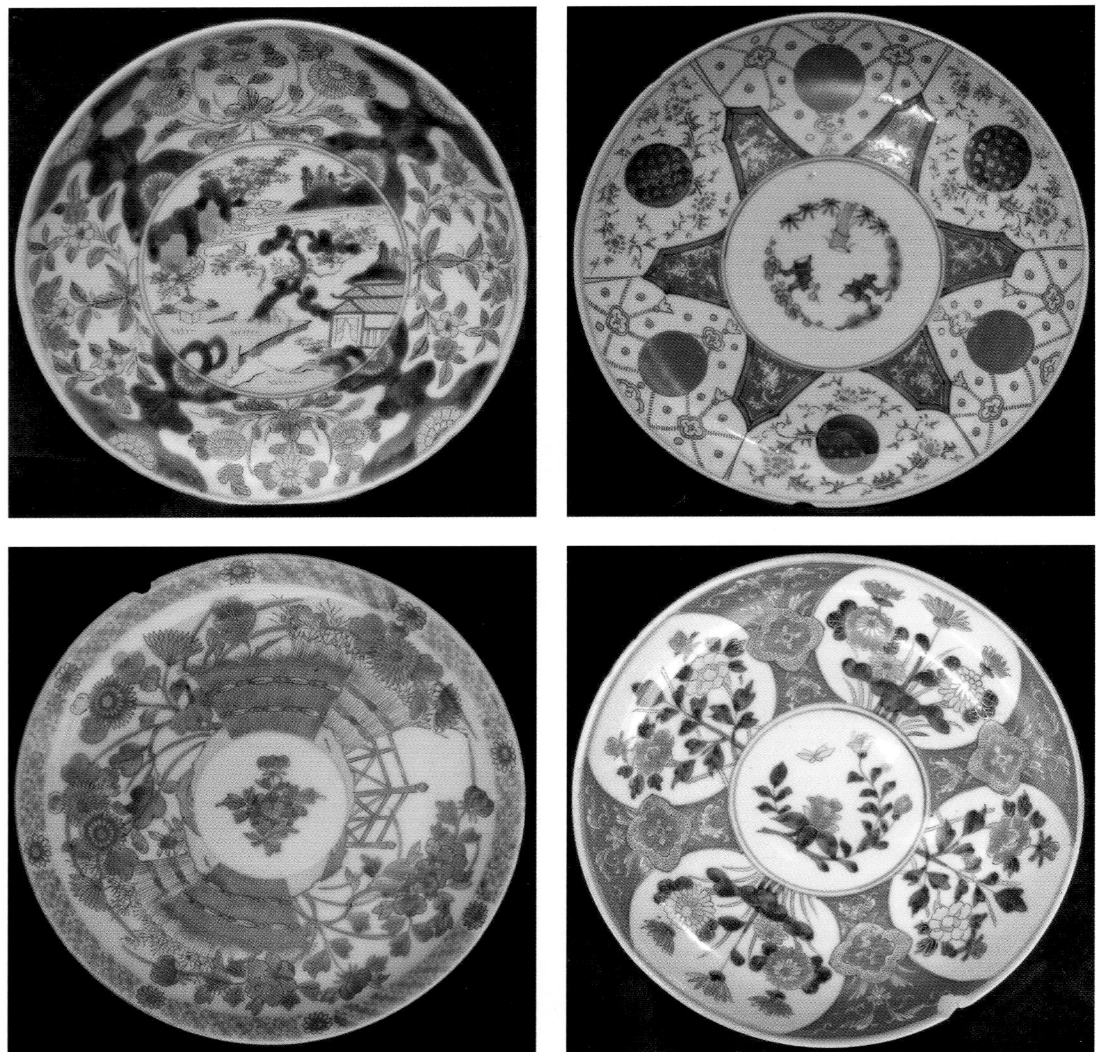

Charlotte Jeans possessed a considerable amount of old Japanese and Chinese tableware, much of which she obtained either in the United States or when she was setting up home in Cambridge. Shown here are four of her Imari bowls (18th–19th Century). Imari — a type of Arita ware — was made in the town of Arita (northwestern Kyûshû, Japan). It was exported to Europe extensively from the port of Imari, Saga. All these bowls are ~20 cms in dameter.

practice the case of equilibrium radiation could not be realized, but this turned out to be incorrect.

From these assumptions Jeans considered the radiation of an accelerated electron would introduce an exponentially decreasing function at small wave lengths. Indeed, when introducing his ratio Jeans employed the laws of

Chantry Dene, Fort Road, Guildford, Surrey, on the Hogs Back overlooking the Weald. An Arts and Craft House, the Jeans's rented home during 1912–13. Roger Fry, the Bloomsbury Group painter had also lived there for a short period.

statistical mechanics which are suitable for any dynamical systems described by Hamilton's equations. However, for long waves the same law was obtained from the electronic theory. Therefore, we can assume that this law is universal. However, the condition of equilibrium between ether and matter is only established after the transfer of all energy to the ether; in the short wave-band, this requires an infinitely long time. The contradiction between theory and experimental data is removed. Thus Jeans defended his theory in 1911 at the first Solvay Congress, however he was criticized by Lorentz and other scientists. It is fair to say that the forum did not lead to a particular outcome. It was still 14 years before the creation of quantum mechanics.

Here is Jeans's opinion about Lorentz's approach to science, comparing it with that of Maxwell: "the goals of both scientists were the same, but their methods were different. For Maxwell, science was an enchanted fairyland, where no one knew what miracle might happen next. For Lorentz, science was a workshop with tools of exceptional accuracy arranged carefully in the direction in which progress was predicted — just as if the development of science followed some preordained plan" [243, p. 278]. Such an approach in an era of 'Sturm und Drang' was unsuitable for the creation of new scientific ideas. Unfortunately, Jeans's own methodology of research was closer to that of Lorentz. He was dissatisfied with the situation in physics and his own efforts to solve the problems, other physicists felt similarly.

Apparently Jeans was deeply disappointed when he was not offered the chair of Astromony vacant after the death of Sir George Darwin in 1912. When his rival Arthur Eddington was elected to that position, he decided to leave his job at the University of Cambridge.

In 1912, he moved to Guildford, at the time one of the most picturesque towns near London — originally a Saxon settlement guarding a gap in the North Downs where the Harrow Way fords the River Wey — but now, it is included in the Greater London built-up zone. Elisée Reclus provides us with a contemporary description:

"Below Godalming the River Wey escapes through a cleft in the Downs. This cleft is commanded by the town of Guildford, whose antiquity is attested by a Norman castle, a grammar school dating from Henry VIII, and an interesting old church. Guildford has an important corn market, and possesses large breweries. In the beauty of its environment few towns can rival it, clumps of trees, carefully kept fields, ivy-clad walls, and shady lanes winding up the hillsides, combining to form a picture of rural beauty and tranquillity." [260, p. 116].

Jeans always liked tranquil and picturesque places, where he could spend his time studying science. However, he did not shy away from congresses and conferences, where in personal contact with other physicists they could discuss the results of their research, learn about new hypotheses, and feel the rhythm of scientific life. In September 1913 he was invited to Birmingham, to take part in the work of the British Association for the Advancement of Science, at which Rayleigh, Rutherford, Lodge, Lorentz, Marie Curie, Larmor and the creator of a new model of the atom, the young Danish physicist Niels Bohr, were present.

This is how Bohr recalls it:

> "This meeting, attended by Madame Curie, held, in particular, general discussion on the issues of radiation with the participation of such well-known authorities as Rayleigh, Larmor and Lorentz; it is necessary to note the presence of Jeans, who made the introductory remarks, devoted to the application of quantum theory to the problem of the structure of atoms. His clear presentation was actually the first manifestation of serious interest by physicists in the consideration of the problems that, outside of the Manchester group [Rutherford's] were generally regarded very skeptically" [257, p. 182].

Olivia Jeans (born 29th February 1912) with her mother and father at their Guildford home.

Jeans began his speech with the words: "Dr. Bohr gave an extremely witty, original, and one can say, plausible interpretation of the laws of spectral cycles". And further: "Today, the only significant confirmation of the correctness of these assumptions is the fact that they operate in practice" [246, p. 170]. A week after the conference, Bohr wrote to his wife: "While things are going so well, nothing better could be desired. Jeans opened the discussion about the problem of radiation with a solid presentation and gave sympathetic appreciation of my theory. I think he believes in some reality of my opinions" [246, p. 170].

At the end of 1913 Jeans again travelled to Brussels for the second Solvay Congress (27th to 31st December) dedicated to the structure of matter. A major report on the structure of the atom was made by J.J. Thomson, who outlined his slightly modified views on this subject. But the general mood in physics at that time was expressed in the discussion on Lorentz's report: "as the Thomson model contains nothing incompatible with the rules of mechanics, it seems highly doubtful that it was possible to deduce from it the correct law of radiation" [288, p. 325].

Jeans had the same opinion. His brilliant physical intuition told him that Bohr was right, and he was one of the first publicly to support that theory. But he could not work in that new, internally inconsistent physics. Consistent

30 participants at the second Solvay Conference on The Structure of Matter.

ɔE PHYSIQUE SOLVAY

E – BRUXELLES 1913

LINDEMANN DE BROGLIE POPE GRUNEISEN HOSTELET
TEIN KNUDSEN LANGEVIN

BRILLOUIN BARLOW KAMERLINGH-ONNES WOOD GOUY WEISS

8 Ormonde Gate, Chelsea, London. The Jeans's home from 1913 to 1918.

quantum theory was only created during the next six years, when he had already left that field for astronomy.

At the Congress Jeans also learned about Max von Laue's discovery of X-ray diffraction in 1912, confirming the wave nature of ionizing radiation. The international collaboration of physicists brought tangible benefits, but the outbreak of the First World War in August 1914 prevented further collaboration for many years.

On the 29th of February 1912 the Jeans's daughter Olivia was born, named in honour of her grandmother, Annie Olivia Tiffany Mitchell. Charlotte's letters to her mother were full of details about the health of the child, its care and other matters, as the little girl was not only bright and attractive, but showed signs of hyperactivity, which increased Charlotte's anxiety.

In 1913, the Jeanses moved to London. They lived for the next five years at 8 Ormonde Gate, in a quiet area of Chelsea much favoured by the creative professions as well as by doctors, lawyers and businessmen. It was close to the river with Ranelagh Gardens and the extensive grounds of the Chelsea Royal Hospital extending to the Thames' Embankment. Walking in its quiet streets, between the well preserved houses with their neat gardens and wrought iron railings, one can understand why they chose this area. And going to the river, it is impossible not to succumb to the scene at dusk and at night of the Thames with its rippled surface, covered with a light mist, sliding silently between the tall buildings on one bank and Battersea Park on the other, shimmering with the reflection of lights and the mysterious outline of Battersea Bridge in the background.

In London, the Jeanses led a rather secluded life. Charlotte suffered further depression, and Jeans was so alarmed by her condition that he wrote to her mother, most likely on the advice of a doctor, asking if there were any evidence of mental illness of their daughter in childhood or in her family. Mrs. Mitchell was upset and tried to reassure him, but acknowledged that "stealth of character and Charlotte's communication problems were inherited from both sides". Charlotte wrote later that she had suffered a "nervous breakdown".

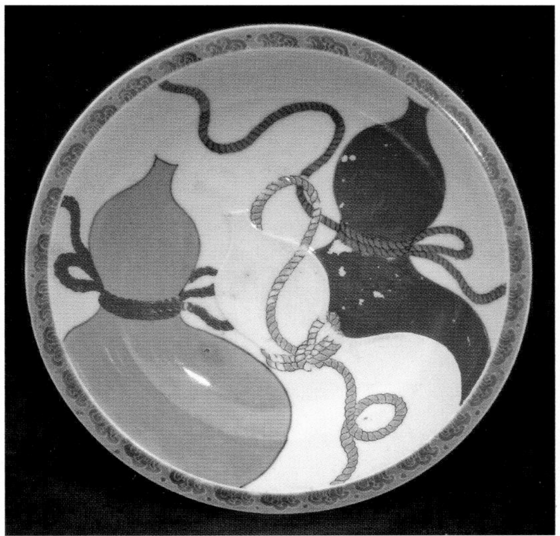

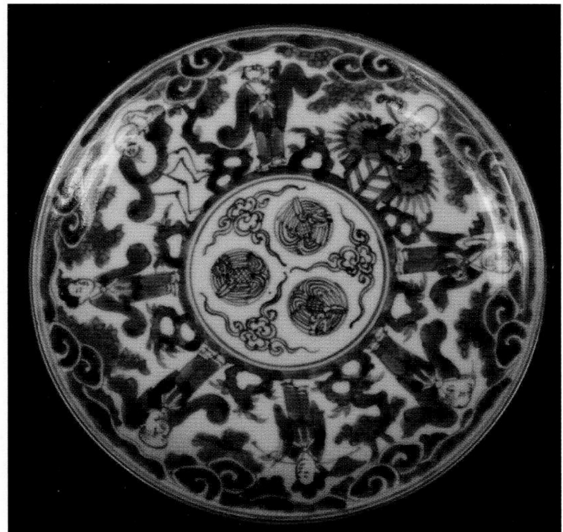

Above: Nabeshima bowl 19th Century, Japan (diameter 21 cms). This was produced in Lord Nabeshima of Saga Domain's kiln at Okawachi near Arita during the Edo and Meiji periods.

Right: Among Charlotte's Japanese ceramics were numerous 19th century plates dramatically ornamented with Kangxi style blue and white patterns. The intense blue cobalt pigment used is considered to have first reached China from Iran in the 14th Century although there is evidence that pigment was already in use at an earlier date but had been forgotten. The pigment was used for under glaze decoration and production reached a peak during the Qing Dynasty (1661–1722).

Despite the war and the complexity of family life, Jeans tried to continue scientific research. In 1914 an extended version of his *Report on Radiation and the Quantum Theory* was published by the Physical Society [37]. It immediately became known to a wide circle of scientists, and by 1919 it was discussed all over the world and contributed to drawing attention to the quantum concept and the orthodox theory of the Bohr atom. Together with Eddington's *Report on the Relativity Theory of Gravitation* (1918), also published by the Physical Society, they both had a decisive influence on the dissemination of new concepts of physics in the UK.

In his *Report on the Radiation and the Quantum Theory*, Jeans applied his ratio to the radiation of an oscillating electron. In that work Jeans also calculated the radiation of a free electron. He managed to find the analytical solution of the equation and again arrived at his ratio for the density of the radiation. This further strengthened the confidence of Jeans in the correctness of the resulting ratios.

Jeans's *Report* consisted of seven chapters. The first one was called Introductory: *On the Need for a Quantum Theory*, the last *On the Physical Basis of the Quantum Theory*. The second and third chapters summarised his own research in the theory of radiation in accordance with classical physics and supported Planck's revolutionary hypothesis. The fourth, fifth and sixth chapters contained Bohr's theory of hydrogen and hydrogen-like atoms and their spectra, Einstein's theory of the photoelectric effect, and the theory of the specific heat of solids by Einstein, Debye and Lindemann. In the final part of his *Report* Jeans wrote:

> "… It may be asserted with confidence that until some kind of reconciliation can be effected between the demands of the quantum theory and those of the undulatory theory of light, the physical interpretation of the quantum theory is likely to remain in a very unsatisfactory state … the explanation of the black-body spectrum demands the quantum theory and nothing but the quantum theory, all the discontinuities of the theory and their surprising physical consequences included. The keynote of the old mechanics was continuity, natura non facit saltus. The keynote of the new mechanics is discontinuity; in Poincaré's words, 'Un système physique n'est susceptible que d'un nombre fini d'états distincts; il saute d'un de ces états à l'autre sans passer par une série continue d'états intermédiaires.' The antithesis is obvious; its resolution will not be easy. Perhaps the present report cannot end better than by a free translation of Poincaré's concluding remarks in his striking article, 'L'hypothèse des Quanta':
>
> 'We see now how this question stands. The old theories which seemed until recently able to account for all known phenomena have suddenly met with an unexpected check. Some modification has been seen to be necessary. A hypothesis has been suggested by M. Planck, but so strange a hypothesis that every possible means was sought for escaping it. The search has revealed no escape so far, although the new theory bristles with difficulties, many of which are real and not simple illusions caused by the inertia of our minds, which resent change.
>
> 'It is impossible at present to predict the final issue. Will some entirely different solution be found? Or will the advocates of the new theory succeed in removing the obstacles which prevent us from

accepting it without reserve? Is discontinuity destined to reign over the physical universe, and will its triumph be final? Or will it finally be recognized that this discontinuity is only apparent, and a disguise for a series of continuous processes? …" [193, p. 18–19].

It was not just by chance that Jeans ended his Report with Poincaré's words. Already at the 1st Solvay Congress Poincaré made a deep impression on Jeans with his mathematical genius, described by Lorentz as "the ease with which he approached the most difficult physical problems, even those that were new". He was also attracted by Poincaré's philosophical approach to the study of nature. Jeans's interests were close to those of Poincaré: quantum hypothesis, theory and figures of rotating gravitating masses, and cosmogony, though in the latter Jeans had yet to make his contribution. In the last years of his life Jeans — like Poincaré — wrote several interesting and profound books for a wider audience, stylishly popularizing the achievements of modern physics and astrophysics.

Jeans's *Report*, published in 1914, was almost his last work in physics. It summarized his unsuccessful attempts to give an explanation of the spectrum of equilibrium radiation on the basis of classical physics. Although Jeans understood the inevitability and necessity of the new approach, yet he could never accept it. One might say 1914 was a year of crisis in his research.

He continued to follow closely the progress of atomic physics and quantum theory, and even published in 1923, a small note on the *Theory of the scattering of α- and β-rays* [71]. The year 1914 may be considered to be the end of the first phase of Jeans's scientific activity in physics. The following 14 years of his life were devoted to astronomy and cosmogony. For the solution to those problems Jeans had the powerful tools of mathematics and theoretical physics at his command. He was one of the first experienced theoretical physicists to begin working in astrophysics.

~~ • ~~

The Jeanses had spent the summer of 1913 on Dartmoor in Devon, an area where there was abundance of wildlife including grouse and partridge. In the autumn the family returned to London. At the beginning of the summer of 1914, they moved to Amersham, shortly before the beginning of the war.

The First World War brought new unrest and uncertainty into their lives. Jeans was not yet forty and could be called up for military service. The role of scientists was not as important as during the Second World War. Life in London at that time strengthened Charlotte's desire for quiet rural solitude. Excerpts from letters to her mother reflect the mood of the family.

Olivia Jeans, aged four, 1916.

James and Olivia, 1916, Boxhill, Surrey. It appears that James and Charlotte made considerable forays in the Surrey countryside looking for a suitable place to settle down in.

September 29, 1916.

I am now well enough. I am so much better for the change in the country, but Olivia is certainly not fit to travel or to have excitement at present, though she is very much better than she was. Still she has to lead a life very different from that of the ordinary child. We see very little of her. We seldom see her both together as she is so much better with just one at a time.

July 26, 1917, on a country holiday.

This valley is so peaceful and lovely and the quiet is so refreshing ... I was interested to hear of your visit to Salem and all you say about Freda's boys. It is well Freda is not of a worrying disposition with so many boys. I am surprised to hear Freda is moving to Washington. [On the entry of the United States into the war in April, 1917, Hiram had obtained an Army commission, and, as a university professor who had learned to fly, he was posted to the War Department to help organize the training of fighter pilots]. Hi is so ambitious and I suppose a University town is too uneventful for him. I expect, if he is taking up politics, etc., that he will never go back to New Haven to live. It is a pity he has to be such a "great man" .... Our two families suffer from diametrically opposed characteristics: Hi is always restless and on the go and sticks to nothing, and Fred is just the reverse, and has the tendency to get into a groove so that it is hard to get him to move at all.

Boxhill on Bank Holiday.

SEARCH FOR A PERMANENT HOME

Top: Contemporary postcard of Boxhill, near Dorking, Surrey on a bank holiday. There were fine views of Boxhill from Cleveland Lodge which the Jeanses purchased in 1918.

Above: Contemporary postcard of Dorking, Surrey, the nearest town to Cleveland Lodge.

> September 23, 1917.
>
> The war seems to be going a little better. It looks as if the end were drawing a little nearer at last. — I have been depressed about Olivia again. You do not realize how different she is from other children. There is a great nervous weakness, but apparently nervous weakness is very common with very clever children. Fred is of course a very delicate man, and can do so extraordinarily little without fatigue, and one of his sisters has gone to pieces completely .... Thanks for the things you said in your last letter and for your sympathy. Fred gets so upset if I am uncheerful that I try to keep up as best I can. He suffers so much from depression too. I fear we are rather a forlorn kind of family.

The beginning of deafness added to Charlotte's trials at around that time. But her letters acquired a happier tone as her constant dream about a country house had finally been fulfilled. "Cleveland Lodge" was a spacious estate of 28 acres at Westhumble, near Dorking in Surrey, located in the gap of the North Downs where the River Mole had cut down through the hills — a well known beauty spot with fine views of Box Hill and the Surrey hills and within easy reach of London. It is where Charlotte and James were to spend the rest of their lives. They purchased it for only £6000 reflecting the decrease in property prices in 1917; and they moved there in January 1918, despite the war.

Cleveland Lodge has an interesting history [305]. It is named after the Duke of Cleveland, who rented the land from two owners, Thomas Boulton and John Daniels. The first one owned 'Westhumble House' and 'Narrow Meadow', and the second owned the land west of Cleveland Lodge (where later a railway was built), 'Great Meadow' stretching to the north and east down to the River Mole, and Westhumble Street.

The last Duke of Cleveland died in 1774, but the title was resurrected in 1833, for William Henry Vane (1766–1842), the new Duke of Cleveland, who rented the land from the two owners in 1838. The family of the Dukes of Cleveland finally ceased to exist in 1890.

Before the Reformation it was probably the site of a large farm rented from a monastery in the nearby village of Mickleham. The old part of the house 'The Westhumble House', as it was then known, was not a residence suitable for a gentleman until 1790. This could be seen in the structure of the building. There were two major alterations, the first in the late classical style at around 1800, and the second in 1830 in neo-Gothic style with Tudor doors and windows, which was done for the Duke of Cleveland.

The war in Europe was coming to its end, and Charlotte returned to a more peaceful life, improving and redesigning the 200-year old house, managing its estate, creating gardens and devoting herself to Olivia's development and education.

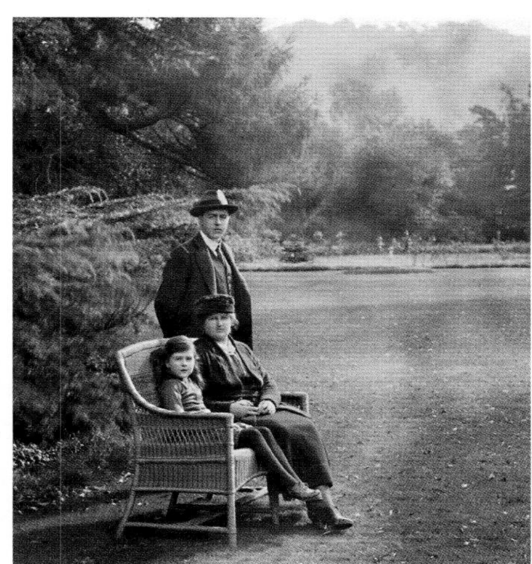

CLEVELAND LODGE

Cleveland Lodge, Westhumble, Dorking, Surrey.
View from the north east and Cleveland Lodge viewed from the east (Waring & Gill, Oxford St., London, sales particulars, 1917).

Perhaps one of the first things that Charlotte Jeans did was to arrange a formal photograph of Cleveland Lodge to send to her mother, Annie Mitchell. Here James, Charlotte and Oliver are sitting on the front lawn, with the rose garden beyond and Boxhill in the background.

Another formal photograph of the Jeans family inspecting the cows in the fields of Cleveland Lodge.
The Rotunda Studio, Dorking ~1920.

James on the tennis courts at Cleveland Lodge. Before contracting tuberculosis in 1899, there is evidence that he was a fit and physically active person … rock climbing in the Lake District with a love of mountains.

The main and rather grand entrance to the house was directly from Westhumble Street. You passed through a glass roofed conservatory before entering a spacious and well-lit hall with bay- and french windows overlooking the gardens. In a lobby a glassed door opened to the garden. A wide staircase led to the first floor bedrooms with white furniture highlighted in gold in the style of Louis XIV, along with bathrooms and some private rooms. On the walls of the staircase hung pictures of American landscapes, acquaintances of Charlotte from her childhood, and in her bedroom there were prints of her favourite Japanese artists Khokusine and Hiroshige.

Through a door from the hall, following a long corridor you came into a vast kitchen. Another door led you to the dining room. A third door led to the drawing room, library and the music room, where Jeans installed a fairly large organ. There was no central heating because it was harmful for the instrument. From the music room with its numerous French windows you had direct access to the garden and a wonderful view of the extensive lawns with Box Hill in the background. In the early morning it was not an uncommon sight to see roe deer foraging in the garden before returning to the surrounding hills. In season, cuckoos and at night owls helped to provide the peace and country sounds that Charlotte longed for.

> May 3, 1918.
>
> Olivia is taking her mid-day meal with us at present and enjoys it hugely. The reason I have not had her sooner is that Fred is always pouring out such streams of information into her mind that it disturbs her meals. Fred is always tempted to talk to her as she is so full of eagerness and curiosity about everything. My difficulty is really in keeping Fred from talking to her too much. He, in the bosom of the family, is not so quiet as he seems to strangers, and he adores chattering to her …. No mother ever spent more anxious time or thought than I do over the management of my two explosive "charges".

Indeed, Charlotte ran the family. For Jeans it was very convenient as he could engage fully in his scientific work with few distractions. He loved to walk in the grounds of his new home or sit on the lawn. During this period, he could ponder at ease over the scientific problems in which he was interested. As a true Englishman, he was very fond of his garden, although he never worked there. With time, Jeans spent more time in his music room playing the organ for several hours a day, only for himself and never before any audience. In 1917 he had his first heart attack, a signal of coming disease, but the quiet life in Cleveland Lodge, surrounded by family and a few servants, allowed him to forget about it for many years.

In that period Jeans continued his theoretical research in the field of astronomy and astrophysics, penetrating deeper into the problems of astronomical science. He wrote works devoted to star clusters, gravitational instability of gas nebulae, the theory of star streamings, the theory of equilibrium figures of rotating self-gravitating masses and other issues in cosmogony. They were published mainly in the *Monthly Notices of the Royal Astronomical Society (MNRAS).*

In 1917 Jeans received The Adams Prize of the University of Cambridge for the work *Problems of cosmogony and stellar dynamics* [58], which was published as a separate volume in 1919. It summarizes the basic research on equilibrium figures of incompressible and compressible rotating self-gravitating masses: the result on the compressible masses is particularly valuable as it applies directly to real astronomical objects — George Darwin, shortly before his death in 1912, had noted that further progress in cosmogony was blocked by the disregard for the development of the theoretical figures of equilibrium of rotating gaseous masses. That work is a great classic; it addressed the issues that attracted attention of mathematicians since K. Maclaurin. One of the conclusions of the monograph was that objects in our Solar System should be rare in the Universe, because their formation is a consequence of an extremely rare event — the close passing of one star by another. Many of the conclusions of that work are no longer accepted, but a number of the mathematical methods and ideas retain their value today. However, modern literature does not generally refer to this work, but cites the monograph of 1928 *Astronomy and Cosmogony* [111; 120], which includes the main results of the earlier work.

The complex issues in Jeans's books are discussed in a simple, figurative language. This, along with the brilliant synthesis of theory and observation, makes them among the best scientific monographs on astronomy ever written. They have encouraged young theoretical physicists and mathematicians to search for the solutions of astronomical problems.

Jeans paid great attention to the illustration and design of his books. That is clear from his letter to George Ellery Hale, Director of the Mount Wilson Observatory:

8, Ormonde Gate, Chelsea, S.W.3 Oct. 11, 1917
Dear Professor Hale,

I am engaged, as far as times permit, in preparing a book on Cosmogony for the Press, on selective [sic] photographs. I am not surprised to find that all the sixteen which I should like to have permission to reproduce come, without exception, from Mount Wilson.

I feel a little embarrassment in asking for permission to illustrate my book entirely from Mount Wilson photographs, but venture to do so, as yours are pre-eminently the best.

Of the sixteen which I should like to have permission to reproduce, six are by Ritchey and ten occur in the recent very fine collection by Pease in the Astrophys. Journal.

I am especially interested in Pease's edgeways spirals as they agree very well with the figures I have calculated for rotating gases. [Bakerian Lecture, Royal Society, 1917; this had not been printed yet.]

If you could give me permission to reproduce these, of course with full acknowledgement, I should be most grateful. I will write separately to Ritchey and Pease also.

My book is being produced in their best style by the Cambridge University Press (Royal 8vo format, similar to Darwin's Collected Works, etc.) and I am sure they can be relied on to do justice to your fine photographs. They ask for actual photographs if these can be supplied. (I have prints of Ritchey's but not of course of Pease's.)
Yours very truly, J.H. Jeans

8, Ormonde Gate, Chelsea, S.W.3 Jan. 1st, 1918
Dear Professor Hale,

I am greatly obliged for your kind letter of Nov. 8 giving me permission to use the Mount Wilson photographs. I have been waiting in the hope of receiving prints from Pease, but am now beginning to fear they must have been sunk or gone astray, so I will write him again.

I am so very glad to hear that the 100-inch telescope is so satisfactory. Besides what you wrote me I heard a glowing account of its success from Dyson, who had just been receiving letters from Mount Wilson. I was greatly interested in the Andromeda nebula results which Dr Adams was good enough to send me.
Again thanking you, and with the Greetings of the Season, Believe me,
Yours sincerely, J.H. Jeans". [193, p. 21–2].

In the first letter Jeans mentions the prestigious Bakerian lecture, which he gave at the Royal Society in 1917 (to receive such an invitation was a great honour). He chose the theme on which he had obtained important results during the last four years. The lecture's title was *The configurations of rotating compressible masses* [59]. It was published as an article in the *Philosophical Transactions of the Royal Society* in 1919.

In 1909 Jeans had been elected a Fellow of the Royal Astronomical Society of Great Britain. Prominent scientists, leading the study of the Universe, came together in that society. It was founded in 1820 and was then called the London Astronomical Society. In 1831, by Royal decree it was given its present name. The patron of the society was the monarch. The society conducted monthly meetings and once a year, usually in February, the general annual meeting. It is interesting that Jeans, being a fellow of that society, did not publish his works in their journal *Monthly Notices of the Royal Astronomical Society* before 1913, i.e. until his main research interests moved to the area of astronomy. He had usually sent his articles to the *Philosophical Transaction or Proceedings of the Royal Society.* However from 1916 to 1928, he often submitted his articles to the *Monthly Notices of the Royal Astronomical Society*, which published a series of Jeans's works criticizing Eddington's theory of the internal structure of stars. Without going into the details of the scientific discussion between Jeans and Eddington, we will note that the discussion was very acute. Eddington was intolerant of criticism and in the discussions he sometimes used quite harsh and insulting expressions. That upset Jeans, who was always a very sincere critic and clearly saw the shortcomings or omissions in his own logical reasoning. As a result of his misunderstanding of Eddington's method of approximation, other researchers were prompted to draw attention to a number of interesting questions in Eddington's theory. Jeans and Eddington had differing views for many years, and their discussions, published in the *Monthly Notices of the Royal Astronomical Society*, significantly increased its circulation. That showed interest not only in the subject of debate, but also in the views of two prominent scientists.

E. Milne writes:

"The outspoken astronomical debates between Jeans and Eddington of 1917–19 had one interesting consequence. Hardy, Jeans's competitor in the tripos and the Smith's Prize, became a Fellow of the Royal Astronomical Society, with some others, in order to have the privilege of attending these debates, and hearing Eddington and Jeans castigate one another in public. And sure enough, Hardy attended the debate of January 1931, and in due course, when the conflict had become triangular [E. Milne joined it. — A.K.], also contributed to it. His contribution was characteristic: he was presenting some analytical results obtained by R.H. Fowler (later Sir Ralph) in connexion with the fundamental differential equations of stellar structure, and he remarked that, amidst all the contending theories of Eddington, Jeans and Milne, of one thing he was certain, namely that, when these theories had all become dead and forgotten, the pure mathematics dealt with by R.H. Fowler would survive." [193, p. 31].

In the debates at the Royal Astronomical Society in 1929–30 Milne sharply criticized Eddington's physical interpretation. At a meeting of the Royal Astronomical Society in November of 1929, E. Milne read his paper *The masses, luminosities, and effective temperatures of the stars* which advanced a fundamental criticism of Eddington's classical works on the subject. Directly after Milne had finished, Jeans got up and said: "I agree with everything Professor Milne has said; I have been saying the same for the past fifteen years". Eddington then got up and said: "I could not follow the second half of Professor Milne's remarks; but no matter, the first half could not possibly be correct." Speaking in January 1931 in the renewed debate, Milne mainly supported Jeans, but criticized some aspects of his theory and developed his own method, but not accurately enough, making Jeans very upset. The debate was very vigorous yet Milne recalled that when he met Jeans later at another meeting of a scientific society, Jeans was very courteous with him. Milne himself felt sympathy and deep respect for Jeans, irrefutable evidence of which is his brief biography of him, which he wrote, being already seriously ill, shortly before his death.

There are, however, critical comments about Jeans: "He could be very charming, when he wanted something of others and very brusque when others wanted something of him".

Milne wrote that "he was modest and unassuming in private life, though he did not exercise 'charm' in the usual sense of that word outside the lecture theatre; on the lecture-platform he had a most winning delivery." Many have thought that his voice was unattractively harsh and high-pitched. [183, p. 136–7] But, as always, opinions about the nature of the person are quite controversial and depend mainly on which facet you observe.

Subsequently Jeans and Eddington kept to their irreconcilable points of view, but avoided the issues that would lead to unleashed stormy polemics. However, William McCrea recalled, one day when they had breakfast together in the club, they were talking about scientific matters on which they were of different opinions. When they rose from the table, Jeans, said: "Anyhow, it won't be settled in our lifetime". "In that case, — Eddington replied, — I'll bet you a harp to a halo that you're wrong" [185, p. 164].

Friday, Christmas 1919
"Merry Christmas, Eva"
exclaimed Winifred.

629

$$v = \frac{\frac{c}{v} + u}{1 + \frac{u}{c^2}\left(\frac{c}{v}\right)} = \frac{c}{v} + \frac{u\left(1 - \frac{1}{v^2}\right)}{1 + \frac{u}{c^2}\left(\frac{c}{v}\right)}.$$

If u^2/c^2 is neglected this reduces to formula (725). In this experiment we have very direct experimental confirmation of Einstein's formula for the composition of velocities.

Reflection of Light from a moving Mirror

688. According to the relativity hypothesis, the velocity of light in free space is always equal to c. If the light is observed by an observer moving with a velocity u relative to the source, the velocity is still equal to c, for we have seen in § 678 that the velocity obtained by compounding a velocity c with any other velocity u is itself equal to c.

This conclusion has been tested by Majorana[+] who examined the light reflected by a moving mirror and found its velocity to be exactly equal to c independently of the velocity of the mirror.

Aberration and the Doppler Effect.

689. As in § 591, the equation of wave-propagation in free space, namely

$$\frac{d^2\chi}{dt^2} = c^2\nabla^2\chi,$$

[+] C.R. 165 (1917) p. 424 and 167 (1918) p. 71.

Olivia's drawings on the back of various manuscript pages including those of her father.

"Winifred's hair began to fall!"

From top left:

Joseph John Thompson
(1856–1940),
English Physicist.
Oil portrait by
Winifred Nicholson 1924.
© Trinity College,
Cambridge.

Ernest Rutherford
(1871–1937),
British physicist born
in New Zealand,
"Father of nuclear physics".
Photo Wikipedia

Charles Scott Sherrington
(1857–1952),
Neurophysiologist,
histologist, bacteriologist
and pathologist.
Photo Wikipedia

THE ROYAL SOCIETY AND THE ROYAL ASTRONOMICAL SOCIETY 1919–1929

In 1919, soon after Jeans was awarded the Gold Medal of the Royal Society, he was elected as their Honorary Secretary of the Physical Sciences, which he held for ten years. There he worked with three presidents, J.J. Thomson (1915–1920), C.S. Sherrington (1920–1925) and E. Rutherford (1925–1930). They said he performed his duties with "very ruthless determination" [185, p. 165].

Among the many congratulatory letters received on this occasion, there was a letter from G.E. Hale:

> "My dear Mr Jeans, I meant long since to send you my heartiest congratulations on your election as Secretary of the Royal Society, or rather to offer my congratulations to the Council, as I am sure that the event is of no small significance in its bearing on the future development of the Society. [Hale was elected a foreign member of the Royal Society in 1909 — A.K.] This is unquestionably a very critical period in the progress of science and the policy adopted by such authoritative bodies as the Royal Society may turn the scale in the right direction. In this country [the United States. — A.K.], and probably England, the conditions are very complex. On the one hand, the increased cost of living and the high salaries offered by the industries are drawing good research men away from the faculties of educational institutions. On the other hand, there is such a marked advance in the public appreciation of science and research and such an obvious necessity of developing more investigators that the opportunity to interest governments and individual donors is greater than ever before. This is manifested in part by the strong expressions of the value of pure science made by industrial leaders. The pamphlet I am sending you under separate cover (Scientific Discovery and the Wireless Telephone) was prepared by the American Telephone and Telegraph Company to accompany their exhibit, of the wireless telephone and its scientific development, first shown at the building of the National Research Council in Washington and now at the American Museum of Natural History in New York. You will see what emphasis they lay upon the importance of research in physics without reference to practical return. If we can convince everyone of this, I am sure we can obtain large new funds for pure science.

Just at present we are attempting to secure a fund of a million dollars for research in physics at the California Institute of Technology (in Pasadena) and from the progress made during the last few days I hope we may complete it before July first. I have had no difficulty in convincing the trustees of this small institution (about 800 students) that research and graduate instruction should have quite as prominent a place in their programme as the ordinary undergraduate work of the average school of technology, and the prospects for the future are very encouraging especially as we mean to limit the attendance in order to raise the quality of the work. It is of course true that the trustees must be given clear ideas of the meaning and importance of research, but there should be very little difficulty in educating any average board, provided one who is familiar with research and its recent developments can have occasional opportunity to present the arguments.

I hope you are going ahead with the organization of National Committees of the various International Unions, and that these may perhaps be ultimately united to form a National Research Council, as I understand from Lacroix (if I have deciphered his letter correctly!) that the French intend to do. American Sections of the Astronomical, Geophysical and Chemical Unions have been formed, and that of the Mathematical Union is now in process of organization. I particularly hope that you are forming a Section of the Mathematical Union, and will be well represented at Strasbourg. Our mathematicians felt that the French went ahead rather rapidly, and are concerned over the fact that the date selected for the Strasbourg Congress coincides with that of the opening of our universities and falls in the same month with the regular triennial mathematical colloquium, to be held this year at the University of Chicago. But in the general interest they have smothered their chagrin, and various national societies are joining in the organization of a strong Section, which plans to send delegates to Strasbourg, where they expect to present a scheme for an abstract journal of mathematics, which seems to be greatly needed. They will be much encouraged if England is well represented there, for in spite of political squabbles and the infernal machines of Sinn Feiners, Egyptian nationalists, Indian Fakirs, and the unspeakable Hearst, England and the United States must work together and do everything possible to put down the many elements that feed on discord.

We are now at work on the definitive observing programme of the 100-inch telescope, and it is hardly necessary to say that your book, which I admire so much, is our chief guide in preparing the attack on the spiral nebulae and on many other questions. I hope you will send me suggestions from time to time, as our programme will be kept elastic enough to follow them." [193, p. 32–4]

GROUP PHOTOGRAPHS
A number of group photographs of scientists taken in the 1920s are extant in the archives of the Royal Society, the Institution of Engineering and Technology, and in Trinity College, University of Cambridge.

Jeans, photographed alongside the winners of the 1922 Nobel Prize for physiology– Archibald Vivian Hill and Otto Fritz Meyerhof.

Left to right: J.H. Jeans, A.V. Hill, O.F. Meyerhof.

This photograph celebrates the presence in London of the American physicist A. A. Michelson who was awarded the 1907 Nobel Prize for Physics. It was taken by A. A. Campbell Swinton on 14 March 1921 at his house; 40 Chester Square, London.

Back row, left to right: W. H. Bragg, J. Petavel, J. Larmor, W. S. McCormick, J. H. Jeans.

Front row, left to right: R. Glazebrook, P. A. MacMahon, A. A. Michelson, C. A. Parsons.

The post of the Secretary made Jeans a highly influential figure as he largely determined the policy of the Royal Society. In a letter to E. Rutherford, then head of the Cavendish laboratory in Cambridge, he wrote:

> Zermatt
> September 1, 1920
> My dear Rutherford
> You spoke of the need of a first-class applied mathematician or math physicist — for Cambridge. I have been wondering what you would think of Albert Einstein. From the Enclosed if seems quite likely that he will be leaving Berlin very soon — there has been a good deal of disturbance over him there, as you have probably seen, he would probably consider an English offer. I should think.
> In my opinion he is just the man needed, in conjunction with yourself to re-establish a school of mathematical physics in Cambridge. The only serious drawback I think of is that he does not — or did not — speak English, but I imagine he would soon learn. His age is 42, nearly 43, and I imagine he has still plenty of creative power left. Anyhow I put out the suggestions in case it has not occurred to you — you can judge of its practicability better than I can. You will never re-establish the school of mathl physics out of the material at present available in England.
> Yours ...
> J.H. Jeans.

The abilities of Jeans as a businessman were useful to put the financial affairs of the Society in order with its capital of more than a million pounds. Its journal since 1800, *Proceedings of the Royal Society*, flourished under his influence. Its series "A" became the leading English journal for the physical sciences. Previously, the most important original papers in physics by Rutherford and his group, Bohr, Darwin, and Jeans were published in the *Philosophical Magazine*. More extensive works were published in the *Philosophical Transactions* (as Rutherford said, — "buried in the mausoleum").

Rutherford, the President of the Royal Society from 1925 to 1930, together with Jeans, tried to select the best and most important articles of British physicists for *Proceedings A*. Although each article was officially reviewed by leading experts in the field, all articles passed through Jeans's hands. He often helped young authors with his usual kindness and attention.

Deep physical intuition allowed him to appreciate the outstanding work of then little known Paul Dirac, who developed the general formalism of the quantum theory on the basis of the ideas of W. Heisenberg. Together with R. Fowler, Jeans contributed to the special publication of Dirac's article in the latest issue of the 1925–1926 *Proceedings A* just two weeks after receipt. Dirac immediately became world-famous. The ability to identify the value of scientific work is very important in such a responsible post, and Jeans possessed it.

W. S. Adams, J. H. Jeans and E. Hubble at the 100 inch telescope at the Mount Wilson Observatory, California, US.

Jeans received the Hopkins Prize of the Cambridge Philosophical Society for 1921–1924 "for his work on the theory of gases and radiation, and the evolution of stellar systems". From 1924 to 1944 he was a Research Associate of the Mount Wilson Observatory and he greatly valued that honorable position. Inviting Jeans to take that post, Hale wrote:

> "If you honored us by accepting, I should be greatly pleased, especially as I feel sure that co-operation would be highly advantageous to us and possibly of some use to you. We should greatly value your occasional suggestions regarding new problems or special lines of observation, and we should be glad to place before you certain questions that puzzle us, though you would never be under any obligation to reply to them if the answers were not evident to you. The purpose of the honorarium is not to pay the Research Associate for work done for us, but to contribute in a modest way towards the pursuit of his own researches in the general field in which we are interested.
>
> I need hardly say that whether you do or do not see your way clear to accept such an offer, assuming it can be made, you will be more than welcome to visit the Observatory at any time and to stay there as long as you choose. I am sure you would find many points of importance to discuss with members of our staff and with Millikan, Epstein, Noyes, Tolman and other investigators now at the California Institute of Technology in Pasadena." [193, p. 36].

In 1923 Jeans gave the Guthrie Lecture of the London Physical Society. Shortly before, he was awarded the Gold Medal of the Royal Astronomical Society for his work in theoretical cosmogony. Handing the medal to Jeans,

OLIVIA AT CLEVELAND LODGE

During her youth Olivia seems to have been a happy child. However, in her late teens she rebelled. According to family legend, her mother gave her money with which she immediately bought a car, packed her belongings, and left home. Olivia and her parents never really became reconciled.

Olivia (age ~10 years) with her parents and dogs, Cleveland Lodge. Early 1920's.

Studio portrait of Olivia Jeans age 13 years by J. W. Moorhouse, September 1925.

Olivia with her new bicycle — possibly a birthday present — at Cleveland Lodge, 1925.

Olivia, Gertrude Jeans (her aunt), Martha Jeans (her grandmother) and James in the front of Cleveland Lodge, 1925.

Charlotte, Olivia and James's mother Martha in the garden at Cleveland Lodge, 1925.

the President, Arthur Eddington, in his welcoming speech did not deny himself the pleasure of reminding Jeans about their disagreements concerning the inner structure of stars. However he made clear his high appreciation of his contribution to astronomical science, including the application of methods used in gas dynamics, star clusters and especially the work on figures of equilibrium of a rotating mass, and the tidal cosmogonic hypothesis.

In particular, Eddington said:

> "I suppose that nothing in astronomy has appealed more to human imagination that the conception of each of the myriad points of light in the sky as a sun giving warmth and light to an attendant circle of planets … It has seemed a presumption, bordering almost on impiety, to deny to them inhabitants of the same order of creation as ourselves. But we forget the prodigality of Nature. How many acorns are scattered for one that grows into an oak? And need she be more economical of her stars than of her acorns? … If indeed she has no grander aim than to provide a home for her pampered child Man, it would be just like her methods to scatter a million stars whereof but two or three might happily achieve the purpose.
>
> Let me repeat that Dr Jeans does not claim to have established that our solar system is a freak system, unusual and possibly unique in the universe; but he has shown how shaky is the opposite view which expects a system of planets to be a normal appendage of a star." [193, p. 38].

~~ • ~~

Jeans had a very high standing in academic circles. He was the President of the Royal Astronomical Society from 1925 to 1927 and gave three speeches of welcome at the award of the Society's Gold medal: to Frank Dyson (1925), Albert Einstein (1926) and Frank Schlesinger (1927). Those were given in his characteristic lively style and at least some excerpts deserve to be cited.

Presenting the award to the astronomer F. Dyson "for his contributions to Astronomy in general, and, in particular, for his work on the 'Proper Motions of the Stars', Jeans started with the words:

> "It has not been the custom of the Society to award its Gold Medal to Astronomers Royal, indeed, only one holder of the Greenwich Office has been so honoured before, namely Airy, who received the medal first in 1833 and again in 1846 …" And further: "The reason why Astronomers Royal seldom achieve medals is not difficult to discover; it was expressed with the utmost clearness from this Chair on the last occasion on which the medal was presented to a Greenwich Astronomer Royal. In presenting the medal to Airy in 1846, Captain Smyth said: 'Our medal

was primarily instituted as a mark of approbation on individual exertion, on labours of love; and not to note our sense of the official merits of public men, or of the rectitude and ability with which they may acquit themselves in their respective offices.'

An Astronomer Royal must of necessity be a busy man; it is naturally somewhat rare to find one who, after the accomplishment of his heavy routine duties, has either the energy or the inclination for astronomical labours of love. It is because the present occupant of the office is such a one that it is my pleasant duty to present the medal to him today." [193, p. 39–40].

At the beginning of the speech awarding A. Einstein for his researches on "Relativity and on the Theory of Gravitation", Jeans told a parable:

"Some of us may remember the story of the children who played truant in order to explore the regions where the rainbow ends. After traveling all day, up hill and down dale, they had to admit failure of the most thoroughgoing kind — the rainbow was, to all appearances, no nearer than when they started .... They must have felt they were the victims of extremely bad luck, for they had clearly seen the rainbow in front of the nearest hill when they started out; could there be some sort of conspiracy on the part of rainbows, hills, and indeed the whole scheme of nature, to prevent their getting close to that rainbow?" [193, p. 42].

Jeans tried to express his understanding of Einstein's revolutionary transformation of physics. Of course, now one cannot agree with it completely, but the imagery is not in doubt.

The third speech was delivered to F. Schlesinger. It manifested Jeans's unusual versatility. He spoke professionally about the problems in the fields of astronomical techniques, photography and determinations of the stellar parallaxes, where he had no special training. The beginning of the speech was very lyrical:

"At the dawn of civilization, when man awoke from his long intellectual slumber, nine muses were appointed to preside over his various activities. Only one muse was allotted to science, and that one was allotted to astronomy. Perhaps the high gods of Olympus who arrange these things had heard of no science beyond astronomy, or perhaps they thought it the only one worth encouragement; we do not know. But it is said that since then the claims of other sciences have been admitted, and a vast crowd of junior muses have been appointed to look after them. When they all meet in conclave, many of the latter report quite extraordinary rates of progress in their particular sciences, and it has sometimes been thought that astronomy, which started first in the race, has at times shown some tendency to lag behind.

To this Urania has always had a ready answer. She can point first to the immensity of her task; sciences such as geography, geodesy and geology, whose field of action is limited to the surface of one tiny planet, can no doubt claim to be well on towards the completion of their tasks, but the exploration of an entire universe offers a task of a different order of magnitude. She can also point to the extraordinary difficulty of this task; after the first obvious steps have been taken, the astronomer can get nothing of value except with instruments of almost incredible precision. Moreover, instead of being able to investigate phenomena when he pleases, he has to wait on Nature, and Nature moves very slowly in comparison with human life — the whole age of astronomy, as a science, bears the same relation to the ages of the stars that it studies as does the last tick of the clock in the dying century to the century itself. Finally, she has often been heard to remark, with a mixture of pride and sorrow in her voice, that her science presents problems of such enthralling interest that only too few astronomers can be found to do their fair share of the fundamental work on which all progress must ultimately be based. We can rest assured that she is well satisfied when, as on the present occasion, our Society singles out for its highest honour one who has done not only a fair share, but a lion's share, of most valuable fundamental work." [193, p. 45].

Indeed, after the first measurements of stellar parallaxes, made almost simultaneously by V.A. Struve, F. Bessel and T. Henderson in 1837–1838, the number of stars with measured parallaxes was growing very slowly, and in 1901 Newcomb's catalogue listed only 72 of the closest stars. This changed completely after F. Schlesinger suggested his photographic method to determine stellar parallaxes. In 1924 *The Shared Directory of Parallaxes* was published, it already contained 1870 objects, and the random errors did not exceed 0.01". The proposed method allowed one to determine — quickly and with high accuracy — parallaxes for a large number of stars. Jeans was particularly proud to have awarded the Gold Medal to Schlesinger.

In 1925 Jeans addressed The General Assembly of the International Astronomical Union (IAU) in Cambridge with a salutatory word as the President of the Royal Astronomical Society:

"We can, perhaps, in a certain sense consider your visit as a pilgrimage to Newton … (the last assembly in Rome, according to Baillaud, was a pilgrimage to Galileo) I can imagine that we (the IAU) will be able to succeed in such a pilgrimage, guided by the history of astronomy. And therefore, we should promise to make a pilgrimage to the country of Laplace, … a birth-place of cosmogony …" [292, p. 88].

J. H. Jeans, O. Lodge and the German physicist A. J. W. Sommerfeld. Possibly 1926 when Sommerfeld was elected a foreign member of the Royal Society

Jeans's activities as President of the Royal Astronomical Society were not restricted to ceremonies and presenting awards; he also tried to improve the inner workings of the society, to contribute to their activities, so that they could respond to the rapid pace of scientific development. He played a leading role in the setting-up and financing the annual Darwin lectures — named after his mentor George Howard Darwin, the President of the Society in 1899 and 1900. In a letter to the Treasurer of the Society F.D.M. Stratton, Jeans offered the Society, a 1000 pounds, the annual income of which was to go towards the expenses of the invited lecturer. He expressed the wish — which was accepted by the Society — that the lecturer should be a brilliant scientist and, as a rule, a foreigner, either from astronomy or a related science such as geophysics, or even physics.

G.E. Hale was invited to give the first Darwin Lecture. He was the honorary Director of the Mount Wilson Observatory, a prominent scientist and an organizer of science in the United States. Thanks to him the Observatories were also perfectly equipped physical laboratories. He was also the initiator of the International Astronomical Union in 1919 and one of the founders of the *Astrophysical Journal.*

Here one should mention the role of Jeans in the setting up of the International Astronomical Union (IAU). In March 1918 H.A. Bumstead began his duties as the scientific attaché at the American Embassy in London. His lengthy letters dated 23rd and 25th July 1918 reported on a weekend with Jeans discussing Hale's plan: "… we are both going to spend all our efforts and persuade A. Schuster (one of the most influential members of the Council of the Royal Society), that the creation of an IAU is not in fact impossible at the present time" [292, p. 41]. Although Schuster was rather

Portrait of G. H. Darwin (1912 by Mark Gertler), Professor of Astronomy and Experimental Philosophy at Cambridge (1883–1912) who inspired Jeans's interest in astronomy — and after whom the annual lecture at the Royal Astronomical Society is named.
© Darwin College, Cambridge.

sluggish and seemed pessimistic, he wrote to Hale on 27 July 1918 supporting his plan. It was very important, as the reach of Schuster's influence exceeded even that of the President of the Royal Society J.J. Thomson, and Hale's plan in some ways criticized Lord Rayleigh as well as A.J. Balfour, then a member of the Cabinet.

Eight years later Jeans invited Hale on behalf of the Council of the Royal Astronomical Society. "Council are most anxious to give it a good start by getting a really eminent astronomer to give the first (Darwin) lecture, and to head the list of lecturers for all time." [193, p. 49]. But, unfortunately, Hale had to refuse for medical reasons. Jeans regretted Hale's ill health and thanked him for the invitation for an extended visit to California. In the same letter, he complains about the heavy work-load as Secretary of the Royal Society, mentions his wish to resign, and writes about the general atmosphere of his life: "All this administration and committee work makes an awful hole in the time and energy available for research, as I expect you realize only too well." [193, p. 51]. Jeans wrote that during five days staying in London he had to attend meetings of 15 committees. It really was a very active period in his life.

The first Darwin lecture *Astronomical photography for precision measurements* was given by Frank Schlesinger in 1927 at the same time as he was awarded the Gold Medal of the Royal Astronomical Society. Since then, outstanding foreign astronomers regularly gave the Darwin Lectures.

Despite his heavy workload, Jeans did not slacken the pace of his scientific activity. In 1922 he delivered the Halley Lecture at Oxford University: *The nebular hypothesis and modern cosmogony* [68]. It gave an overview of the development of cosmogonic ideas, starting with Laplace's *The System of the World* (1796) up to his own research. In 1925 Jeans gave the Rouse Ball Lecture [97] at the University of Cambridge. It was devoted to the quantum theory of the atom and showed that he was closely watching the development of new physics, although not participating in it.

JEANS Add 7653/J2

RS

CLEVELAND LODGE
DORKING.

Jan 20. 29.

My dear Rutherford —

I feel rather worried about Eddington's paper & his intensive advertising campaign. It makes the R.S look rather foolish, & I am afraid they may think I have let them down. Also Millikan may feel he has a real grievance.

I can't take any action, but I want you to know the facts.

The paper was received at the R.S on Dec. 10th. The offices closed on Dec 22nd for Christmas, so that I had either to rush it through in 12 days or hold it up for 7 weeks. The original MS contained a definite statement (struck out in proof) that Siegbahn had obtained a value for e (given, but I forget the figures)

First page of a four page letter from Jeans, Secretary of the Royal Society to Rutherford (President), concerning a paper by Eddington and his intense advertising campaign … © Royal Society

Jeans continued to work most actively in the field of astronomy. In the *Monthly Notices of the Royal Astronomical Society*, between 1913 and 1928 he published more than 45 works, which are brought together in *Astronomy and Cosmogony* [111], published in 1928, the last year of his active scientific work.

In the twenties the Jeanses repeatedly visited America making up for their lack of visits after leaving Princeton and during the war years. Charlotte's father had died in 1911. Her mother, Annie Mitchell, had inherited the extensive fortune, property and holdings on behalf of the family. Daunted in the first instance, she sensibly arranged it to be placed in trusts administered by lawyers. With the outbreak of the First World War, fearing German submarines, the "Folly" in Jamaica was vacated. In February 1920, the Jeanses made a long postponed journey to visit Charlotte's

Arthur Eddington (1882–1944). Gold medallist of the Royal Astronomical Society, 1924.
© Royal Astronomical Society.

Frank Watson Dyson (1868–1939). Gold medallist, Royal Astronomical Society, 1925.
© Royal Astronomical Society.

Albert Einstein (1879–1955). Gold medallist, Royal Astronomical Society, 1926.
Image Wikipedia

Frank Schlesinger (1871–1943). Gold medallist, Royal Astronomical Society, 1927.
© Yale University. Photograph by Harris and Ewing, Washington DC

15th WEDDING ANNIVERSARY IN SALEM
Old Mumford House, Salem, Connecticut, US. Celebration of James's and Charlotte's 15th wedding anniversary: Olivia is in front of her parents, to her left is Hiram Bingham, Alfreda (Charlotte's sister). Annie Tiffany Mitchell is behind James and Charlotte. 1922.

mother in Miami. In summer 1922 they visited New London and Salem in Connecticut and celebrated the 15th anniversary of their wedding, with photographs being taken on the porch of the old Mumford house where they got married. Granny by this time was about eighty. She spent her time knitting, and in a number of Jeans's letters to her we can find his thanks for his "well fitting" socks.

During these years Jeans's scientific work was widely recognised. At the Leiden Congress in 1922 he and Charly were met at the railway station by a delegation, which included Einstein, Kamerlingh Onnes and many other celebrities. Charlotte wrote: "people (were) invited from across the Netherlands" to meet us. Soon after his return to England Jeans spoke at a gala dinner attended by several hundred dignitaries, including the Duke of York ("who stuttered"), Ramsay McDonald, and Sir J.J. Thomson, who 'made the best speech'. Two months later, Jeans gave the Halley lecture in Oxford *The nebular hypothesis and modern cosmogony* [68]. It gave him the reputation as 'the best lecturer in England' — Oxford University awarded him an honorary degree of Doctor of Sciences.

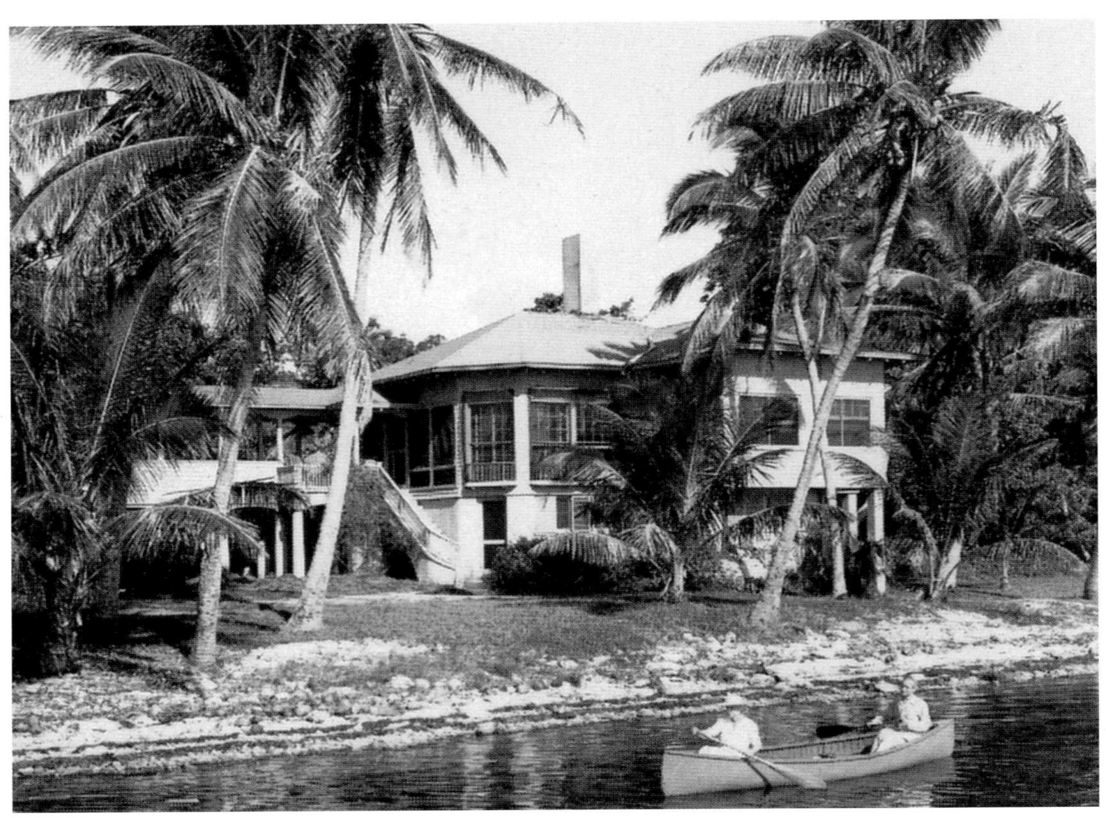

TIFFANY & CO.

23 AND 25, MADDOX STREET, REGENT STREET, LONDON.W.1.
25, RUE DE LA PAIX & PLACE DE L'OPÉRA PARIS.
FIFTH AVENUE & 37th STREET, NEWYORK.

London, 28th July, 1924.

The American Consul-General,
American Consulate,
London.

Sir,

It is with very great pleasure that we introduce to you Dr. J. H. Jeans, of Cleveland Lodge, Dorking, who with Mrs. Jeans is shortly sailing for America on a visit to Mrs. Jeans' mother.

Mrs. Jeans is the grand-daughter of the founder of our House, and we can well testify as to the uprightness of character, health, and financial responsibility of her husband.

We have the honor to be, Sir,
Your obedient servants,

pro Tiffany & Co.
A.W. Heavenyead

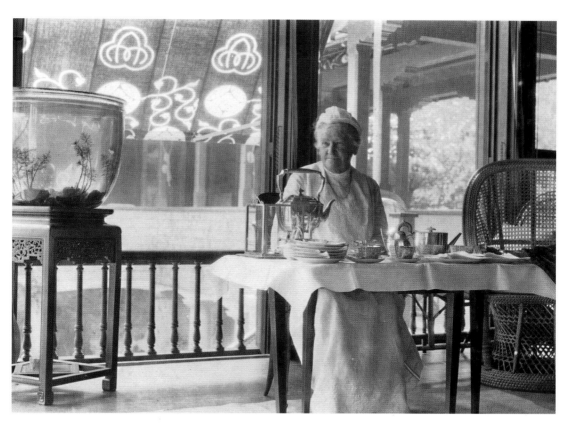

BIRTHDAY OF ANNIE MITCHELL, CHARLOTTE'S MOTHER

'Sweet Ways', Miami, Florida, US. Annie Mitchell's home, modified recently with an extension built in 1922 (from The Tiffany Fortune 1996).

Letter of reference from Tiffany concerning the suitability of James to obtain a visa for their 1924 visit to the United States. This visit was to coincide with Annie Mitchell's 80th birthday.

Annie waiting for her guests for tea, Sweet Ways, Miami.

Charlotte and Annie joking with James. Sweet Ways, 1924.

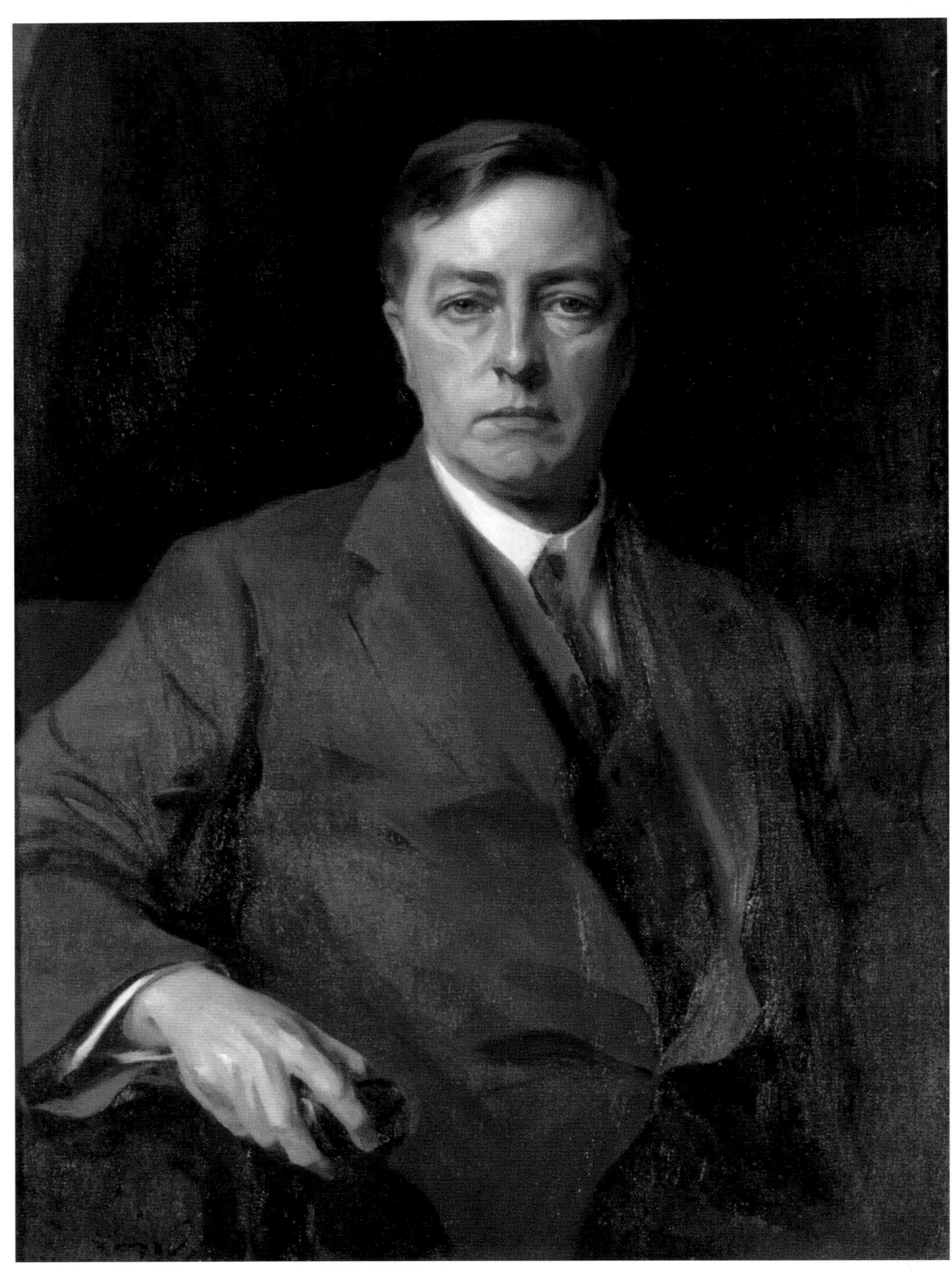

Portrait of J. H. Jeans by Philip de László dated 1924 that now hangs in the Royal Society at Carlton Terrace, London.

STELLAR DYNAMICS

When Jeans started working on stellar dynamics, a completely new field of astronomy, his interest focused on applying the mathematical tools that had been developed for his work on the kinetic theory of gases.

In 1913 his article *On the Kinetic Theory of Star Clusters* [36] was published in the *Monthly Notices of the Royal Astronomical Society*, the pre-eminent astronomical journal in the UK. The main problem was to determine the deviations in the directions of motions of the stars arising from their being close to each other. Jeans adopted an estimate by Lord Kelvin that 10^9 stars lie within a distance of 1000 parsecs and assumed the average mass of a star was five solar masses. He further made an informed estimate of the relative velocities of the stars as 60 km/s. For these parameters Jeans found that it would take 3.2 x 10^9 years for a star's direction of travel to be deviated by 1°, 8 x 10^{11} years for 2° and 5 x 10^{12} years for 5°. The last two time intervals exceed our current understanding of the age of the Universe and so today they seem physically meaningless.

Jeans describes the results of his research very vividly:

> "... let us take a definite instance of a star-stream in which the stars all start with equal and parallel velocities of 4x10^6 cms. per sec. Let us suppose that a star is still considered to belong to the main stream as long as its direction of motion makes an angle not greater than 2° with the main stream. After 100 million years, the stream will have lost only one in 8000 of its original members, and the remainder will make angles with the main stream of which the average amount is only 10'. After 3200 million years, the loss will be one in 250, and the average angle will be 1°. After 80,000 million years, one-tenth of the original members have been lost by violent encounters, but the average angle of the remainder is 5°. Thus the stream has been mainly dissolved, not by collisions or violent encounters, but by gradual scattering." [36, p. 111–12].

Consequently Jeans believed that the Galaxy was not in a steady state. Today, however, based on the known age of the Universe, we would come to the opposite conclusion. Indeed, during the lifetime of the Universe of approximately 10 billion years, any scattering of stars in the Galaxy would be negligible.

In 1915 Jeans tried to explain theoretically the apparent presence of two star streams in the Galaxy, a concept suggested by the Dutch astronomer J.C. Kapteyn when interpreting his extensive observations on the movements of stars. He presented it first at the Astronomical Assembly in Saint Louis, Missouri, in 1904, and then, in 1905, at the Congress of the British Association in Cape Town where Jeans was the secretary of section A (Mathematics and Physics).

Kapteyn's concept was as follows: If we construct a diagram of stellar velocities relative to the Sun, we would expect it to be stretched toward the anti-apex, the direction opposite to the peculiar motion of the Sun. But it turns out that stellar proper motions pick out *two* preferred directions, points that Kapteyn called "vertices". Kapteyn considered it was most natural to interpret this picture as a superposition of the movements of the Sun and two groups of stars, moving in opposite directions. Moreover, it was thought that these two star streams penetrated each other. After corrections to remove the effect of the motion of the Sun, 'true vertices' were identified. They were located at opposite points of the sky: one in the constellation of Orion, another in the constellation of Scutum. Their coordinates were respectively $\alpha_1 = 91°$, $\delta_1 = +13°$, and $\alpha_2 = 271°$, $\delta_2 = -13°$. At the time it seemed surprising that these vertices were in the Milky Way, and that one was close to the centre of the Galaxy and the other in the opposite direction. These facts were naturally explained in later studies.

At this point we should mention the work of A. Eddington and the German astrophysicist K. Schwarzschild. Eddington showed that the stars of both streams are present in any volume of space. This implied that the stars of these flows were perfectly mixed. In this respect, the two-stream concept was too implausible. Schwarzschild's point of view was more logical. He rejected the two-stream model and just assumed that residual stellar motions exist in a preferred direction coinciding with Kapteyn's vertices. Proceeding from the fact that the projections of the velocity in these directions are distributed according to Maxwell's law, Schwarzschild managed to determine the velocity dispersion of the stars and concluded that the highest dispersion of velocities was along the line of vertices. Jeans also contributed to the clarification of that problem. He examined the general conditions under which the distribution of stellar velocities of Schwarzschild could be ellipsoidal, applying the laws of the kinetic theory of gases to the stars. That served as a model for future research. In 1916 he considered the details of mutual penetration of stellar streams and realised the difficulty of the solution. Summarizing it, Jeans wrote: "In conclusion, we must again repeat that the problem we discussed is too complicated to yield a complete solution" [43].

The correct explanation was found by the Swedish astronomer B. Lindblad but not until 1921. He demonstrated that patterns in the distribution of proper velocities of stars were the natural consequence of the rotation of our Galaxy. Most of the stars move around the centre of the Galaxy, and nearly circular orbits and more inclined and elongated orbits create the observed deviations. Lindblad's point of view was fully confirmed and it was further developed in the works of the Dutch astronomer Jan Oort. In 1927, Oort not only confirmed Lindblad's hypothesis of large-scale rotation in the Galaxy, but was also able to identify subsystems of stars on the basis of the effects of differential rotation. He showed that the stars in the spherical component of the Galaxy differed in a number of properties from the stars of the disc component.

Despite the fact that Jeans failed to discover the correct interpretation of the proper motions of stars, we should remember his outstanding contribution to the development of stellar dynamics. B. Lindblad wrote in a classical review paper *Dynamics of Galaxies*: "we can say that the study of galactic dynamics began with the fundamental works of Eddington and Jeans" [266, p. 39]. He goes on to discuss Jeans's work in more detail: "Jeans developed a more general theory, classifying the function of the distribution as a function of integrals of motion. Applied to ellipsoidal distributions Jeans's analysis is limited to homogeneous expressions of the second order for the velocities; the average differential motion in the system is not taken into account. Kapteyn formulated a dynamic theory for the 'typical stellar system', derived from his statistical work on the distribution of stars. The analysis of this 'typical system' was significantly developed by Jeans in an important study, containing a host of mathematical techniques, used for research in the field of galactic dynamics." [266, p. 40]. (see Jeans's article *Motions of Stars in Kapteyn's Universe* (1922)).

In his review *Star Clusters*, Sawyer-Hogg sets out Jeans's views on this issue. "Exploring the accumulation of destructive forces, Jeans, in his pioneering work, *The Dynamics of Moving Clusters* (1922) suggested that our galactic system as a whole could be formed from the remnants of broken clusters which arose in the plane of the Galaxy and consisted of stars more closely bound than now" [266, p. 203].

Jeans's works on stellar dynamics have retained their significance up to the present time due to the rationality of his methods. He developed a method of studying a pair of convergent stars, and suggested that convergence could be so strong that the orbits of stars undergo a mutual gravitational effect which would change the direction of motion of the centre of mass. Jeans obtained a ratio, which provided a very full solution of the problem.

STELLAR STRUCTURE AND DYNAMICS TODAY

Kumar Chitre and Adam Jermyn

The study of stellar structure began as a field during Jeans's life, and so is quite young compared with the millennia-old study of astronomy as a whole. This is not surprising because so many disparate and deep laws of nature are required to properly understand how stars work, and so it was only recently that this exploration became a feasible undertaking. Theories of gas behaviour, radiation, nuclear fusion, and fluid dynamics, to which Jeans made many significant contributions, coalesced in the 1900s–10s and provided the groundwork for understanding, as it were, what makes stars tick. These physical laws are like the rules of chess: without them one cannot hope to understand the game, but the game is vastly richer than the rules themselves would suggest.

As soon as all the rules were known astronomers turned to their consequences, to "playing the game", and progress was rapid. Subrahmanyan Chandrasekhar (1910–1995) was perhaps the most prolific, explaining the structure of white dwarfs, predicting the mass at which they become unstable, exploring the structure of rotating stars, to name just a few of his contributions. Donald Lynden-Bell (1935–2018) examined the magnetic fields of stars and Hermann Bondi (1919–2005) studied the way in which interstellar gas falls on to stars. Other giants of the time include William Fowler (1911–1995) and Fred Hoyle (1915–2001), who provided in broad strokes the currently accepted explanation of the origin of the chemical elements as products of fusion in stars. This work is the origin of Carl Sagan's famous phrase, "We are all star stuff.", and has had a profound impact on our understanding of the universe and our place within it.

In the 1960s a numerical investigation was taken up to study the stability of galaxies initially based on N-body simulations of tens of point masses. Lyman Spitzer (1914–1997) did seminal work on the evolution of N-body systems for studying the evolution of globular clusters. With advances in available computing power, the numerical simulations can now handle millions of point masses to simulate the disks, bulges and halos of galaxies. Jeremiah Ostriker (1937–) and his colleagues later went on to examine specific mechanisms like shocks and tidal-capture binaries to investigate the evolution of globular clusters demonstrating the depletion of the inner parts of galaxies owing to dynamical friction-induced inspiral.

The second half of the twentieth century saw the extensive investigation of the formation of nuclear regions of galaxies and the origin of massive black holes in galactic nuclei. More recently, over the past quarter of a century there has been intensive study of the mechanism of galactic cannibalism whereby satellite galaxies, orbiting in the halos of massive galaxies, induce wakes behind them. These cause a drag from the gravitational forces, resulting in the spiralling of the satellites with eventual merging into the central galaxy.

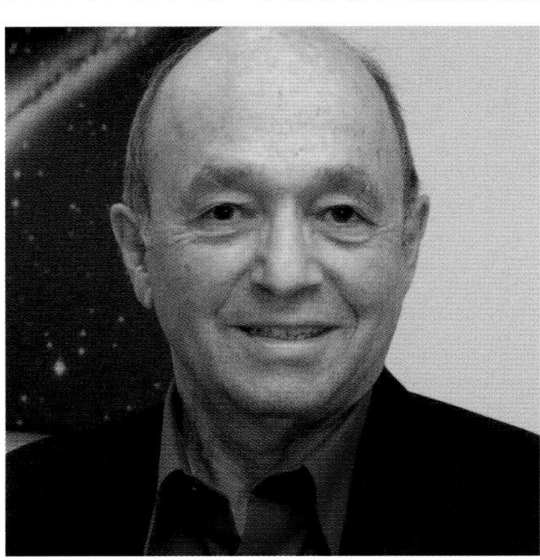

Top to bottom
Subrahmanyan Chandrasekhar (1910–1995).
© University of Chicago.
Donald Lynden-Bell (1935–2018).
Wikipedia.
Hermann Bondi (1919–2005).
© European Space Agency.
William Fowler (1911–1995). © Caltec.
Fred Hoyle (1915–2001).
© Royal Astronomical Society.
Lyman Spitzer (1914–1997).
© Princeton University.
Jeremiah Ostriker (1937–).
© Princeton University.

He examined the effect of multiple weak encounters. In this approximation, even when taking the combined effects into account, the overall outcome is negligible. From the modern point of view of galactic orbits, the vast majority of stars are not experiencing disturbances from their neighbours.

Jeans's main achievement in stellar dynamics was to introduce methods derived from the kinetic theory of gases. For stars, he introduced Hamiltonian coordinates and momenta and constructed a six-dimensional phase space. Then the equation of motion of stars can be easily written using the Hamilton function $H(p, q)$. This equation for stellar systems was first used by Jeans in 1915 [43]. His method was widely used by subsequent researchers. Lindblad applied it in 1925 to explain the dependence of the asymmetry of stellar motions on their dispersion of velocities, discovered by E. Strömgren. A method of studying a close conjunction of the stars was applied and developed in the works of K. Charlier in 1917 and S. Chandrasekhar in 1942. In stellar dynamics the law of the constancy of the phase density became known as Jeans's theorem, and his monograph *Problems of Cosmogony and Stellar Dynamics* [58] was one of the main guidelines in this area for many years.

~~ • ~~

As a physicist, Jeans, of course, could not be satisfied only with the dynamical study of stellar motions. He was interested in the energy sources of radiation and internal structure of stars. But the general level of development of physical science of that time was the reason why his work in this area was not of such a fundamental nature as that on stellar dynamics, despite a number of brilliant conjectures and ingenious solutions. In *Astronomy and Cosmogony*, summarizing his astronomical research, Jeans puts the basic extragalactic questions:

> "What, in ultimate fact, are the stars? What causes them to shine, and for how long can they continue thus to shine? Why are binary and multiple stars such frequent objects in the sky, and how have they come into being? What is the significance of the characteristic flattened shape of the galactic system, and why do some of its stars move in clusters, like shoals of fish, while others pursue independent courses? What is the significance of the extragalactic nebulae, which appear at a first glance to be other universes outside our own galactic universe, comparable in size with it, although different in general quality? And behind all looms the fundamental question: what changes are taking place in this complex system of astronomical bodies, how did they start and how will they end?" [120, p. 29].

Interested for many years in the problem of the source of stellar energy, Jeans offered various solutions at different times. In 1904, he suggested that the energy of stars, including the Sun, was caused by annihilation of matter. Based on his hypothetical assumptions he criticized other earlier proposed sources of stellar energy, such as the common initial store of heat or gravitational energy of the stars. The inability to explain the duration of existence of a radiating star led Jeans to the search for subatomic energy sources. This is what Geoffrey and Margaret Burbidge wrote about it in their retrospective review *Stellar Evolution*:

> "They can be divided into three categories: 1) radioactive sources, 2) a kind of mass annihilation, 3) synthesis of heavy elements from lighter ones. The use of natural radioactivity as a source of energy immediately created great difficulties, as radioactivity is a spontaneous quantum effect, not depending on the conditions inside the star. Further, the liberation of energy, if we assume terrestrial abundances of uranium and thorium, would be insufficient to increase the time scale. Artificial radioactivity was not considered at that time. Jeans was an ardent defender of some polyatomic annihilation process, such as the annihilation of protons and electrons. His arguments were based on his sustainability criteria. He concluded that all interactions between the atoms, between atoms and electrons or between atoms and radiation were excluded, because they violated these criteria. He even believed that the synthesis of helium from four protons could lead to explosive instability, although he did not consider that this synthesis could occur as a result of catalysis or a number of consecutive reactions. He also ruled out one of the conditions imposed by Russell, namely, that there was a threshold temperature below which a source of energy is inactive. The source proposed by Jeans was like radioactivity in that it was independent of all external physical parameters. The time scale simply expressed the time necessary to convert a mass equal to the solar mass into radiation, which is a period of the order of 10^{13} years [254, p. 143]".

Jeans rightly believed that the energy released by the annihilation of matter greatly exceeds that released during any chemical reaction, but he wrongly assumed the possibility of annihilation of a proton and an electron. A mistake was also his suggestion that the source of stellar energy is superheavy radioactive transuranic elements, although the prediction of their existence was fair (this assumption did not appear out of nowhere, it was due to the research in physics at the time).

In 1923 Kramers determined ratios for the coefficients of X-ray absorption by hydrogen atoms and other heavier elements. Jeans, aware of the high temperatures in the interior of the Sun and stars and, consequently, the prevalence there of shortwave radiation, immediately realized their importance for astrophysics. According to Kramers' ratios the rate of absorption is proportional to Z^2/A, where Z is the atomic number and A is the atomic weight. It is easy to see that the heavier the absorbing element, the greater this ratio and the greater, therefore, the value of the absorption coefficient. But the absorption coefficient can alternatively be established by the ratio of the luminosity of the star and its mass, which are determined from observations. Thus, Jeans had an opportunity to assess Z^2/A for stellar matter, which was done in 1926 [100]. The value obtained for Z^2/A matches hypothetical elements heavier than uranium. In addition, for young stars, according to Jeans's ideas, that ratio was greater than for old stars. Thus, the genesis of his thoughts on generating energy in the interiors of stars due to the fission of transuranium elements into lighter ones becomes clear.

Unfortunately, at that time the understanding of the evolution of stars was imperfect, and it soon became clear that Kramers' formula could not be applied to heavy elements, though it gave good results for hydrogen-like atoms. Thus Jeans's hypothesis did not have firm foundations. Eddington in his classic monograph *The Internal Structure of the Stars* (1926) noted that the opacity value obtained from Kramers' theoretical approach differed from the value of the opacity determined by astronomical observations, and referred to it as the "gloomy cloud" on the horizon of the theory of stars. He was correct in not following Jeans with his hypothesis of stars consisting of speculative superheavy elements. For this, however, Jeans criticized Eddington:

> "I should, perhaps, merely indicate that Eddington and others approached the issue from the other end, attributing Z^2/A values on a hunch on the basis of our information about the elements in the atmosphere of the Sun and stars. This path, however, is very risky. The stellar spectrum gives no indication about which elements are present in the interior; at least, there is reason to believe "a priori" that the elements inside the stars are totally different from the elements on the surface. What mistake would an observer make on another celestial body, if he assumed that none of the other chemical elements existed, besides those in the atmosphere!" [168, p. 22–3].

This illustrates the fact that in conditions of limited observational data, logically justified but mutually conflicting points of view can exist and only the further development of science allows the extraction of the truth. However, in the studies that Jeans carried out on the internal structure of stars, there are a number of ideas that have had a huge impact on the further development of astrophysical science.

Jeans developed the Lane-Ritter-Emden theory of the equilibrium configurations of stars with the polytropic equation of state $P = K\rho^{(n+1)/n}$ where the constant n is known as the polytropic index and K is a constant of proportionality. This equation of state, namely the dependence of the pressure P of stellar matter on its density ρ via a power law, was widely used in the 19th century, when it was assumed that the transfer of energy in stars was achieved by convection. In 1917 he first suggested that at the temperatures prevailing in stars, matter should be in an ionised state, with ionised nuclei and free electrons both contributing to the pressure. This deduction led to the important result that the mean molecular weight of the stellar material is reduced and as a consequence the central temperature is decreased. The modern value of the temperature at the centre of the Sun differs from the value obtained by Jeans by only a factor of two or three.

Jeans noted the important role of radiation pressure in stars in equilibrium. He rightly argued that this effect becomes significant for massive stars. As Eddington later confirmed, for stars of approximately a solar mass, radiation pressure can be neglected, but for stars of a hundred and more solar masses it becomes dominant.

Developing the theory of the internal structure of the stars, Jeans drew particular attention to the mechanism of energy transport. He showed that heat transfer by conduction would be insufficient to explain the powerful radiation from the surfaces of the Sun and stars. Jeans correctly believed that the bulk of the energy transfer was by radiation. Jeans then took on the task of the unification of the theory of radiative equilibrium with the theory of polytropic configurations. Although using approximate methods, he came to the correct conclusion that a star with specified parameters will always be able to come to an equilibrium state. However, in the case of the polytropic index $n = 3$, Jeans observed that "the addition or subtraction of the slightest amount of mass causes the star to rush through the whole range of values [of the central density] from $\rho_c = 0$ to $\rho_c = \infty$." [120, p. 82]. This result led him to criticise Eddington's theory based on the $n = 3$ polytrope in which Eddington had argued that the luminosity depended only on the mass and did not depend on the nature of the energy source. The case of $n = 3$, however, is very interesting and important because it describes the state of the matter in white dwarfs, in large hot stars, and even in the Sun, very well. But when building a polytropic equilibrium model with $n = 3$, three features need to be taken into account: 1) equilibrium is possible only at a certain value of the mass (if K is constant), 2) the total energy of the star is equal to zero, 3) the radius of the star is arbitrary [222].

Jeans showed that a polytrope of index $n = 3.25$ corresponded to the equilibrium configuration of a star composed of matter with a constant molecular weight and evenly distributed energy sources. Similar formal exercises allowed him to calculate the pressures and temperatures in the central regions of stars within the framework of polytropic equilibrium models. It is very interesting from a modern point of view that Jeans considered models on the assumption that the region of energy generation was concentrated towards the centre. This enabled him to decrease the central stellar temperatures by nearly a factor of two. Jeans also pointed out that the strong ionisation in stellar material meant the ideal gas law might be invalid. He wrote "Such a condition can be properly described as a liquid, or semi-liquid, state" [120, p. 108]. Although Jeans's criticisms of Eddington's equilibrium gas sphere model of a star were unsound, his analysis was to be confirmed in later studies of the evolution of white dwarfs. The cooling white dwarf plasma ions form a Coulomb liquid, then a lattice and, finally, a quantum liquid [202]. But Jeans's observation that stable stars cannot be wholly in a gaseous state has been rejected. Nor was he right in opposing H.N. Russell's suggestion that the generation of stellar energy can be ignored until the temperature reaches a certain critical value. (In the modern view, thermonuclear reactions are possible only above a certain critical temperature.) And his assessment of stellar ages, 10^{12}–10^{13} years, certainly does not tally with current views. The age of the Universe, as we have already noted, is estimated at $(13–15) \times 10^9$ years, and naturally the stars cannot be older. But we cannot blame Jeans for these errors, because when he studied the internal structure and evolution of stars, the source of their energy was unknown. We have to marvel at how much Jeans, Eddington and Milne and others were able to achieve in the study of stars without knowing the basic physical processes taking place within them.

An example of Jeans's deep insight is the work in which he spoke about the viscosity of radiation in a star (a phenomenon he first remarked upon in 1926). It seemed natural that since radiation carries momentum, it generates a pressure, but, as Jeans showed, radiation carrying momentum from one layer to another in a rotating star would create an apparent viscosity, thereby smoothing the gradient of the velocity. Jeans attributed a strict physical basis to this effect, calculated the coefficient of viscosity of radiation and re-evaluated the mechanism of transfer of momentum in a moving environment. He showed that in stars, radiation viscosity could be comparable with the conventional gas viscosity [99]. In this context, Jeans put forward the interesting idea that the flux of radiation from the central region of the star passing through the outer layers could have an inhibitory effect, disrupting solid body rotation. Jeans's thoughts on the rotation of stars were significant because they were the first suggestions of the possibility of differential rotation. That possibility was further developed in the works of E.A. Milne, and the problem of differential rotation was studied theoretically by J. Wasiutynski [325] and J. Jardetsky [311]. S.I. Blinnikov demonstrated the possibility of differential rotation of polytropic configurations [206] and investigated the influence of differential rotation on their shapes and gravitational fields [228]. Jeans's idea about the possibility of differential rotation in celestial bodies was very fruitful.

~~ • ~~

A number of Jeans's works relate to the field of geophysics. In 1923 Jeans published an article *The Propagation of Earthquake Waves* [72]. He started with a methodically exact statement of objectives: "A complete understanding of the propagation of earthquake disturbances demands a solution of the problem of the vibrations of an elastic sphere in which the mutual gravitational attraction of the parts is taken into account, as well as the variation of the physical constants of the Earth's material with distance from the centre" [72, p. 554]. Accounting for the effects of the curvature of the Earth and gravity becomes necessary for waves with periods of about 1 minute and above. Jeans was one of the first to build, to a first approximation, a theory of the free oscillations of the Earth for a spherically symmetric model. His work was a direct response to the needs of seismology, since oscillation periods can significantly exceed a minute (the former limit of detection), and periods of longer than 3 minutes are typical of the free oscillations of the Earth. For large n, free oscillations can be considered as the superposition of surface waves. Jeans derived the fundamental relationship that links the order n of the surface harmonic with the period T and the phase velocity v of the propagation of the relevant surface wave:

$$(n + \tfrac{1}{2})/a = K = 2\pi/vT,$$

where a is the radius of the Earth and K is the wave number. More details of the theory of this topic are given in [220, p. 223].

Using this relationship and the connection between n and the angular frequency $\omega = 2\pi/T$ obtained from the accepted model of the Earth, the dependence of the phase velocity on the period can be calculated. Desirous to confirm his findings numerically as usual, Jeans compared the theoretical results with real data from seismic observations.

In his work of 1902, as we have already noted, Jeans even touched on the question of the theory of the shape of the Earth. He discussed the problems associated with deviations of the shape of the Earth from spherical symmetry and the stresses that are necessary for their maintenance. Jeans thought the areas of greatest stress concentration should have the greatest seismic activity. He tried to confirm this with the available seismological data, but these were inadequate. Today, this idea is not accepted, since the origin of stress concentration resulting in earthquakes is associated with a number of complex processes in the upper layers of the planet that were unknown in Jeans's time. In 1917 Jeans addressed the problem of the shape of our planet in the article *Gravitational instability and the figure of the Earth*, [48].

As we have already noted, Jeans considered questions of the theory of the figures of celestial bodies in the first of his works on astronomy. However, he repeatedly returned to these questions later in his studies.

Jeans investigated Maclaurin spheroids and Jacobi ellipsoids. His writings contain a table of various parameters of rotating configurations, where for the variable parameter he takes the angular speed of rotation. These tables are included in all textbooks on the theory of figures of celestial bodies. He showed that, by the principle of the conservation of angular momentum, increasing the density was mathematically equivalent to increasing the angular momentum at a constant density. Using these tables Jeans constructed a diagram (Fig. 2) representing a linear series of Maclaurin spheroids and Jacobi ellipsoids.

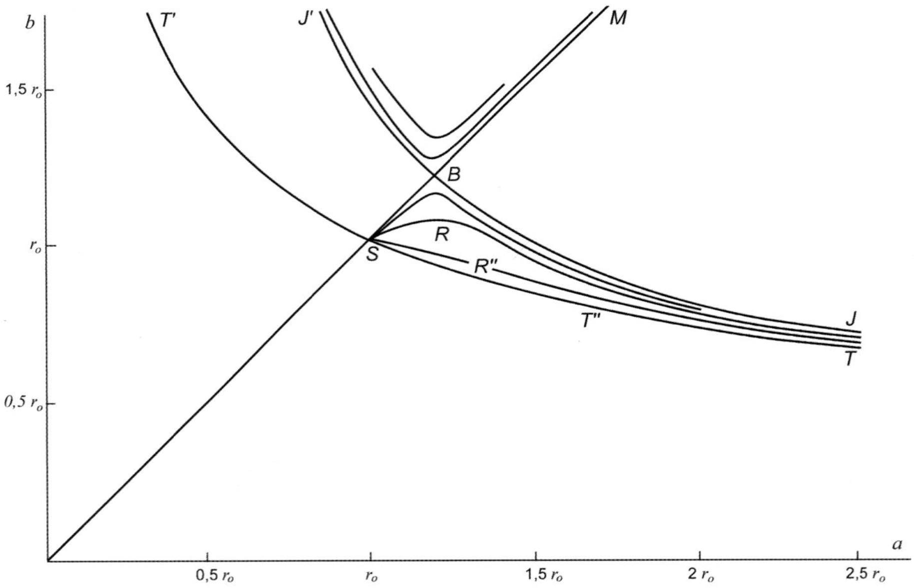

Fig. 2. Jeans's linear series of equilibrium configurations

Jeans's special achievement was his attempt to solve the difficult problem of stable pear-shaped figures. For this work, Jeans developed a new method, differing from both Liapounoff's original and very cumbersome mechanism and Darwin's method, using the theory of elliptic functions. He tried to find out whether the moment of inertia would increase or decrease with the passage through a bifurcation point from a series of Jacobi ellipsoids to a pear shape. Following Poincaré's general principles, a decrease implies instability, an increase means stability.

To address this issue Jeans calculated the gravitational potential of a perturbed ellipsoid where the perturbation was specified in the form of a particular function of the position of a point of bifurcation, multiplied by a small parameter e (the eccentricity). The expression for the gravitational potential on the boundary of the perturbed ellipsoid and its interior points turned out to be similar in form to the expression for the potential of an unperturbed ellipsoid and coincided with it in the case $e = 0$. The position of the point of bifurcation thus identified by Jeans was the same as that derived by Darwin, although obtained by another method. However Jeans noticed a mistake in Darwin's work, which only considered an approximation of second order of smallness e^2, and he showed that the investigation of the stability of pear-shaped configurations required accuracy up to the third order of smallness e^3. Calculation with such a degree of accuracy was extremely time-consuming work, and here Jeans again showed his brilliant mathematical skills. In the end, Jeans came to the conclusion that I, the moment of inertia of the pear-shaped figure, was related to I_0, the moment of inertia of the critical Jacobi ellipsoid, by the relation

$$I = I_0 (1 - 0.06765 e^2).$$

This means that $I < I_0$, i.e., the moment of inertia decreases on passage of a bifurcation point. Following on from this, Jeans deduced that rotating pear-shaped configurations become unstable and break up into two separate bodies. This conclusion followed on from the results of the work of 1902, which examined the two-dimensional case in which three-dimensional bodies were represented by cylinders. Jeans concluded that investigation with the words: "Thus we may with fair confidence assert that the two-dimensional series ends by fission into two detached masses, and in view of the close parallelism which we have discovered between the two-dimensional and the three-dimensional problems, it seems highly probable that the three-dimensional series also will end by a similar fission into detached masses" [58, p. 115].

Jeans highlighted the importance of these results for cosmogonic models. He put forward an original hypothesis for the formation of double stars from dividing fast-rotating single stars. He thought that Cepheids were stars in the process of fission. Jeans believed that the core of a Cepheid was a pear-shaped configuration surrounded by a spherical atmosphere. As the pear configuration is unstable, the Cepheid cores vary, which along with their rotation causes a change in the brightness of the stars.

We will not go into the criticism of this hypothesis in detail here but simply say that Jeans's theory of Cepheids was never confirmed and has long been abandoned. However, for quite a long time it was believed that at least close binary stars occurred as a result of fission. Today it is clear, however, that the problem of the breakup of a body through the development of instability is a fully nonlinear problem and its solution requires further research. In the bibliographic review *Figures of Equilibrium* V.A. Antonov said:

> "It seems that pear-shaped figures (which, according to Liapounoff, are unstable) were never specifically studied after the work of Darwin and Jeans. As the Jacobi ellipsoid becomes distorted into a needle shape, new instabilities continue to arise. For high-order harmonics here we are essentially dealing with the gravitational instability of a fluid cylinder with respect to its decay into separate spherical clumps." [201, p. 35].

Furthermore, the treatment was of homogeneous configurations of an incompressible fluid, but real celestial bodies are inhomogeneous and stars have a strong concentration of density towards the centre. James researched the rotational instability of polytropic configurations [306]. He showed that depending on the polytropic index n, i.e. depending on the degree of concentration of density towards the centre, the instability develops at different angular speeds of rotation, and confirmed Jeans's view that under certain conditions matter is expelled from the equator of a fast-rotating star. Specifically, for $n > 0.8$, when the dimensionless moment of inertia is less than 0.28, and the critical speed of rotation is achieved, matter is expelled from the equator that forms a very thin disk; if $n < 0.8$ and the moment of inertia is greater than 0.28, ellipsoids can progress through a series of pear shapes. Jeans's idea of the loss of matter from the equator of a star led Otto Struve in 1931 to an interpretation of the spectrum of the so-called B-stars as fast-rotating stars with a gas nebula surrounding the equator. In his work Jeans also examined compressible matter, but this will be discussed below.

Jeans classified the problems of investigation of equilibrium configurations of interest to astronomy as follows:
1) The basic problem of rotating configurations;
2) The tidal problem, in which a primary mass of incompressible fluid is under the influence of a distant point-mass satellite: the problem is the shape and stability of the primary as a function of the satellite orbital parameters;
3) The problem of binary stars, in which both bodies revolve around the common centre of mass in unchanging relative positons: this is in a sense a combination of the two previous problems.

When studying the tidal problem, he obtained a series of equilibrium configurations in the form of prolate spheroids, later given the name 'Jeans spheroids' [279].

Jeans vividly illustrated the solution in a now classic diagram (see Fig. 2) [58]. The two coordinates are the two semi-axes of the ellipsoid *a* and *b*, directed perpendicularly to the axis of rotation *c*. As the volume of the incompressible fluid is constant, $abc = r_0^3$, where r_0 is the radius of the sphere of equivalent volume. The spherical configuration is represented by point *S*, corresponding to zero angular velocity. For the Maclaurin spheroids, $a = b$ and they are represented by the line *SBM*. The branch *T'ST* represents the prolate tidal spheroids. The point *B* is the point of bifurcation on the series of Maclaurin spheroids and is also the focus of the curve *J'BJ*, representing Jacobi ellipsoids with three unequal axes. The point infinitely distant along *SM* corresponds to a very thin slowly rotating disk of large radius. The point infinitely distant along the curve *BJ* corresponds to a very long needle-shaped configuration, the limiting Jacobi ellipsoid, also slowly rotating. Along the line *SB*, the angular velocity of the Maclaurin spheroids increases, and along *BJ* it steadily decreases. Ellipsoidal solutions of the double star problem are determined by two parameters: the ratio of the masses and the distance separating them, and occupy the whole area *TSBJ*. Only the earlier parts of the tidal series *ST* and the various double stars series are stable.

Jeans was one of the first to study the equilibrium configurations of a compressible fluid. These configurations are much more similar in structure to real celestial bodies than homogeneous bodies, the consideration of which has mainly a purely mathematical and academic interest. When awarding Arthur Eddington the gold medal of the Royal Astronomical Society, Jeans emphasised the importance of his research by saying: "It's not enough to deal with theoretical liquid masses. An astronomer wants to know how results will change when we take into account the heterogeneity or gaseousness of actual stars" [279, p. 279].

Jeans divided the study of compressible masses into three main areas:
1) the Roche model: a point nucleus with a very high density surrounded by an atmosphere of negligible density;
2) a generalised Roche model, with a finite incompressible core;
3) an adiabatic model: a gas mass in adiabatic equilibrium.

Exploring heterogeneous configurations, Jeans concluded that the Roche model exhausts all possible cases of exact integration of the equations of equilibrium. However, polytropic gas masses also form an equilibrium shape compressed at the poles. He called these figures respectively pseudo-spheroids and pseudo-ellipsoids, by analogy with Maclaurin spheroids and Jacobi ellipsoids. The mathematical study of equilibrium figures of inhomogeneous bodies is a very complicated task and Jeans took only the first steps. The form of Jeans's pseudo-spheroids was more rigorously studied by S. Chandrasekhar, but only for the case of small deformations. [279]

Jeans also tried to explore the fission of these configurations at the critical points both in the case of pure rotation and of tidal interaction. However, his estimates were not mathematically rigorous. Later R. James showed that rapid rotation changes the Roche model into a lenticular configuration with a pointed rim along the equator, away from which matter may flow [306].

Based on these models and the available observational material, Jeans thought that the spiral nebulae were probably formed at the equator of a rotating body of compressed matter. He believed that the condensations of matter in their arms had a mass comparable to that of stars in our Galaxy. The analogy of galaxies with a rotating fluid now seems unrealistic. But Jeans's thoughts are of interest because they were made long before the extragalactic nature of these nebulae was understood, at a time when A. van Maanen's measurements of the rotation periods of the nebulae had not yet been refuted. Interestingly, although Jeans's views on this issue were never to be confirmed, they influenced the first detailed classification of galaxies proposed by E. Hubble in 1925. Hubble himself admitted: "Although a conscious attempt was made to find a descriptive classification quite apart from theoretical considerations, the result was almost the same as that which Jeans obtained from purely theoretical models" [276, p. 187].

~~ • ~~

Jeans's work on the theory of figures of rotating self-gravitating masses exerted a strong influence on his cosmogonic ideas and, we might say, largely shaped them. When he extended this work to the tidal hypothesis of the formation of the Solar System in 1916, it brought Jeans considerable fame.

The idea underlying the hypothesis was not new. In 1749 (before Kant proposed his nebular theory in 1754, later named the Kant-Laplace theory), the famous French scientist and translator of the works of Newton, Georges-Louis Leclerc, Comte de Buffon suggested in his *Natural History* [295] the first hypothesis of the origin of the Solar System, the beginning of the so-called 'catastrophic' hypotheses. He thought that the Sun once collided with a comet or some other body and at the moment of impact a part of its mass separated from it, and then formed a planet. Today these views seem quite simplistic. They already seemed implausible in Jeans's times, but he considered a modified form of the main idea — a close passage of two bodies (Jeffreys in 1929 also suggested a collision of the Sun with a star as an explanation of the high orbital angular momentum of the planets. [233])

At the start of the 20th century, Buffon's hypothesis was revived by two American scientists, the astronomer F. Moulton [318] and the geologist T. Chamberlin [296], who proposed the so-called 'planetesimal' hypothesis. This name arises from the fact that Chamberlin and Moulton assumed rapid cooling and solidification in the protoplanetary nebula and the formation of fragments of matter — planetesimals. The emergence of this nebula, they supposed, was due to the close passage of another star past the Sun, causing two great opposing tidal extensions.

Despite the naivety of this idea, the concept of planetesimals remains in modern scientific cosmogony. Many scientific ideas, even though unconfirmed by the further development of science, contain a grain of truth, which sometimes 'grows' along quite different directions.

P. Laplace's nebular hypothesis was published in his popular book *The System of the World* in 1796, and was probably proposed independently of several similar hypotheses previously advanced by the philosopher I. Kant. In the preface to it Laplace wrote:

> "Of all the natural sciences, Astronomy is that which presents the longest series of discoveries. There is an immense distance from the first view of the heavens, to that general view by which, at the present day, we comprehend the past and future state of the system of the world. In order to arrive at this it was necessary to observe the heavenly bodies during a long succession of ages, to recognise from their appearances the real motion of the Earth, to develop the laws of the planetary motions, and from these laws to derive the principles of universal gravitation, and to redescend from this principle to the complete investigation of all the celestial phenomena, even in their minutest details. This is what the human understanding has accomplished in astronomy.
>
> The exposition of these discoveries, and of the most simple manner in which they may arise one from the other, would have the double advantage of presenting a great assemblage of important truths, and the true method which should be followed in investigating the laws of nature. This is the object I propose in the following work". [238, p. 9]

Laplace drew attention to the following features of the Solar System. The seven planets that were known at that time orbit around the Sun in the same direction, which is the same direction as the orbits of their fourteen satellites around their planets, and all the known rotational motions of the Sun, planets and satellites on their own axes are also in the same sense. Each orbit and rotation takes place in a plane with low inclination to the others. The eccentricities of all these orbits are small, so that they are almost circular.

On this basis Laplace came to the conclusion that all the bodies of the Solar System must have a common origin. Going into more detail than Kant's hypothesis, Laplace considered an initially rotating protoplanetary nebula. The nebula was an extensive hot atmosphere of the emerging Sun. According to Laplace, the atmosphere rotated as a solid body, so its outer regions had a higher linear speed than the inner. Eventually, it gradually cooled and shrank under the action of forces of self-gravitation, and it therefore contracted. Due to the law of conservation of angular momentum, as it contracted its rotation accelerated. When the equatorial centrifugal force balanced the force of gravity, material separated off in the form of a ring. In this way a system of rings was formed in the equatorial plane of the nebula. Due to the heterogeneity of the rings, the material gathered in clumps from which the planets were formed.

In this scenario, the planets would have to move in circular orbits, all in the same direction, and the direction of rotation of the protoplanetary nebula and all the orbits would lie in one plane, the plane of the equator of this nebula.

According to Laplace the satellites of the planets were formed in the same process, when rings separated during the contraction of a clump forming a planet.

Laplace did not given any mathematical justification of his proposed hypothesis. The first mathematical model was constructed in the middle of the 19th century by the French mathematician E. Roche. He showed that rotation would flatten the nebula into a lens-shaped form and the separation of material would occur from the edges of the lens.

Even so, it was unclear how a giant low-density gas disk could divide into denser rings. To overcome this difficulty Roche suggested the process was intermittent, resulting in the separation of continuous layers, and narrow rings. But no clarification of this model was given.

By the beginning of the 20th century many other artificial assumptions were obvious in the Kant-Laplace hypothesis. Furthermore, new data about the Solar System that had emerged during the previous 150 years as a result of improved observational capabilities in astronomy could not be explained satisfactorily in the framework of classical nebular hypothesis [296].

Critical analysis of the nebular hypothesis by Jeans led him to the conclusion that it could not explain the small angular momentum of the Sun compared with the orbital angular momentum of the planets. The Sun, containing more than 99.8 % of the mass, has less than 2 % of the total angular momentum of the Solar System. Moreover, even in 1861 Babinet had pointed out that the total age of the Solar System was clearly insufficient for the system to collapse under rotation [290]. This guided Jeans to the Moulton-Chamberlin idea of the close passage of a star relative to the Sun and its catastrophic tidal effects [51]. Assuming that the passing star had a large mass and momentum relative to the Sun and is able to impart sufficient angular momentum to the planets, Jeans seemed to solve the problem of the distribution of the angular momentum in the Solar System.

Jeans thought the advantage of his tidal scheme was firstly that it was not necessary to introduce the hypothetical planetesimals. According to his theory, planetary masses are formed directly from the material ejected from the Sun as a result of condensation by gravitational instability. Secondly, his theory was a natural explanation of the inclination of the plane of the ecliptic at an angle of 6 degrees to the equatorial plane of the rotating Sun. Jeans wrote: "The tidal theory explains this naturally by supposing that the present invariable plane records the plane of passage of the tide-generating mass, whilst the present plane of the Sun's rotation coincides approximately with that of the rotation of the original mass" [193, p. 119].

However, the problem of the distribution of angular momentum in the Solar System was solved very artificially. In the first version of the theory it was supposed that at the time of the close passage, the Sun had dimensions of the order of Neptune's orbit. With a protosun on this scale and a minimum distance to the disturbing mass of three radii of Neptune's orbit, even with an initially low angular speed of rotation of the protosun the angular momentum imparted to the material extracted from the Sun (per unit mass) could get close to that possessed by the planets. But the subsequent development of the theory of stellar evolution and the refinement of the age of the Sun and the planetary system showed that the notion that the size of the Sun 5 billion years ago was significantly greater than today was unrealistic. In addition, Jeffreys [312] observed that such an assumption would have two consequences: 1) the mass of the Sun would have to be as large as that of the giant stars and 2) if the formation of planets took place at the distance of Neptune, there would have to be a mechanism that reduces their orbits to their present values.

In the second version of his theory Jeans imagined that at the moment of encounter the Sun had almost the same size as at present [111; 120]. But, as in the first scenario, it was assumed that the orbital angular momentum of the planets was generated by a star passing in a hyperbolic orbit around the Sun. The mass of the star was considered to be very large, implying that a sufficient amount of angular momentum could be imparted to the planets.

H.N. Russell was the first to point out the fallacy of this conclusion in 1935. He wrote:

"A much graver difficulty arises when we consider the distribution of angular momentum — not the total amount this time, but the angular momentum per ton. As has already been said, this is proportional to $\sqrt{p}$, the square root of the semi-parameter of the orbit, for all the planets. For the star's motion around the sun it will be proportional to $\sqrt{(p(1+x))}$ where x is the ratio of the star's mass to the Sun's — since the combined attraction of the two increases their orbital velocity at a given distance.

For a parabolic orbit, p is twice the perihelion distance; for an elliptic orbit less, for a hyperbolic more. The star had a hyperbolic orbit; but the correction on this account would be but a very few per cent unless its velocity, before being perceptibly increased by the Sun's attraction, was much greater than the average for actual stars.

Now, to produce tidal eruptions, the star must have almost grazed the Sun. If it was of the Sun's size and mass the perihelion distance could not have been much more than a million miles, or no ejection of matter would have taken place. To be liberal, let us call it 1½ per cent of the Earth's distance, or 1,400,000 miles. The parameter p is then 0.03 astronomical units ... to put so much angular momentum into the ejected material during the encounter would seem to be impossible." [261, p. 86–7].

In the USSR Pariyskiy was the first to draw attention to this situation. He agreed with Russell: "As far as we know, Russell did not make a strict calculation of the maximum angular momentum that the passing star may have imparted to the tidal stream, but his qualitative arguments are convincing" [247, p. 77]. Detailed calculations were done later by Pariyskiy on a limited hyperbolic three body problem.

He came to the final conclusion:
"in none of our calculated cases did we get positive angular momentum of the amount of the 'planets' motion per unit mass that would exceed that of the passing star, i.e. we did not get orbits similar in size and momentum to actual planetary orbits. Therefore Jeans's theory, at least if we take the present size of the Sun at the moment of its meeting with the passing star, appears to be untenable from a purely dynamic point of view" [248, p. 28].

We have to remember that the cosmogonic theory needs to be able to explain the appearance of small planets (asteroids) and the satellites of the planets as well as the major planets. Jeans presented the origin of the satellite systems as a (scaled down) copy of the formation of the planetary system. However, the process of formation due to fragmentation as a result of gravitational instability is not viable for all the satellites and asteroids. Their masses are so small that they cannot have been gaseous at the moment of formation. This difficulty was perfectly understood by Jeans himself [111]. It is difficult to suppose that small solid or liquid bodies develop from gaseous planets.

In Jeans's hypothesis great difficulties also arose in the explanation of the Earth-Moon system.

The level of development of science at that time allowed Jeans to analyse his cosmogonic hypothesis mathematically using only a rather formal representation of the basics.

He considered the problem of the relative motion of two deformable bodies: the Sun (*S*) and a star (*S'*). As expected, in this scheme, the force of attraction between the bodies plays a central role; it defines their mutual movement and their shape. However, even with such an extremely schematic arrangement the problem is too difficult for mathematical analysis. Jeans assumed that regardless of the change of shape of the second body *S'* its gravitational field was equivalent to the field of a point mass *M'*. He further assumed that the size of the bodies *S* and *S'* could be neglected compared with the distance between them and assumed that the body *S* attracted the body *S'* like a point mass *M*. Then the trajectory *S'* with respect to *S* is a conic section. But to simplify his task further, Jeans assumed some distortion of the real situation. The orbit of *S'* relative to *S* is assumed to be rectilinear and to pass through the common centre of gravity so that the distance *R* between the centres of *S* and *S'* stays constant. Jeans called this artificial scheme a scheme of slow meetings.

When analysing the circumstances of approaching stars Jeans considered two extreme cases: 1) the body *S* is uniform and incompressible and 2) all the mass *M* is concentrated in the core (Roche's model).

He comes to the following conclusion:

"In both the extreme cases of an incompressible mass of uniform density and of a mass with its density distributed as in Roche's model, we have found that a sufficiently close encounter with another star will result in the break up of the mass into detached pieces. In the former case, however, the final broken up pieces are each of a mass comparable with that of the parent star; in the latter case, the fragments which are pulled off by tidal action are of comparatively insignificant mass, so that the mass of the parent star is only slightly reduced by the process of disruption. A comparison with the actual facts of the Solar System makes it clear that the parent sun must have approximated much more closely to Roche's model than to the incompressible mass."
[120, p. 405–6].

A detailed analysis of Jeans's approximation of the Sun by the Roche model is given by Rhine in her famous work *The methodical analysis of Jeans's cosmogonic theory. The origin of the Solar System* [258]. Our treatment next relies on the work of Rhine and Pariyskiy [259].

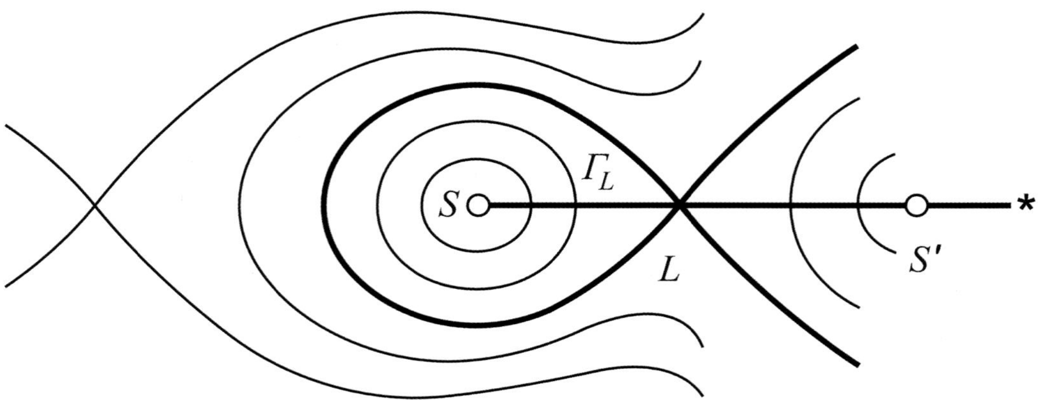

Fig. 3. The Roche model

Consider the motion of particles in the solar atmosphere in the fields of two gravitational points *S* and *S'*. The equipotential surfaces are also surfaces of zero velocity of a particle with respect to S. A cross-section of these surfaces through *S* and *S'* is shown in Fig. 3. The curve bounding the largest closed surface surrounding *S* is the cross-section of the critical surface. If *R* is the distance between *S* and *S'* and, by Jeans's assumption, $M'/M = 2$, then a singular point of the surface *L* lies at a distance $r_L = 0.457R$ from *S*. If r_0 is the radius of the sphere of the equivalent volume of the critical sphere cavity, $r_L = 1.313r_0$. Jeans easily obtained values for *R*, in which the outer layers of the Sun are limited to a closed surface with critical point $R = 2.28(M'/M)^{1/3}r_0$ or $R = 2.87r_0$.

As Jeans thought, the existence of a critical point of the surface bounding the atmosphere of the Sun demonstrates the possibility of the separation of some of its parts. It is through this point that matter is ejected in a gaseous state, and, according to Jeans, it was a fairly slow process. He argued:

> "The rate of ejection of matter would be slow at first, it would increase to a maximum when the passing star was at its distance of closest approach, and would subsequently diminish to zero. The result ought to be a filament of matter of which the line density would be zero at each end and would increase to a maximum near the middle. As this filament lost heat by radiation, the ends would experience the greatest

> fall of temperature … after a time the ends of the filament might be mainly liquid while the middle region was still almost entirely gaseous. During this process of condensation, gravitational instability would result in the formation of furrows, leading to ultimate fission into separate masses" [58, p. 283].

A planet formed at the end of the filament would naturally form from the more dense material and therefore could have smaller mass. But if planets formed in the central areas of the filament, they should be much more massive. Jeans concludes:

> "In this way the tidal theory readily explains the great inequality between the masses of Jupiter, Saturn and the other planets, while explaining at the same time why the two largest planets occur in the middle of the chain. The theory indicates that the smaller planets must have been mainly liquid or solid from their birth, while Jupiter and perhaps also Saturn may have always been almost entirely gaseous" [58, p. 283].

The plane of the orbits of planets formed like this must lie very close to the Sun's equator. Jeans uses this fact to explain the formation of satellite systems. The Sun exerts tidal effects on the planet. He writes: "This hypothesis accounts at once for the directions of revolution of the majority of the satellites, and explains why their orbital planes are, for the most part, close to the orbital planes of the corresponding planets" [58, p. 283].

Concerning the shape of planetary orbits, Jeans, like Moulton and Chamberlin, assigned a significant role to the action of the interplanetary medium. The process of formation of the planets means that the original shape of their orbits is very different from circular. The resistance of the medium can greatly reduce the eccentricity of the orbits, especially of the inner planets, to their modern values.

However, of course, Jeans understood the preliminary nature of these inferences. "The time for arriving at conclusions in cosmogony has not yet come," he wrote at the end of his essay in 1919 [58, p. 288].

In the early 1960s Woolfson [327] published a modification of Jeans's hypothesis. He suggested that the planets were formed from a tidal bulge pulled from a low-mass low-density star during a close passage by the Sun [328]. Although Woolfson's hypothesis did not offer a complete explanation of all the features of the Solar System, it is another example of Jeans's ideas reappearing in modern cosmology [298].

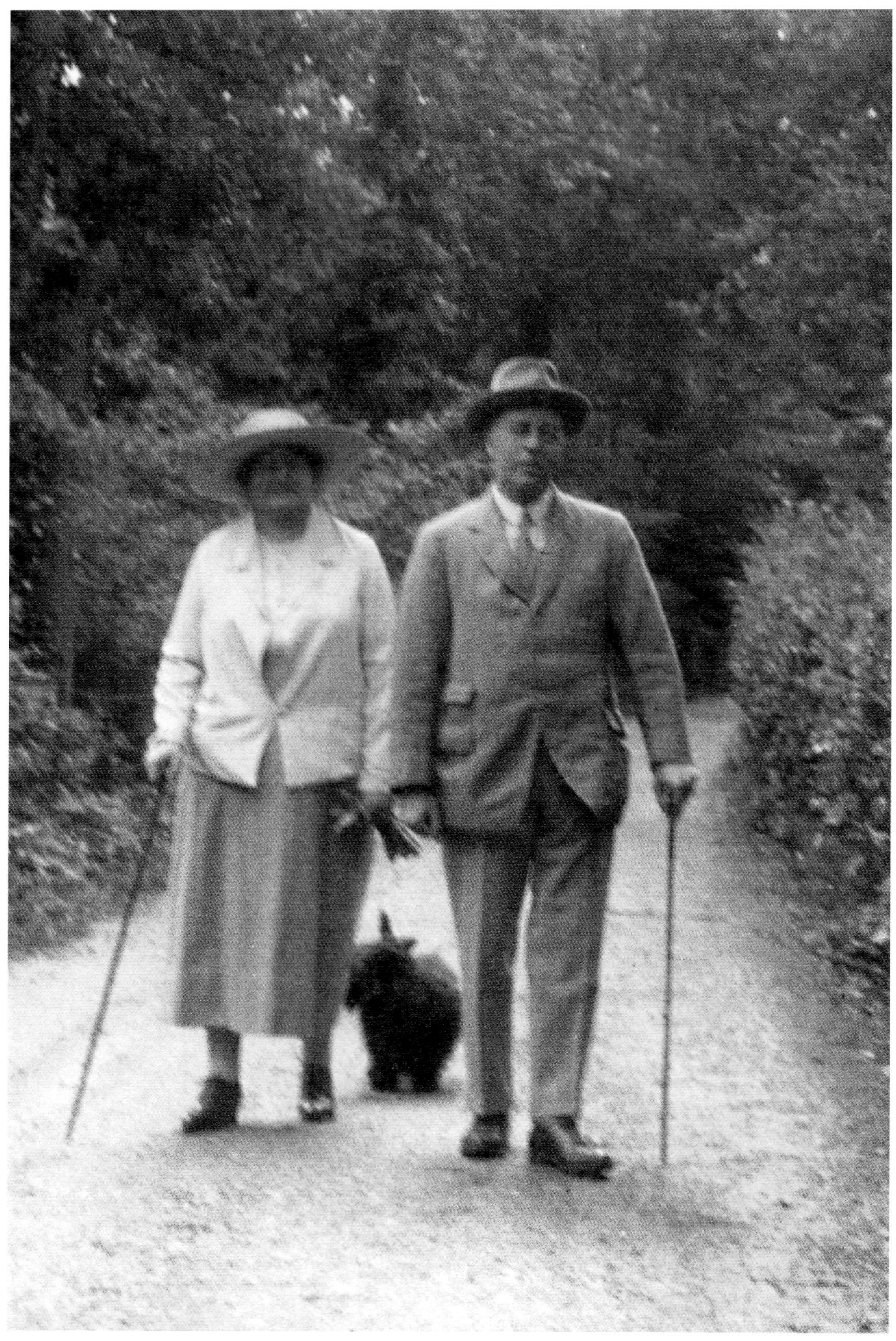

James and Charlotte returning home along Cherry Tree Lane from a walk to the Norbury Park Estate that forms the west side of the River Mole Valley. Date unknown.

THE TWILIGHT YEARS, POPULAR WRITING AND PUBLIC OUTREACH

When there were no meetings or lectures in London, Jeans spent whole days at home — working, reading, playing the organ or listening to music. He had a large collection of gramophone records of virtuoso performers. He could think well, while playing music or walking alone. At that time one could cross the River Mole near the Burford Bridge Hotel and climb to the top of Box Hill and the Old Fort without meeting anyone. To-day there are many more people walking in these hills admiring the views.

However, the calm of the area was badly affected by the events that shook the country after the First World War. Britain sought to strengthen its position as a global financial centre. In April 1925, Winston Churchill, the Finance Minister in Baldwin's Conservative Cabinet, restored the gold standard. The pound sterling rose to an exchange rate of $4.86 dollars as it had done before the war. The new exchange rate hit exporters' competitiveness to sell goods made in the UK. There were calls to 'tighten their belts' in order to allow for modernization of industrial enterprises. Prime Minister Baldwin proclaimed: "all the workers of our country should accept lower wages in order to help put industry on its feet." The employed were not happy with that solution. State subsidies supporting the wages to miners and some other categories of workers were granted for 9 months, postponing a social explosion. Nevertheless, on the 1st May the miners did not go to work, and on the 4th, the General Strike started, the first in the history of the country. Life in the UK was completely paralyzed. The General Strike was a threat to the security of the "Empire on which the Sun never sets".

Newspaper workers went on strike, and so did bus drivers, but the trains, with changed timetables, were manned by volunteers despite strikers picketing at the stations. The volunteers were unskilled workers, intellectuals, and other representatives of the middle class and even the aristocracy. They all realized the danger to their homeland. Jeans also understood the dangers in the unfolding events but, faithful to his principles, preferred not to interfere in the political confrontation. Naturally he stocked up on coal and dry products, so that the family would survive for some time even if all the shops were closed. Another danger may have troubled his thoughts — the development of Bolshevism. Jeans saw clearly the shortsightedness, if not the incompetence, of the political leaders of the country. Fortunately common sense prevailed, and on the 12th May, the General Strike was formally called off, although in some places workers did not return for several days, and miners continued to strike for almost 7 months.

In the 1920s Jeans increasingly thought about man's place in the Universe. He corresponded with Sir Oliver Joseph Lodge, who had been a Fellow of the Royal Society since 1887. Lodge had contributed to the study of electrolysis, the conditions of propagation of electromagnetic waves, the development of the theory of electromotive force, and to the problem of the ether. After 1910, he became interested in spiritualism. A letter from Lodge, below, illustrates Jeans's breadth of interests.

Normanton House,
Lake,
Salisbury.
30th May 1927
My dear Jeans,
I am delighted at getting a letter from you: it is full of interesting information. And I am glad to see you have an open mind even in the direction of telepathy, at any rate between people close to. I should however expect, rather, that when you stood over your pupil a sort of shudder at his incipient wrongnesses may have been audibly or feebly sensible to him, and served as a check. We have to be very careful in telepathy experiments to control breathing and every other kind of indication, though the best plan is not to watch the results as they are being produced.

I can assure you that we were very cautious in our telepathy experiments as reported in the PROCEEDINGS of the S.P.R. (Society for Psychical Research). I forget if any of us used numbers of two digits as a test. I did not. But if they are on record I should like to look them up. It seems there is much more predilection for special numbers than one would have expected; though I have known the number 7 exercise a sort of fascination over otherwise sensible people. A curious instance of that is in my mind, but it is too long to write about.

I hope my article in THE OBSERVER was sufficiently clear. It is but a partial report. A complete report needs still more working out, but I think the numbers and facts were correct as far as they go, though they were not correct in the first account, rather hastily published by THE RADIO TIMES before publication was fully intended.

I am surprised and pleased that this rather trivial sort of experiment has attracted your attention.
Yours sincerely,

The end of the 1920s was marked by the industrial and commercial decline of England. Political life was characterized by internecine fights between party leaders. In 1929, after a brief interval of relative stability, a period of deep economic crisis began. It started in the autumn of that year in the United States, and then spread over Europe. It hit England's trade balance and that was reflected in the exchange rate of the pound sterling, which started to fall. By 1931 it was 30% below the gold standard and on the 21st September the standard was abandoned. During that difficult time Jeans must have been concerned about his financial situation. Jeans became well-to-do through his first marriage. When he died in 1946, his fortune was valued at £256,054, one of the very largest ever left by a British scientist. As his brusque manner suggested, he was a very capable businessman. The stranger meeting him in the train coming up to London from the country might easily have taken his neat, round, bustling figure, clean-shaven face and clear, alert head for that of a wealthy stockbroker with intellectual hobbies." [183, p. 104–5].

In 1928, Jeans was knighted for services to science and to the Royal Society.

Jeans himself was fully aware that, with increasing age, original research became more difficult and one's mathematical abilities declined. Milne wrote in 1952 "He had great scientific achievements to his credit; in 1929 he was fifty-two; and nothing is more pathetic in the biography of a great scientist than when the stream of original papers, instead of drying up suddenly, becomes a trickle of inferior quality. Jeans had probably passed the height of his powers as a mathematician. Probably he recognized this. The less he concerned himself now with the technical details of mathematical investigation, the more he could stand back and survey what he himself and others had accomplished, and interpret it for the benefit of the intelligent non-specialist." [193, p. 73]. Indeed, in the last two decades of his life Jeans turned to the popularization of science and understanding of its results from a philosophical point of view. He abandoned his independent scientific researches and started a new career as a popularizer. That was for Jeans a difficult, but a deliberate choice as he was talented not only as a scientist and musician, but also as a writer. He had a great accuracy of language, clarity of exposition and a crispness of comparison. The breadth of his knowledge, and his gift with language put him in the first league among the popularizers of scientific research.

His monograph *Astronomy and Cosmogony* (1928) [111], brings together much of his research. The final chapter summarizes the contents in clear figurative language with lively illustrations and without the help of mathematical apparatus. That chapter had attracted the attention of R. Fowler — Professor of Mathematics at Cambridge (son-in-law of E. Rutherford) — who mentioned it to the Secretary of the University Press, S.C. Roberts. Roberts immediately appreciated the lively style of writing and told colleagues that the perfection of his style is not inferior to the *Oxford Book of English Prose*. Roberts encouraged Jeans to write his first popular book, and he related the event in the introduction to the Jeans's biography by Milne:

> "I remember very clearly Ralph Fowler coming in to my room at the Press and asking me whether I had read Jeans's latest book. I took the enquiry to be a jocular one and reminded Fowler, in reply, that I was not obliged to read every book that I published. Then, more seriously, Fowler said: 'Ah, yes, but you should look at the last chapter.' It was good advice and I realized, especially after promptings from my colleague, R.J.L. Kingsford, that cosmogony might contain the potentialities of best-selling beyond the dreams of academic avarice.
>
> At that time I frequently travelled by road to Worthing, where my parents lived. Jeans's home at Dorking was only a few yards off the main road and accordingly I proposed myself for lunch on a day when I was due to go to Worthing. It was the first time I had seen Jeans at home and he gave me a most friendly welcome. He produced an admirable claret and after lunch we retired to his study. After a few preliminary *pourparlers*, I approached my main topic and asked Jeans whether he would consider the writing of a popular book. His reply was characteristic. Looking at me with a kindly but slightly scornful expression, he said: 'Oh, yes, several publishers have approached me about that.' 'Well', I replied, 'what about us?' 'Oh', he said, 'you're the finest mathematical printers in the world — but you couldn't sell a popular book'. 'Well, have you ever written one?' I countered. From that moment onwards the situation was easier. I could see that Jeans set a definite value on being published by a press famous for its high standard of printing; and, as I afterwards realized, he was also keen to maintain his friendly rivalry with Eddington, whose *Nature of the Physical World* was one of the publishing successes of 1928.
>
> Jeans never haggled over royalties and an agreement was signed in April 1929 for a book to be entitled *The Universe Around Us*. We took a good deal of trouble over the illustrations and the book was published in September. The first edition was one of 7500 copies and was sold out during October. By the end of 1929 11,300 copies had been sold. At the Press we were, of course, delighted and so, in his own way, was Jeans." [193, p. ix–x].

According to colleagues, Jeans was glad about the success of *The Universe Around Us* and from then on concentrated on writing popular books on astronomy and physics.

In the Preface to the first edition of *The Universe Around Us* [163, p. V] Jeans wrote: "The present book contains a brief account, written in simple language, of the methods and results of modern astronomical research, both observational and theoretical. Special attention has been given to problems of cosmogony and evolution, and to the general structure of the universe. My ideal, perhaps never wholly attainable, has been that of making the entire book intelligible to readers with no special scientific knowledge."

The excerpts below can serve as examples of a popular presentation of complex scientific and philosophical issues.

"Galileo's telescope now showed that, precisely as Copernicus had foretold, Venus passed through the full cycle of phases, so that, in Galileo's own words, we "are now supplied with a determination most conclusive, and appealing to the evidence of our senses, of two very important problems, which up to this day have been discussed by the greatest intellects with different conclusions. One is that the planets are not self-luminous. The other is that we are absolutely compelled to say that Venus, and Mercury also, revolve around the sun, as do also all the rest of the planets, a truth believed indeed by the Pythagorean school, by Copernicus, and by Kepler, but never proved by the evidence of our senses, as is now proved in the case of Venus and Mercury."

"These discoveries of Galileo made it clear that Aristotle, Ptolemy and the majority of those who had thought about these things in the last 2000 years had been utterly and hopelessly wrong. In estimating his position in the universe, man had up to now been guided mainly by his own desires, and his self-esteem; long fed on boundless hopes, he had spurned the simpler fare offered by patient scientific thought. Inexorable facts now dethroned him from his self-arrogated station at the centre of the universe; henceforth he must reconcile himself to the humble position of the inhabitant of a speck of dust, and adjust his views as to the significance and importance of human life accordingly.

"The adjustment was not made at once. Human vanity, reinforced by the authority of the Church, contrived to make a rough road for those who dared draw attention to the Earth's insignificant position in the universe. Galileo was forced to abjure his beliefs. Well on into the eighteenth century the ancient University of Paris was teaching that the motion of the earth round the sun was a convenient *but false* hypothesis, while the newer American Universities of Harvard and Yale taught the Ptolemaic and Copernican systems of astronomy side by side as though they were equally tenable. Yet men could not keep their heads buried in the sand for ever, and when at last its full implications were accepted, the revolution of thought initiated by Galileo's observations of January 7th 1610, proved to be the most catastrophic in the history of the race. The cataclysm was not confined to the realms of abstract thought; henceforth human existence itself was to appear in a new light, and human aims and aspirations would be judged from a different standpoint".

"This oft-told story has been told once again, in the hope that it may serve to explain some of the interest taken in astronomy to-day. The more mundane sciences prove their worth by adding to the amenities and pleasures of life, or by alleviating pain or distress, but it may well be asked what reward astronomy has to offer. Why does the astronomer devote arduous nights, and even more arduous days, to studying the structure, motions and changes of bodies so remote that they can have no conceivable influence on human life?"

"In part at least the answer would seem to be that many have begun to suspect that the astronomy of to-day, like that of Galileo, may have something to say on the enthralling question of the relation of human life to the universe in which it is placed, and on the beginnings, meaning and destiny of the human race. Bede records how, some twelve centuries ago, human life was compared in poetic simile to the flight of a bird through a warm hall in which men sit feasting, while the winter storms rage without."

"The bird is safe from the tempest for a brief moment, but immediately passes from winter to winter again. So man's life appears for a little while, but of what is to follow, or of what went before, we know nothing. If, therefore, a new doctrine tells us something certain, it seems to deserve to be followed."

"These words, originally spoken in advocacy of the Christian religion, describe what is perhaps the main interest of astronomy to-day. Man — **only knowing Life's little lantern between dark and dark** — wishes to probe farther into the past and future than his brief span of life permits. He wishes to see the universe as it existed before man was, as it will be after the last man has passed again into the darkness from which he came. The wish does not originate solely in mere intellectual curiosity, in the desire to see over the next range of mountains, the desire to attain a summit commanding a wide view, even if it be only of a promised land which he may never hope himself to enter; it has deeper roots and a more personal interest. Before he can understand himself, man must first understand the universe from the dust of which his body has been formed, and from the events of which all his sense perceptions are drawn. He wishes to explore the universe, both in space and time, because he himself forms part of it, and it forms part of him." [163, p. 4–6].

An increase of interest in astronomy at that time was the result of the revolutionary new views about the Universe, associated with the revolution in physics, beginning in the 20th century. It had become absolutely impossible to understand what was happening in the Universe without knowledge of the new physical concepts, and Jeans tried to present them in the most accessible way. An important part of the book is his own personal cosmogenic hypothesis.

In 1930, the following year, A.B. Ramsay — Vice-Chancellor of Cambridge University and Master of Magdalene College — invited Jeans to give the Rede Lecture. Once Roberts had learnt about that invitation, he

Sidney Roberts (Secretary of Cambridge University Press, Jeans's publisher), James Jeans and Arthur Eddington dining at the Athenaeum Club, 10th May 1935. Eddington had published his first popular scientific book *Nature of the Physical World* in 1928, whereas Jeans published *The Universe Around Us* in 1929. According to Roberts, Jeans was keen to maintain his friendly rivalry with Eddington.

wrote to Jeans that he would like to publish the Lecture. He asked for a copy to be sent to him so that it could be printed immediately after the lecture. But Jeans had his own idea on how to promote the proposed book. He not only promised to send the manuscript in advance, but also gave a warning that it would be much more than just a lecture, actually a book. Just a few weeks before the lecture Roberts printed the first edition of the book *The Mysterious Universe* [122].

Jeans gave the Rede Lecture in the Senate House of the University on the 4th November. It was a resounding success. Already the next morning one could read about it in *The Times* and during the following months it was discussed in detail in many papers and journals. Even country vicars included some of its visions in their sermons, because Jeans's philosophical interpretation of the achievements of astronomy was consistently creationistic. In his lecture Jeans first expressed his idea that the Creator of the Universe had to be a mathematician. A few weeks after the lecture *The Mysterious Universe* was selling at 1000 copies per day — comparable with the circulations of bestsellers of the time. The book was beautifully illustrated and Roberts emphasized that the printer Walter Lewis had gone to great trouble. Jeans considered *The Mysterious Universe* [122] a sequel to the *Universe Around Us*, but it was written so that it could be read independently as an essay in its own rights. Despite its slim size, about 150 pages, it gives a full picture of the development of the Universe in its five chapters *Extinguishing the Sun, New world of modern physics, Matter and radiation, Relativity and ether, Staring into the abyss.*

In the same year, a small popular essay *Eos, or the wider aspects of cosmogony* [121] focused on ideological issues, and tried to show how the achievements of physics and astronomy influenced the direction of philosophical thoughts.

The flyer for *Through Space and Time*, the book by J. H. Jeans published in 1934, based upon his Royal Institution Lectures for Christmas 1933.

Part of the flyer advertising Jeans's popular books in the United States (~1944)

The dust cover of the American edition of *The Mysterious Universe* (1930) with wood cuts by Walter T. Murch . Published by the Macmillan Company, New York, USA

Murch's woodcut as the heading to Chapter IV, American edition of *The Mysterious Universe* (1930)

Through

Space and Time

The Royal Institution Lectures for Christmas 1933

SIR JAMES JEANS

224 pages *54 plates* *About 8s. 6d. net*

Ready in October

POPULAR OUTREACH BOOKS

Jeans and his publisher S.C.Roberts were fully aware of, and, took advantage of all means to bring before the general public the nature of the Universe and humans' position in it. The roles of astronomy and astrophysics were emphasised.

They coordinated popular books with articles and reviews in journals and newspapers, and public lectures and radio broadcasts. Jeans with his clear and elegant style, with journalism in his genes, knew how to inform the general reader and listener through words, illustrations and sounds. But he also knew how to challenge their thoughts. At the end of the Foreword to *The Mysterious Universe* 'he wrote 'Many will disagree with it — it was written to this end." Among his papers there were details obtained from the BBC of the optimal rate of word delivery as well as the concentration period of the average listener. Included here was a confidential report on his own radio talks he had obtained from the Director of the BBC.

The reaction of some other scientists to Jeans's change of direction has been described in Graham Farmerlo 's life of Paul Dirac (The strangest Man. Faber and Faber, 2009)

"Rutherford had no time for petty jealousy but was not above making a thinly disguised attack on his recently retired colleague Sir James Jeans, whose *The Mysterious Universe* had been a best seller since it first appeared in the bookstores the month before. Rutherford was as down to earth and, at the same time, as snobbish as anyone in science. As the recorder of the dinner wrote: Sir Ernest Rutherford 'deplored the writing of popular books by men who had been serious scientists, to satisfy the craving for the mysterious exhibited by the public'. This was a common opinion in Cambridge. A few months later, his idoliser C.P.Snow — a scientist about to become a writer — sneered at science popularisers for doing a job that was just too easy: 'There is no argument and no appeal, just worshipper and worshipped'. The result Snow declared, a 'great evil' ".

SIR JAMES JEANS

O.M., M.A., D.Sc., LLD., F.R.S.

As one of the foremost astronomers and mathematical physicists of our time, Sir James Jeans has won many distinguished honors for his contributions to science. But it is his remarkable gift for revealing, in clear and dramatic language, the discoveries made concerning the universe and what those discoveries mean to man, that has made his name known the world over. More than 705,000 copies of his popular scientific books in English have been sold in addition to translations in thirteen languages. Each of these books has been acclaimed in superlative terms as a brilliant contribution to our understanding of the universe. To every intelligent reader Jeans' books will give a knowledge of the great advances of science, show how they were made and how they have affected man's thinking.

Chapter IV

RELATIVITY AND THE ETHER

We have seen how modern physics reduces the universe to systems of waves. If we find it hard to imagine waves unless they travel through something concrete, let us say waves in an ether or ethers. I believe it was the late Lord Salisbury who defined the ether as the nominative of the verb "to undulate." If this definition will serve for the moment, we can have our ether without committing ourselves very far as to its nature. And this makes it possible to sum up the tendency of modern physics very concisely: modern physics is pushing the whole universe into one or more ethers. It will be well, then, to scrutinise the physical properties of these ethers with some care, since in them the true nature of the universe must be hidden.

It may be well to state our conclusion in advance. It is, in brief, that the ethers and their undulations,

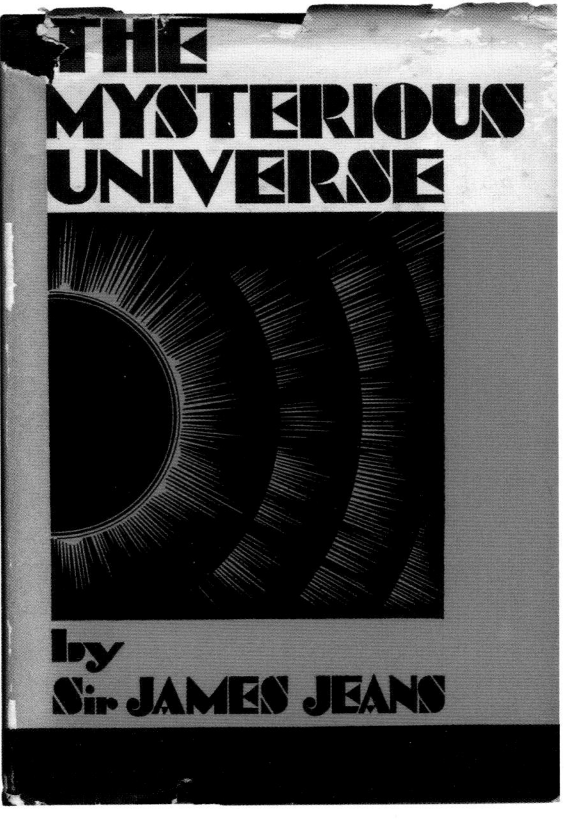

These publications enhanced Jeans's reputation as a writer. One popular book followed the other, and he was invited to give a series of radio broadcasts. Roberts recalled that sometimes there were difficulties and misunderstandings. The book *The Stars in their Courses* (1931) [126] was based on the series of broadcasts, and its first part, submitted for publication in the *Sunday Express*, happened to be quite similar to one of the broadcasts printed in *The Listener*. The Editor of the *Sunday Express* found that unacceptable and the case went to court. It took considerable effort for Jeans and Roberts to deal with the conflict and reach an agreement.

To Jeans's fame as a scientist and popular writer was now added a high reputation as a lecturer for the widest audiences. His popularity was not limited to the UK. His books were much read in the United States and were translated into many languages. *The Mysterious Universe* was published in France, Germany, Italy, Portugal, Denmark, Norway, Sweden, Finland, Poland and some other countries. In the 1930s Jeans was one of the most famous foreign astronomers in the USSR.

~~ • ~~

Jeans worked hard, but his life style seemed to have been very agreeable. A journalist, who visited him in 1933, noted the following details:

> "A rose, moist from the mists of morning, lies on the sparkling breakfast table at Cleveland Lodge, near Box Hill, Surrey.
>
> It lies beside the plate of Lady Jeans. It was put there by Sir James Hopwood Jeans.
>
> It is the daily tribute of a devoted husband and gardener to his charming wife.
>
> Sir James, who is astronomer and author by profession, handsome barrister in appearance, gardener and musician by inclination, got up very early to pick that rose.
>
> His custom is to wake before anyone else in the house and go out.
>
> He comes back in time to write a lot before breakfast. His best-known work is putting the Universe on paper so that something of its nature can be grasped by us careless, ignorant folk without telescopes.
>
> *Rough on Ronald*
>
> He is the publicity agent of the eternal stars. He makes them seem more exciting than the comets and meteors of Hollywood.
>
> "The Mysterious Universe", for instance, sold 123,000 copies.
>
> At the peak of its vogue, Ronald Jeans, playwright, strolled into the foyer of a theatre where his latest play was on.
>
> "This man Jeans", remarked another stroller, "is a genius — one of the greatest brains of our time!"
>
> Playwright Jeans blushed. A great exaggeration, of course, but a most pleasing conversation. Then it continued:
>
> "Such a graphic way of writing. I enjoyed every word. I'm no scientist, but I could read that book again and again — *The Mysterious Universe*, you know."

Exit Playwright Ronald Jeans.

Sir James Jeans likes to pass unnoticed and talk to people who do not know who he is. Travelling between London and Cambridge, a man in the train once told him he was interested in science, but believed that half these scientist fellows are not convinced by their own arguments.

"What grounds have you for thinking that?" asked Sir J. Jeans, *incog.*

"Well," said the man in the other corner, "I've been reading that Jeans chap — jolly clever and all that; but seems like an idealist."

"And is not present-day science favourable to idealism?"

The traveller rather shied off this question. ... At Cambridge he saw a book by Sir James on a stall. The showcard above bore a portrait of the man he had been talking to.

Sir James writes his books in longhand. But whereas most scientists, including Lord Rutherford and Sir Oliver Lodge, write tinily and neatly, Sir James writes like a journalist — i.e., script, big, bold and free.

An expert in graphology would say that his writing showed imagination even more than precision.

Typewriter Banned

The writing is done in a large room with creamy walls and simple furniture. Two sides are lined with bookshelves, and there is a quantity of drawings, maps, globes.

From his chair at the big desk, Sir James can see through the window a vast view of Surrey hills and woods.

This sanctum holds an atmosphere of peace. In fact, Sir James insists on peace. He must have it to think out his books and lectures.

That is why he writes everything in longhand. Dictation or a typewriter would be too disturbing.

All over the house, there is this quiet. Sir James aged 56, doesn't like modern furnishing. But the old-fashioned stuff must be simple and comfortable.

Mahogany reflects cut glass, and there are flowers in every room. Lady Jeans sees to that.

She, by the way, was an American, Miss Charlotte Tiffany, of Connecticut.

That may account for Sir James's liking for North America. He came home recently from Toronto; he has many astronomer friends in the United States, and has done much research at Mount Wilson Observatory, California.

Skilled Pianist

World-traveller Jeans looks nothing like the traditional professor. Features clear-cut, complexion fresh, keen blue-grey eyes, well-groomed air, smartly-cut suits ....

Blue-grey eyes, yes — and blue-grey suits. And a blue or a grey silk tie.

Nothing absent-minded and frowsy there. Nothing, either, resembling the traditional musician.

Yet he loves to play upon his beautiful grand piano, and he is a skilled pianist with a "professional" touch and manner.

This talent is kept strictly for his private life. He spends many happy evenings thus with Lady Jeans and their daughter for an audience.

No popular stuff mars the old-world atmosphere. Sir James's passion is Bach, whom he interprets extremely well.

He also plays the organ, and has installed one at Cleveland Lodge.

When he has time away from home, he goes to a classical concert.

He owns a radio set and a gramophone but does not use them much.

People who can express their own musical feelings don't need canned noise.

So that when Sir James has finished playing the piano, he reads or discusses daily problems with wife and daughter.

He is an omnivorous reader — and that includes novels.

He will eat anything — whatever they put in front of him. He likes fruit and sometimes a glass of wine.

If you are his guest, and smoke cigarettes, he will do the same. But he would rather fill his pet pipe and puff away thoughtfully.

Games? No.

Not while he has the glittering Universe to play with." ["The Man Who Brought the Stars to Earth", The Passing Show, October 28, 1933]

~~ • ~~

Jeans's wife, Charlotte was somewhat of a recluse and seemed to feel safe only in Cleveland Lodge. She was worried about her husband's administrative workload in London, and about the health of their daughter Olivia and her schooling. She again felt her poetic calling and in the 1930s resumed writing poetry, which she had practically given up in the first years of marriage. Romantic passion, love and death remained her topics, but there was a new freshness and the power of imagery in her Wordsworthian vision of nature and people. Her poems were published in various periodicals; more than ten can be found in the journal *Poetry Today.*

Charlotte now felt more settled. The stress of James's responsibilities at the Royal Society were no longer there. The couple spent their free time together, travelling to Cornwall, Scotland, Switzerland, Spain, and took a cruise around the Mediterranean. There were three visits to America (1930, 1931, 1934); during the first two Jeans gave a series of lectures, and Charlotte lived with her mother. During one of these visits 'Granny' gave a ball in honour of Olivia. In 1931, Hiram Bingham, his brother in law, then a U.S. Senator, invited Jeans to an official dinner in Washington, given in his honour.

In 1931 the Franklin Institute in Philadelphia awarded him the Franklin Medal. On 24 February of the same year Jeans wrote to Hale:

"At last, to my great pleasure, I find it is possible to visit Mount

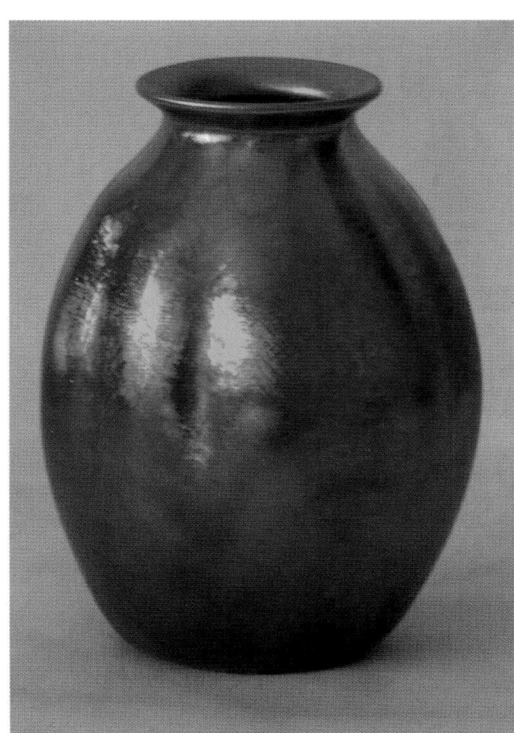

"FAVRILE" GLASS AT CLEVELAND LODGE

Charlotte's uncle, Louis Comfort Tiffany (1848–1933) — the eldest son of Charles Lewis Tiffany and founder of Tiffany & Co. He was a major influence in the decorative arts movement in the United States particularly in the use of decorative glass. Best known for his development of iridescent "Favrile" glass with unusual beauty of colour produced by the exposure of molten glass to various metallic oxides — a process that he patented in 1894. Four small "favrile" vessels survive from Charlotte's household. Three appear to have been experimental pieces with a unique number scratched on their base, the other is probably a commercial product sold over the counter.

"Favrile " vase (9454; height 12 cms)
"Favrile" bowl (Û4133; diameter 11 cms)
base of Û4133
Commercial "Favrile" Tiffany vase (height 26.4 cms)

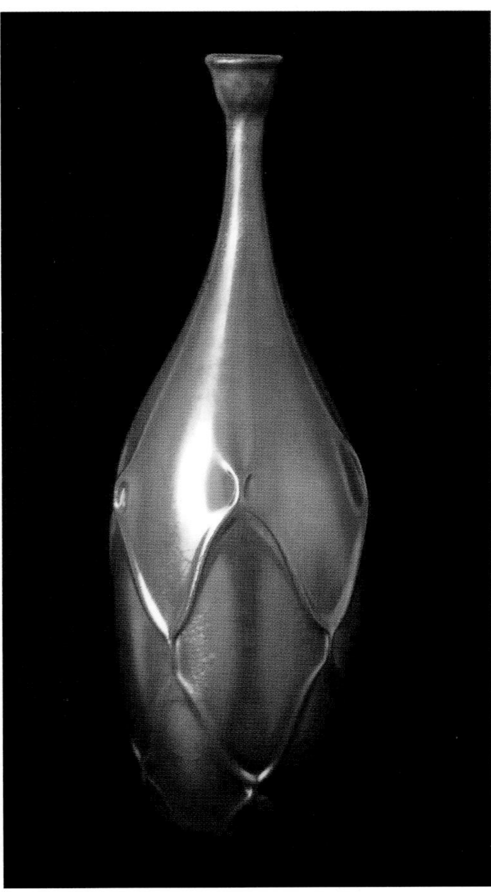

AN EXPORT CHINESE TEA SET

Lurking in a safe room at Cleveland Lodge after the death in 1993 of Susi, James's second wife, was a brilliantly colourful Kwon-Glazed Porcelain tea set painted with Chinese scenes, practically glowing amidst the piles of papers, manuscripts and music. This tea set was never used during Susi's time as James — judging by the tone of the pictures, furniture and rugs in his big music room — had a sombre taste, it may have never been used at Cleveland Lodge. The tea set is likely to have come from Charlotte's side of the family judging from her Cambridge home where there is brightly coloured Japanese ware in the glass fronted cupboard in the dining room and a colourful Qashqai rug on the floor of her study.

These tea sets are famous for their beautiful lines and brilliant colours combining traditional Chinese painting with classical western ornamentation. They were made in China during the Qing Dynasty from the mid part of the C17th up to 1912. The biscuit porcelain blanks were manufactured in Jingdezhen and then transferred to Guangzhou where they were painted and fired to the requirements of foreign customers. In recent years their production has restarted and continues today.

JEANS'S MANUSCRIPTS.

James Jeans was left handed. According to his sister Gertrude (letter dated 22 February 1950), as a boy he practised cricket but being left-handed he felt it a handicap in playing with others.

Below: A mathematical script, date unknown.

Page 606 (510) from the manuscript for "Astronomy and Cosmogeny" published by Cambridge University Press, 1928.

Right column:
Jeans lighting his pipe with his left hand, date unknown.

Page 134 (629) from the manuscript for "The Growth of Physical Sciences" published by Cambridge University Press, 1947.

Notes on Tone Colour and Electrical Music from a Royal Institute lecture in April 1928.

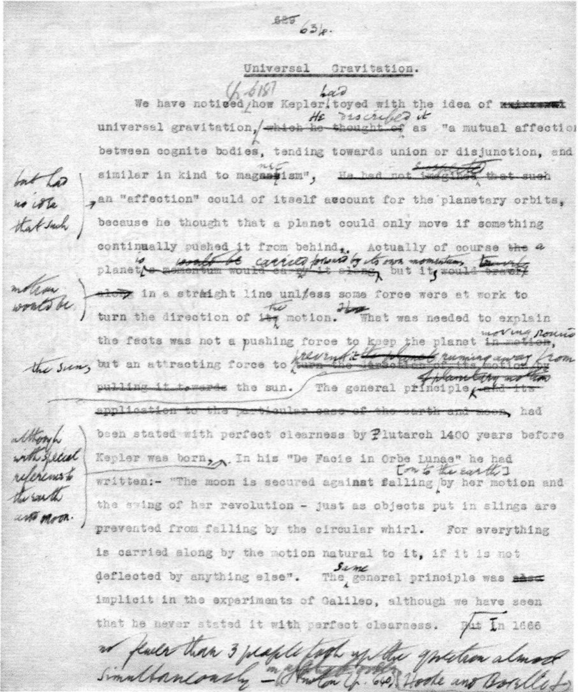

634

Universal Gravitation.

We have noticed how Kepler had toyed with the idea of universal gravitation, He described it as "a mutual affection between cognite bodies, tending towards union or disjunction, and similar in kind to magnetism", but had no idea that such an "affection" could of itself account for the planetary orbits, because he thought that a planet could only move if something continually pushed it from behind. Actually of course a planet is carried forward by its own momentum, but it would travel in a straight line unless some force were at work to turn the direction of its motion. What was needed to explain the facts was not a pushing force to keep the planet moving round the sun, but an attracting force to prevent it from running away from the sun. The general principle had been stated with perfect clearness by Plutarch 1400 years before Kepler was born. In his "De Facie in Orbe Lunae" he had written:- "The moon is secured against falling [on to the earth] by her motion and the swing of her revolution - just as objects put in slings are prevented from falling by the circular whirl. For everything is carried along by the motion natural to it, if it is not deflected by anything else". The same general principle was implicit in the experiments of Galileo, although we have seen that he never stated it with perfect clearness. In 1666 no fewer than 3 people took up the question almost simultaneously — Hooke and Borelli

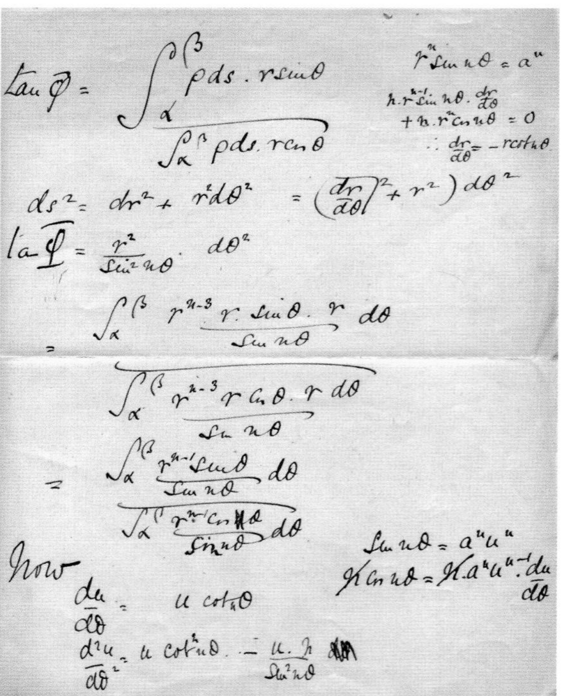

$$\tan\Phi = \frac{\int_\alpha^\beta \rho\, ds \,.\, r\sin\theta}{\int_\alpha^\beta \rho\, ds\,.\, r\cos\theta}$$

$$r^n \sin n\theta = a^n$$

$$ds^2 = dr^2 + r^2 d\theta^2 = \left(\left(\frac{dr}{d\theta}\right)^2 + r^2\right) d\theta^2$$

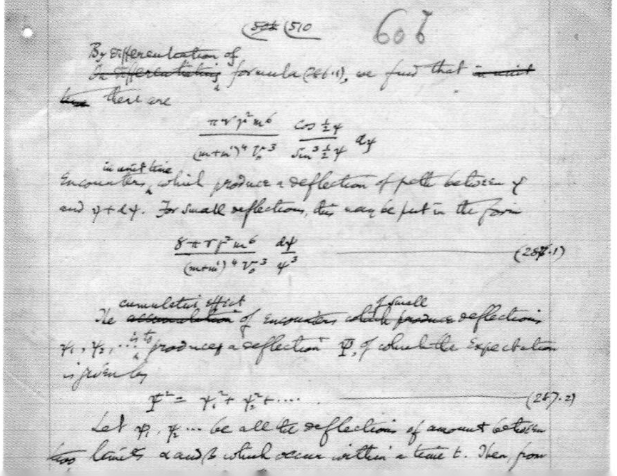

606 (510)

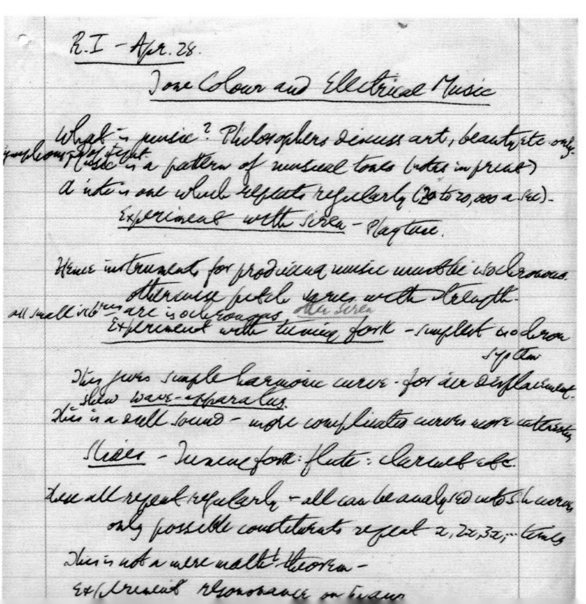

R.I - Apr. 28.

Tone Colour and Electrical Music

> Wilson, as far as I can tell in the first fortnight in May. I am writing at once to enquire whether there is any prospect of seeing you at that time in Pasadena, or if you will not be there, where you are likely to be. You have probably seen in the newspapers that the Franklin Institute have been good enough to award me their Medal, and I am crossing to receive it on May 20th. I shall leave here as soon as Olivia returns to College, which I think is the 17th April, and shall come almost directly to the Observatory." [193, p. 74].

Hale in response to the letter expressed satisfaction with the high distinction bestowed by the Franklin Institute and invited Jeans to take part in the Congress of the American Association for the advancement of Science in Pasadena, organized by W. S. Adams and R. Millikan from 15th to 20th June. The latter invited Jeans to speak at the Congress. Jeans, however, had to stick to his plans to visit Pasadena earlier and wrote to Hale on 16th April:

> "I was sorry I was unable to do as you, Adams and Millikan suggested and visit Pasadena in June for the meeting of the American Association. The difficulty is that I am not altogether a free man. Olivia is now at College at Cambridge and as my wife is coming with me to California, we have to fit our trip in within the limits of a College term, which ends in the middle of June. This made the latter date quite impossible. If I had known that the American Association was meeting in Pasadena at that time, I might have tried to make other arrangements for Olivia, but it was too late to do this when the invitation reached me." [193, p. 75–6].

During the award ceremony of the Franklin Medal Jeans spoke on 'The Origin of the Solar System' [129].

The visit three years later (1934) was less successful, possibly because Hiram was no longer a Senator.

This is the only surviving letter from Jeans to Hiram Bingham and it is not without humour:

> "Sweet Way
> Twenty-twenty-five Brickell Avenue
> Miami, Florida
>
> My dear Hi —
> This is just a line to thank you for your excellent and highly appreciated gift of whisky and of supplies in the cocktail cupboard. It was really awfully good of you to supply so many good things in this thirsty land ["Prohibition" had just come to an end], and all of us are enjoying them

GIFT TO THE FITZWILLIAM MUSEUM

Late in 1933 Charlotte Jeans was much taken with Epstein's bust of Professor Einstein displayed by Arthur Tooth & Sons Ltd of New Bond Street not far from their London flat in St. James' Court, Buckingham Gate. After consulting with James and the director of the Fitzwilliam Museum, Sydney Cockerell, it was donated to the Museum at the end of the year.

hugely. Granny is gradually — under Charly's instigation — increasing the strength of her Scotch Highballs, and is now up to a thimbleful of whisky to a glass of soda, remarking immediately after each glass that it doesn't seem to have done her any harm. Less good results followed when Granny insisted that Judge Foster [her lawyer] must of course have a full glass of Manhattan cocktail — the glasses provided were claret glasses.
We look forward to seeing you.
Yrs, J.H.Jeans"

Charlotte's health was failing, though how seriously no one seemed to realise, not even James. In 1934 she died. Soon after he wrote to his old friend Hale:

"My whole life has been changed by the death of my dear wife which occurred at the end of May. She had been suspiciously ill for some time, but we went to Florida in March, and if she had proved to be well I had hoped we might cross over to Pasadena then, or possibly come again in the autumn. But in Florida she got actually worse and we hurried home only for her to die after a few weeks. Happily she passed very peacefully after only a few days of acute illness. It has been a terrible shock to me as we had been such good friends and inseparable companions — especially as she got more deaf and was reluctant to see friends or strangers.

I still hope I may get to California before long and hope to take up my research more actively than has been possible in the last few years. At present Olivia is living with me but she is temporarily out of action with a strained heart.

We have had Hubble over here as you know, but have been able to see very little of him. It was good to hear from him that there is real improvement in your health. May it continue to improve.
My warmest regards to Mrs. Hale and yourself." [193, p. 77].

After the death of his wife, Jeans became very depressed. His friend Roberts whose wife had died two years before (1932), wrote. "He was desperately lonely and unaffectedly glad to welcome me. His daughter was ill in bed and he was clearly pleased to have someone to whom, in some measure at least, he could confide his troubles. Sitting in his lovely garden, he tried to tell me how he felt. 'Sometimes', he said, 'I wish I'd been a games-master at Eton.' Later in that summer of 1934 Jeans stayed a week-end with me at my house in Barton Road (Cambridge). He was still tired and depressed, but I think he was cheered by the change of scene and company. My mother was also staying with me and I noted with pleased surprise how docilely he listened to her words of old-fashioned advice and comfort." [193, p. XII].

Jeans recovered slowly after Charlotte's death. When Sir William Hardy [biologist and food scientist, 6th April 1864 — 23rd January 1934], President-Elect of the British Association, suddenly died shortly before assuming office in autumn 1934, he gallantly took his place. He delivered a typically vibrant and challenging presidential address — widely reported upon in the Press — at the opening of the annual meeting in Aberdeen in the evening of the 5th of September 1934 before an audience of more than 2000. The subject was the fundamental one "What is the real value of science to humanity?"

The main part of the address, which dealt with "The new world-picture of modern physics" was largely devoted to showing that we have more control over our own actions and destiny than the old physics, with its insistence on "determinism", would allow. The last part dealt with the practical interface between science and humanity and the economic problems of the times.

"The contribution of the new physics", said Sir James," to this problem [of free will] is not that it had given a decision on a long-debated question, but that it had reopened a door which the old physics had seemed to slam and bolt."

"We had an intuitive belief that we could choose our lunch from the menu or abstain from housebreaking or murder; and that by our own volition we can develop our freedom to choose. We may, of course, be wrong. The old physics told us that we were, and that our imagined freedom was all an illusion; the new physics tells us it may not be."

"The old physics showed us a universe which looked more like a prison than a dwelling-place. The new physics shows us a building which is certainly more spacious although its interior doors may be either open or locked — we cannot say. But we begin to suspect it may give us room for such freedom as we have always believed we possessed; it seems possible, at least, that in it we can mould events to our desire and live lives of emotion, intellect and endeavour. It looks as though it might form a suitable dwelling-place for man, and not a mere shelter for brutes."

He stressed that mankind needed a new morality and religion, and the fact that these "should be consistent with our new knowledge of psychology and the established facts of science". He also discussed how civilization could be saved from the dangers that threaten it — dangers resulting, mainly, as he believed, due to the fact that human nature is too slow and always lags behind the development of human knowledge.

Jeans offered a more consistently organized life for man on the basis of scientific principles:

"... psychology, which holds out hopes that, for the first time in his long history, man may be enabled to obey the command 'Know thyself';

Meeting of the British Association for the Advancement of Science, University of Aberdeen, September 1934:
The Principal's Lodge. Lilian Adam Smith — the Principal's wife — her guests and family.

From left to right:
Kathleen Thomson (née Smith),
James Hopwood Jeans, Alick Buchanan Smith [later Lord Balerno], Lilian Adam Smith,
George Paget Thomson, Charles Galton Darwin.

to which I, for one, would like to see adjoined a morality and, if possible, even a religion, consistent with our new psychological knowledge and the established facts of science; scientific and constructive measures of eugenics and birth control; scientific research in agriculture and industry, sufficient at least to defeat the gloomy prophecies of Malthus [who believed war and epidemics were necessary to prevent population growth — A.K.] and enable even larger populations to live in comfort and contentment on the same limited area of land."

Jeans went on to deal with the economic problems of the time:
"This last brings us to the thorny problem of economic depression and unemployment. No doubt a large part of this resulted from the war, national

Punch September 12, 1934. Cartoon based around Jeans's presidential address to the 1934 annual meeting in Aberdeen of the British Association for the Advancement of Science.

PUNCH, OR THE LONDON CHARIVARI—SEPTEMBER 12, 1934
BRITISH ASSOCIATION ANNUAL MEETING. ABERDEEN.
ANOTHER ANTHROPOLOGICAL DISCOVERY.
PROFESSOR JEANS (*earnestly*). "BEFORE WE ALL GO AWAY FROM THIS GREAT CITY I WANT TO EXPLODE THE THEORY OF THE PRIMITIVE ABERDONIAN MEAN MAN, WHOSE SKELETON IS SAID TO HAVE BEEN DISCOVERED HOLDING A SMALL BRONZE TOKEN IN THE PALM OF HIS RIGHT HAND."

Opposite:
News Chronicle of 6th September 1934 had an extended article discussing Jeans's presidential address in Aberdeen implying he was juggling with the Universe and human society

rivalries, tariff barriers, and various causes which have nothing to do with science, but a residue must be traced to scientific research; this produces labour-saving devices which in times of depression are only too likely to be welcomed as wage-saving devices to put men out of work. The scientific Robot in Punch's cartoon boasted that he could do the work of 100 men but gave no answer to the question 'who would find work for the displaced 99?' He might, I think, have answered — 'the pure scientist', in part at least, for scientific research has two products of industrial importance — the labour-saving inventions which displaced labour, and the more fundamental discoveries which originated as pure science, but may ultimately lead to new trades and new popular demands providing employment for vast armies of labour."

"Both were rich gifts from science to the community. The labour-saving devices lead to emancipation from soul-destroying toil and routine work, a greater leisure and better opportunities for its enjoyment. The new inventions add to the comfort and pleasure, health and wealth of the community. If a perfect balance could be maintained between the two there would be employment for all, with a continual increase in the comfort and dignity of life. But, as I see it, troubles are bound to arise if the balance is not maintained, and a steady flow of labour-saving devices with no accompanying flow of new industries to absorb the labour they displace, cannot but lead to unemployment and chaos in the field of labour."

"At present we have a want of balance resulting in unemployment, so that our great need at the moment is for industry-making discoveries. Let us remember Faraday's electromagnetic induction [one of the foundations of the electrical industry — A.K.], Maxwell's Hertzian waves [which led to wireless communication — A.K.], and the Otto cycle [basis of the internal combustion engine — A.K.] — each of which has provided employment for millions of men. And, although it is an old story, let us also remember that the economic value of the work of one scientist alone, Edison [whose work led to the gramophone and many other developments — A.K.], has been estimated at three thousand million pounds."

"Unhappily, no amount of planning can arrange a perfect balance. For as the wind bloweth where it listeth, so no one can control the direction in which science will advance; the investigator in pure science did not know himself whether his researches will result in a mere labour-saving device or a new industry. He only knows that if all science were throttled down [as had sometimes been suggested — A.K.], neither would result."

Jeans painted a gloomy picture of the world without science:
"... the community would become crystallised in its present state, with nothing to do but watch its population increase, and shiver as it waited for the famine, pestilence or war which must inevitably come to restore the balance between food and mouths, land and population."

"We meet in a year which has to some extent seen science arraigned before the bar of public opinion; there are many who attribute most of our present national woes — including unemployment in industry and the danger of war — to the recent rapid advance in scientific knowledge. Even if their most lurid suspicions were justified, it is not clear what we could do. For it is obvious that the country which called a halt to scientific progress would soon fall behind in every respect as well — in its industry, in its economic position, in its naval and military defences, and, not least important in its culture. But can we admit that the suspicions of our critics are justified? If science has made the attack more deadly in war, it had also made the defence more efficient in the long run; it shows no partiality in the age-long race between weapons of attack and defence. This being so, it would, I think, be hard to maintained in cold blood that its activities are likely to make wars either more frequent or more prolonged. It is at least arguable that the more deadly a war is likely to be, the less likely it is to occur."

The "News Chronicle" of the 6th of September 1934 commented on Jeans's presidential address with an article entitled "**Science seeking new morality. Sir James Jeans Outlines His ideal World**" suggesting that he had left his listeners disappointed. He had omitted to define the morality and religion he wanted, only saying they should be "consistent with our new psychological knowledge and the established facts of science", leaving his audience wondering what he would do with the Bible, how the Churches would fare at his hands, and what he would base it all on [319].

This address showed that Jeans was a follower of the views of Sir Francis Galton, the founder of modern eugenics and a grandson of Erasmus Darwin and a cousin of Charles Darwin. He defined eugenics as 'the study of the factors that are under social control and which could improve or worsen the properties of race, both physical and moral' [289, p. 472]. What may have particularly impressed Jeans, is that Galton sought in these studies to apply mathematics extensively, agreeing with the opinions, from Kant to Kelvin, that every science is as scientific as mathematics. According to Galton, eugenics passes through three stages: first, it should be seen as a purely academic matter; secondly, its practical feasibility should be considered; thirdly, it must penetrate into people's conscience as the religion of the future [289, p. 472]. "Helping nature, should strive to ensure that land possessed the most perfect human beings. What nature provides blindly, slowly and cruelly, mankind will do consciously, quickly and with love" [289, p. 472–3] — Galton also had no doubt that the improvement of the human species is one of the goals of mankind — We do not know its final fate; one only there is no doubt that improving himself the most worthy of it, and the degradation of the most disgraceful" [289, p. 473]. Galton was sure that "man could not only physically improve his conditions, but, with greater biological knowledge could create a better self" [289, p. 473]. This has only come about in the 21st century, it could only have been a dream for Jeans.

Monart Glass Vase (height ~18 cms).

Another example of Charlotte's sharp eye and love of colour is a vase that is still in the Jeans Family. Salvador Ysart, a French glass worker was originally recruited in 1915 to work on the British war effort in Scotland producing much needed laboratory ware. In 1922 he was recruited by John Moncrieff to make laboratory glass in Perth, Scotland. His other three sons from France joined him. In the following year Salvador using colours he had brought from France made a beautiful vase and Mrs Isabel Moncrieff was so taken by it that she encouraged him to develop a range of art glass. This was called Monart combining Moncrieff with Ysart. It was a great success and continued in production until 1939 when the Second World War disrupted production (based on the Glass Encyclopedia).

Sic Itur Ad Astra.

 Sir James Jeans

Punch, February 27, 1935

A MUSICAL MARRIAGE. SUSI HOCK

In 1935, the Royal Institution in London established a professorship in Astronomy and, and the 58 year old Jeans was invited to this position which he held until 1946, when his deteriorating health forced him to resign. His successor was the then Astronomer Royal, Harold Spencer Jones. However in the same year a more important event took place in Jeans's life. He married Susi Hock, an Austrian organist of international renown. They were introduced by Lady Heath, and Jeans decided to continue his courtship in the Swiss Alps as he knew that the young musician was fond of mountaineering. He invited his publisher and friend S.C. Roberts to come along with him, and Roberts described this trip in his introduction to Milne's biography [193, p. ix–xvi].

"It was my first experience of Switzerland and I entered upon the expedition with a pleasantly ingenuous feeling. What pleased me was that, although I was too old to learn to climb in the technical sense, one could do quite a lot by stout walking. Jeans showed me the Morteratsch glacier in the course of our first day, but his knee was not very reliable and once or twice I went off on my own. One day we went over to St Moritz and spent the day with Helen and Harley Granville-Barker. After an exquisite meal out of doors, described as a picnic, we went over the Maloja Pass and wandered round the picturesque corners of Soglio. Over some very poor beer at the inn, Jeans with the rest of us, became quite hilarious and Granville-Barker proposed that we should send a picture post-card to someone whom all of us knew. We fixed upon Winstanley, then Vice-Master of Trinity and sent him some doggerel beginning:

As duodecimo to folio
Bears very slight affinity
So is the beer of Soglio
To Audit Ale at Trinity ....

But Jeans had another expedition to Italy in mind. He persuaded me that it would be a good plan to drive over the Stelvio Pass and spend a few days at Solda just over the Italian border. He added that he had been asked by his friend Lady Heath to look up a young musician whom he had met at a party in London. At the time I did not realize the significance of this supplementary motive for the journey.

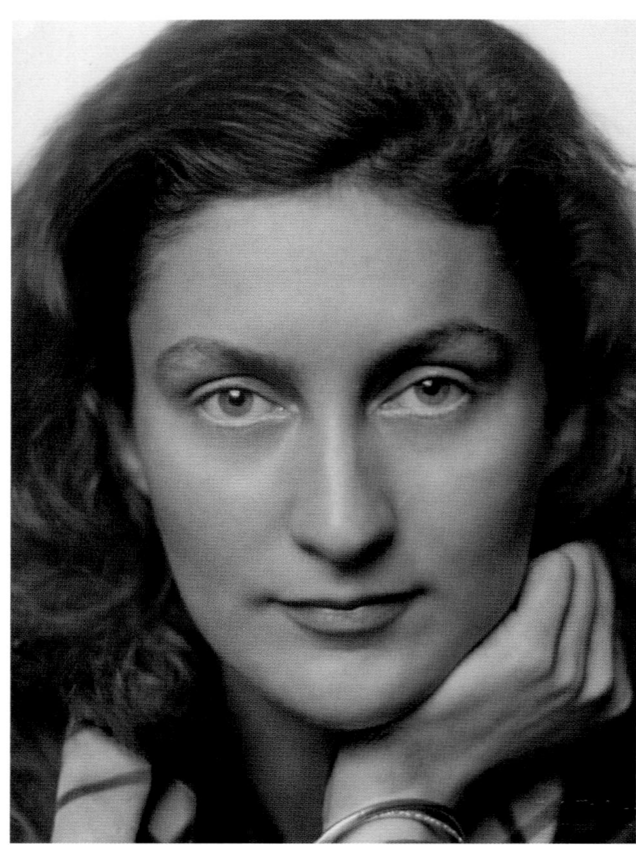

SUSI HOCK

Portrait by Trudi Fleischmann,
Vienna, 1933.

With her father in the Otztal, Austria.

At Sankt Florian, Upper Austria, known internationally for its sacred music and the composer Anton Bruckner.
Photo 1935

Studio portrait, late 1930's by Gerti Deutsch of Vienna, London.

Grand Hotel Kronenhof in Pontresina, Switzerland, where the two widowers, James Jeans and Sidney Roberts stayed after their visit to Solda.

Sir Thomas and Lady Heath with James Jeans at Cleveland Lodge ~ 1936–7. Ada Heath, a professional musician had introduced James to Susi Hock in 1935. Thomas Heath was the Permanent Secretary to the Treasury and an authority on Greek Mathematics.

Sidney Castle Roberts (1887–1966) Jeans's Publisher, Secretary of Cambridge University Press (1922–1948), Vice Chancellor Cambridge University (1949–1951) photo 1938.

We had an interesting drive over the pass, partly because the car we had hired frequently showed signs of giving out at the steep parts of the ascent. But we arrived at Solda without mishap in the late afternoon. After we had been allotted bedrooms, I came down to the entrance hall of the hotel. Most of the people were Italian tourists, but suddenly a most elegant and individual figure approached — a tall girl in a white climbing-suit. She looked inquiringly at me and we introduced ourselves: she was Susi Hock, the young Viennese musician whom Jeans had met at Lady Heath's party. Then Jeans appeared and our introduction was formalized. Susi had just done a little climb (about 10,000 feet) and went to change for dinner. After dinner we went out on to the hotel terrace. It was a brilliant starlit night and Susi asked many questions about the stars, which Jeans was only too ready to answer. There was also much talk about music. Feigning weariness after a long day, I announced that I was going to bed early. There was no protest. The situation was becoming quite clear to me.

The weather next day was not very good. We climbed up to a nearby hut in the morning. Jeans was a little slow and it was quite easy, and convenient, for me to act as pathfinder. Later in the day Jeans asked me with some embarrassment, whether I would mind if Susi came back with us to Pontresina. I assured him, with complete sincerity, that I should be delighted. The holiday was acquiring an element of romance and excitement for which I had been wholly unprepared. We decided to return to Pontresina by a different route and I quickly announced my desire to sit in front with the driver. On our return to the hotel we aroused some interest. Two days before, we had left — a pair of detached and unromantic widowers. Now we returned with our elegant prize. The dowagers of the Kronenhof [Grand hotel in Pontresina, where Jeans and Roberts were staying — A.K.] were agog with curiosity. But our gaiety was not damped. We went up the Schafberg by the funicular and had lunch at a hut on the way down. There were some odd characters in the hut and we rioted over the silliest jokes. I had never before seen Jeans shaken with helpless laughter.

A day or two afterwards I returned to England. About ten days later I received the following letter from Jeans from Vienna:

'Just a line in haste to tell you — before you see it in The Times — that I hope soon to marry Susi Hock.

'I expect this is no surprise to you and fear you must think I owe you an apology for Pontresina and Solda. I am really sorry if you felt it broke up into a 2+1 party, but I had not quite foreseen how things would turn out. Anyhow I hope we may all three meet again soon.'

Thus was the seal set upon my friendship with Jeans. I had a share in the happiest adventure of his later life and although it was always difficult for him to confide frankly in anyone, he would from time to time consult me in a jerky, sceptical way about problems other than those relating to books and publishing. I became godfather to his elder son, Michael, and some years before his death I had agreed to be one of his executors, but I did not know, until his will was read, that he had nominated me as co-guardian, with Susi, of his three children. It was characteristic of him that he had not brought himself to the point of asking me during his lifetime.

Jeans was not a man of many friends, partly because of his temperamental shyness and reticence and partly because of his intolerance of what he deemed to be second-rate. With his own quick perception he lacked the patience which would have enabled him to understand and appreciate a slower-moving mind and consequently he missed those intimacies which he fundamentally desired," [193, p. xiii–xvi]

Music was one of the strongest links in his second marriage. Jeans accompanied Susi on a concert tour in America in 1937. She gave him the idea to write a book in which music was analyzed from a scientific point of view. His book *Science and Music* (1937) [150] was dedicated to her. There are chapters on the theory of pure tones, natural harmony, the structure of musical instruments and acoustics of concert halls as well as the history of music. The book became widely known as one of the most valuable introductions to the scientific aspects of music.

However, Jeans was not the first physicist to write about music from a scientific view point. The physicist Max Planck — a wonderful pianist and a connoisseur of classical music — had already written a book in a similar vein *Gleichschwebende Temperatur, gleichschwebende Stimmung* (1893). Musical abilities often accompany a mathematical talent.

In 1937 Jeans became the honorary Director of the Royal Academy of Music, and in 1938/1939 was the President of its Student Union.

~~ • ~~

Susi Hock was born in Vienna on the 25th of January 1911, to Oscar and Jekaterina Hock, a family of paper manufacturers. She had a younger brother Peter and sister Lisl who were twins, and an even younger brother, Nikolas. They lived at 71 Kobenzl Strasse, Grinzing, the 19th district of the City, in the same street as the writer Robert Musil — author of the famous novel *The Man without Qualities*. Their home was designed and built by the famous architects Oskar Strnad and Oskar Wlach in 1910–1912 and is now known as Villa Hock.

SUSI'S FAMILY

The Hock family home at 71 Kobenzlstrasse, 19th District, Vienna. Designed and built by Oskar Strnad and Oskar Wlach during 1910–12. Oskar Strnad (1879–1935) played a leading role in creating the Vienna School of Architecture. Now refurbished it is known as Villa Hock (Die Presse, 14–15th August 1971).

The Hock family after Susi's father was invalided out of the 1st World War after contracting cholera. Left to right: Lisl, Oscar, Susi, Peter, Jekatarina.

Susi's mother, Jekaterina Hock, at their home, 1937.

Susi's father, Oscar Hock (1874–1948), at their home, 1937. Born in Prague of Jewish parentage.

As a result of his parents' financial circumstances Oscar aged 16 had to leave Prague and school — for Vienna. Joining the paper-manufacturing firm of Lenzing he soon became head of it.
On his 60th birthday in 1934 The Firm presented him with an album of photographs of their two paper mills (Lenzing, Pettighofen) and their sawmill at Shörfling on the Ager River, Atter See. His firm was confiscated and in spite of being asked to run it by the Nazi authorities, he refused. In 1938 it became Zellwolle Lenzing A.G. and has now evolved into one of world's largest producers of textile and non-woven cellulose fibres.

Stefan Zweig wrote of Vienna: "Hardly any other city in Europe thirsted for culture as passionately as Vienna. Precisely because Austria for several centuries had no political ambitions, did not have special success in their military campaigns, their national pride manifested itself in the strong desire to dominate in the arts. … immortal constellations of musicians shone from here over the world: Gluck, Haydn and Mozart, Beethoven, Schubert, Brahms, and Johann Strauss; it was here that all the currents of European culture met. Royalty, aristocrats, and the German-speaking people were vitally connected with the Slavic, Hungarian, Spanish, Italian, French, and Flemish cultures. The real genius of Vienna was to combine all these contrasts into a harmonious and particularly Austrian music". [283, p.18–19]. The Hock family was also international, her mother was a Serbo-Croat born in Semlin near Belgrade and her father was a Czech Jew born in Prague. And the family had a strong passion for art.

Susi at 14 years old, was admitted to Vienna's Academie für Musik und Darstellende Kunst (music and fine arts), where her teachers were Franz Schütz for organ and Franz Schmidt for piano and music theory. Schmidt later dedicated many of his works for organ to Susi. After graduating from the Academie with the highest grades, she moved to Leipzig, where she studied with Karl Straube, specializing in the organ music of Johann Sebastian Bach as well as that of his predecessors and contemporaries. She also studied in Paris with the outstanding composer and organist Charles-Marie Widor.

She made her debut when she was just 18 years old in Vienna before an audience of more than two thousand. The program included music by Bach, his predecessors, a composition by Reger, and two works by Schmidt. That was followed by performances in France, Belgium, Germany and the UK. They were accorded brilliant reviews in such newspapers as *Figaro*, the Belgian national, *The Times*, *The Musical Times* etc. In 1935 she gave a concert of organ music in Cambridge at the Handel festival. This is where Jeans first came across this young musician.

Susi recalled her first visit to Cleveland Lodge and her later life there:

"I can still vividly remember my first visit to Cleveland Lodge. It was in July, 1935, when Sir James Jeans invited my Viennese friend Dea Gombrich and me to a dinner party and asked us to make music afterward. Dea, a brilliant young violinist, and I had already given several joint recitals in England and we were looking forward to playing at Cleveland Lodge and to meeting the great astronomer of whose interest in music we had heard before."

PROGRAMME

SUNDAY JUNE 9TH

9.0 p.m. ORGAN RECITAL AND CHORAL MUSIC

Works by Handel and his contemporaries in Germany.

At the Organ: SUSI HOCK.

The Choir of St. John's College.

Conductor: DR. CYRIL ROOTHAM.

IN THE CHAPEL OF ST. JOHN'S COLLEGE. *Admission by Programme.*

MONDAY JUNE 10TH

5.0 p.m. LECTURE ON HANDEL.

PROFESSOR E. J. DENT.

IN THE ARTS SCHOOL. *Admission free.*

9.0 p.m. CHAMBER CONCERT.

Works by Handel and his contemporaries in Italy.

The Cambridge University Musical Club.

IN THE GUILDHALL. *Admission by Programme*

TUESDAY JUNE 11TH

2.45 p.m. First dramatic performances of Handel's

"THE CHOICE OF HERCULES"

"SUSANNA"

MABEL RITCHIE, GEOFFREY DUNN, FREDERICK WOODHOUSE, IRENE FLANDERS

Members of the C.U.M.S., and of the C.U. Madrigal Society.

Producer: CAMILLE PRIOR.

Conductors: BERNHARD ORD and HUBERT MIDDLETON.

OUTSIDE GIBBS' BUILDING, KING'S COLLEGE (in the Hall, if wet). *Admission by Ticket.*

MINSTER RECITAL

Austrian Organist in York

It is probably quite safe to say that the organ recital in York Minster last evening was the first given by a woman player in that building.

Miss Susi Hock is a young Austrian, who studied first in Vienna and later under Dr. Straube, who is the successor of J. S. Bach at St. Thomas's Church, Leipzig. She has given recitals in Austria, Switzerland and France, and last year played for the first time in England, at the invitation of the Organ Music Society in London.

On this her second visit to this country she is playing, besides in York, at the Handel Festival at Cambridge, and also in London, Oxford, Peterborough, Leicester, etc.

Miss Hock has made a special study of the works of Bach and his predecessors. Of these latter works she selected two by German writers, Georg Muffat (1645-1704), and J. G. Walther (1684-1733). This last-named was a near relative and close friend of Bach, and was a great master of the variation form The third example was by Buxtehude (1637-1709), a famous Danish organist, to hear whom Bach walked 50 miles. The Prelude and Fugue in F, by which he was represented, is interesting for the curious curly subject of the fugue.

Bach's own works were two choral preludes, a "Concerto after the style of Vivaldi," which I do not remember hearing before, and the big Toccata in F, with its long "pedal points" and exigent pedal work.

The outstanding feature of Miss Hock's playing was her clean and crisp touch, which successfully overcame the blurring resonances of the Minster. Her choice of stops was admirable (though she has a distinct partiality for "Swell to Mixtures"), and her avoidance of the more powerful stops was in keeping with the period of the music she played. Her technique is of a very high order, and her playing of the Bach Toccata was brilliant in its execution.

REGINALD ROSE.

Programme for the Cambridge, Handel Festival 9–11th June 1935

Review of the organ recital in York Minster, Yorkshire Herald 25th May 1935

SUSI HOCK, ENGLAND 1934–5

Susi Hock came to England on concert tour in June 1934 and then again in May and June 1935. She gave recitals including ones in St Margaret's Church (Westminster), King's College Chapel (Cambridge), St John's College Chapel (Cambridge), York Minster, St Paul's Church (Bedford), St Mary's Church (Woburn), and Peterborough Cathedral as well as taking part in the Cambridge Handel Festival and playing for the Organ Music Society at St Mary Abbot's Kensington, London. It is clear from the reviews that she had an unrivalled technical skill and an understanding of how the music of 17th Century and 18th Century composers such as J.S.Bach, his predecessors and contemporaries was actually played and sounded.

On her first visit she was a guest of John Christie of Glyndebourne. He had recently installed in his home in Sussex the largest organ outside a cathedral. On her second visit she was a guest of James Jeans who had been a keen organist since his teens. He had installed an organ in his home near Dorking, Surrey.

MARRIAGE:
SUSI AND JAMES IN VIENNA, 1935

Below:
On the Leopoldsberg.

Top right:
At Villa Hock, then 71 Kobenzlstrasse, Grinzing, Vienna.

James and Susi's marriage took place in "a picturesque little Protestant Church" in the Viennese suburb of Waehring on the 30th of September 1935. Left of Susi is her brother Peter; part hidden is her younger brother Niki. The two bowler hatted gentlemen are possibly from the British Embassy.

Bottom right:
In the Wiener Wald.

VEGETABLE GARDEN AT CLEVELAND LODGE

The formal vegetable garden at Cleveland Lodge in Surrey extended over nearly two acres (~8000 m^2) and contained heated glass houses and cold frames. For Susi this must have been a novelty. She was brought up in her parents' home built on the steep slopes overlooking Vienna where level ground was rare. But grapes, peaches, apricots and other more sensitive fruit and vegetables flourished outside in their garden, orchard and vineyards.

Southern aspect of the glasshouses and cold frames in the vegetable garden at Cleveland Lodge (~1935/6).

Susi in the formal vegetable garden inspecting her new domain (~1935/6).

"It was a lovely day and we arrived early. As our host had not yet returned from London, we decided to explore the gardens. Cleveland Lodge was well over 200 years old. Its original name was "Birds and Abbots" and it was only in the nineteenth century that the house acquired its present name. The house had a reputation for having had musical owners and at one time it belonged to Mendelssohn's aunt, whose musical parties were very popular in the neighborhood. Mendelssohn is said to have stayed there frequently and I could well imagine his enjoyment of the gardens and the fine view on Box Hill. I did not muse very long because I was too keen to see the organ. I slipped into the music room and there it stood at the end of the room behind white shutters. It was played from a console about six yards away, and soon our host, who had arrived in the meantime, proudly demonstrated its various tonal resources. I remained silent and began to wonder how I could ever find suitable registrations for all the Bach, Buxtehude and Lübeck pieces which I intended to play. I had just come from France, where I had

MICHAEL JEANS, THEIR FIRST CHILD

James and Susi on the way to the Royal Garden Party at Buckingham Palace, July 1936. Susi was 7 months pregnant with her first child, Michael (Portman Press Bureau, London)

Michael Jeans's christening tea party at Cleveland Lodge, summer 1937. S. C. Roberts, holding his godson, with his mother and daughter.

James with Michael (~10 months) at Cleveland Lodge, summer 1937.

James and Michael Jeans at Cleveland Lodge, summer 1939.

played some of the new Gonzalez organs, and I was full of enthusiasm for the baroque type of instrument. After dinner — when I ate the best ice cream in my life — I had to get down to the registration problem and found that contrary to my expectation James was very interested in the baroque sounds which I reproduced on this typically English instrument built by William Hill & Son and Norman & Beard in 1924/5. James had never heard any of the Continental baroque organs, but when 12 years old, he was brought up on a Snetzler organ which he played at school. From that time onward he collected organ specifications and was very much interested in organ building. He was a very good player, who not only played all Bach's organ works but who was also very well acquainted with romantic and contemporary organ music. However, he did not like to play before others and that evening I had to play and play. I am sure that all the other guests were very tired, but he wanted more and more organ music. It was very late when at last Dea and I left, and it was on the way back to London that Dea made the astonishing remark that she was quite certain that our host would marry me. I could not help laughing at Dea's prophecy, but she must have been gifted with second sight because two months later James and I were married and Cleveland Lodge became my home. I could have wished that I had this gift of second sight too, because, when a few years later Dea announced her marriage to Sir John Forsdyke, then director of the British Museum, it came to me as a complete surprise."

"Soon after we were married James found that one organ was not sufficient for two organists and decided to present me with a baroque chamber organ with tracker action. I was more than overjoyed at the idea of possessing such an instrument, especially after years of struggling on a two-manual pedal harmonium at my home in Vienna. James made plans for building a new and much larger music room for his organ, which was to be altered and enlarged by Hill, Norman & Beard. The old music room was to be my music room and the baroque organ was to stand in the old organ chamber. The difficulty now was where to get my baroque organ. At that time baroque organs were not built in England and we thought we would try to get one in Germany. We were, however, afraid of action trouble, as the new German tracker actions were still not very reliable, and so we decided on a compromise: to have the organ case and tracker action built in England by Hill, Norman & Beard and to get all the pipework from Germany. We went to Germany, where I wanted James to hear all the Silbermann organs which I knew so well from my student days in Leipzig. After all, was it not the beautiful big Silbermann organ at the Dom in Freiberg which had converted me to old organs and old organ music? I had fallen in love with it at first sight, or better, first hearing, and even now after so many years I can remember exactly the beauty of its sound."

The partially built new music room, autumn 1936.

"While visiting several of the Silbermann organs near Leipzig, we heard that some of the restoration work on these instruments had been carried out by the firm of Hermann Eule, organ builder of Bautzen. We liked Eule's work so much that we wanted him to build my organ. When we arrived at Bautzen we found to our surprise that the whole business was run by an elderly Miss Eule and that it was Fritz Abend who supervised all the organ building. We were very impressed by Abend's work and were delighted when he agreed to design all the pipework for my baroque organ and come to England to voice it. The specification of my organ was drawn up by J.N. David, the well-known Austrian organ composer, who taught at that time at the Kirchenmusikalische Institut in Leipzig and was one of the keenest pioneers in the baroque organ movement. Highly satisfied with the results of our German trip, we returned to England. At Cleveland Lodge the builders were now busy and when the new music room was finished it turned out to be a great success. James had taken infinite trouble over its acoustics and before it was built a small cardboard model was made of it and tested at the National Physical Laboratory in Teddington. Not until it proved satisfactory did the building begin. In the curved ceiling of the music room there were seventeen tons of concrete. James had also carefully worked out how many square yards of carpets and curtains the room could take without impairing its acoustical properties. In September 1936, his organ stood in its big chamber behind a nice wrought iron grill and was ready to be played. My baroque organ was also finished. Fritz Abend had done the voicing to our complete satisfaction. Hill, Norman & Beard had made the tracker action so light and easy to play

Inside of the new music room at Cleveland Lodge. Jeans's double partner's desk stacked with papers. The organ console is to the left, August 1937.

The rotating and tilting chair in which James did all his writing. After his death in 1946 its use continued until ~2010. Now restored and back in use within the Jeans Family.

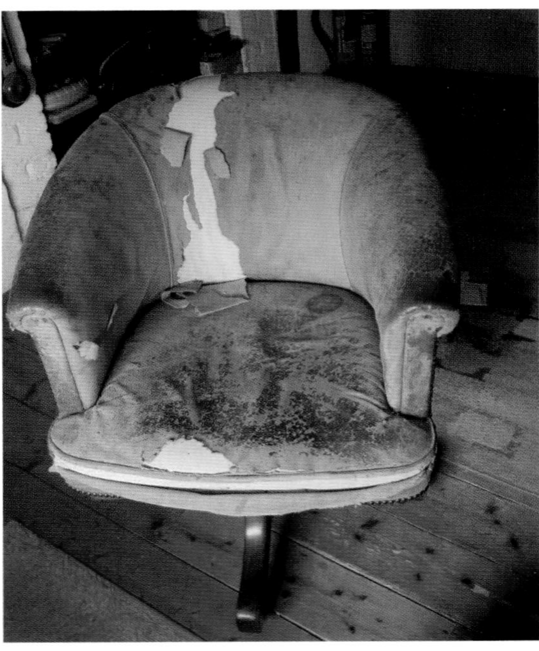

NEW MUSIC ROOM

The design of the new music room — the "big Music room" as it was called — was entrusted to the well known Liverpudlian architect Harold Chalton Bradshaw (1893–1943). He had been the first Secretary of the Royal Fine Art Commission, a man with a considerable reputation as a Roman Scholar with a classical taste who had been involved during the 1920's with the Imperial War Graves Commission in the design of the Ploegsteen, Cambrai, and the Guards Division Memorial. The new music room was to be essentially freestanding although it was to be linked by a double door passage way to Susi's music room where her new baroque organ stood. It was to be ~19 feet high to the apex of its curved ceiling, ~21 feet wide, and ~47 feet long including the organ chamber. The acoustics of a scale model were tested at the National Physical Laboratory at Teddington prior to construction. The suspended roof of the room contained 17 tons of cellular concrete. The organ pipework was situated behind an ornamental wrought iron grille and the electric action console was situated in the opposite end of the music room.

The room was designed to act as James's study and music room but not as a concert hall although after his death in 1946 it was used to accommodate Susi's annual music festivals and master classes from 1951 until her death in 1993. It was later used for the same purpose by the Royal School of Church Music. Cleveland Lodge was sold to developers in 2007 and its famous music room — reputed to be the best in England — was demolished.

Harold Bradshaw was also involved in improving and building new living quarters for the staff employed at Cleveland Lodge. The Elizabethan Cottage, Catbells, was altered. A capacious garage with two flats and a very fine pair of semi-detached gardener's cottages were added to the estate to ensure that the staff was more than adequately housed. This work was completed in 1939. James must have got on well with Harold because he asked him to be a godparent for his second son, Christopher, who was born on the last day of 1939.

NEW MUSIC ROOM : CLEVELAND LODGE : DORKING

LONGITUDINAL SECTION

CROSS SECTION

GROUND FLOOR PLAN

NORTH ELEVATION

EAST ELEVATION

ONE EIGHTH INCH SCALE
N.B. FIGURED DIMENSIONS TO BE FOLLOWED IN PREFERENCE TO SCALE

H.C. BRADSHAW. F.R.I.B.A
DWG No 995.CT 2/36

Plans of James's new music room designed by H. C. Bradshaw. It was constructed during 1936–37 to house his own organ built by William Hill & Son and Norman & Beard (1924–25) which had been altered and enlarged.

James's bookcase from his big music room in which he kept all his books, their many editions and translations. Here you see it in use in the well-known antiquarian booksellers G David of St Edward's Passage, Cambridge. They acquired the remainder of his library in 1993 after the death of Susi, and with it the bookcase.

SUSI'S NEW NEOBAROQUE ORGAN

The new Hermann Eule-Hill, Norman & Beard neobaroque organ. After the Royal School of Church Music left Cleveland Lodge in 2006 it was restored and is now in the Birmingham Conservatoire.

Susi at her new organ 1936–37 (A. W. Carr, Coulsdon).

James and Susi Jeans, Cleveland Lodge, ~1937.

Susi and James Jeans on the Liverpool Cathedral organ with Harry Goss-Custard who was the organist from 1915 to 1955. Photo ~1936.

James Jeans with his pipe at Cleveland Lodge, ~ summer 1937.

that we were really delighted. Another great event took place at the same time: our first son Michael was born and his arrival was duly celebrated by playing the organs."

"Many people came to hear our organs, and many were, I am afraid, rather shocked by the unusual sound of my baroque organ. But I was very happy with it and would not have anything altered. In 1938 James decided to ask Henry Willis to do some alterations to his organ; these involved re-voicing some stops and the addition of a few new ones."

"We were not to enjoy our organs for more than a few years. The war broke out and six months later we had to move to the west-country. We packed Michael and our second son Christopher, who was only a few months old, into a station wagon and took only our most necessary belongings with us to our temporary home in Somerset. Our hearts were heavy when we left the organs. Would we see them again? Cleveland Lodge was taken over by the army until the end of the war. The organs were out of bounds and not played except on the rare occasions when I returned to our house for a broadcast. I shall always remember one of these broadcasts when I had to play while an air raid was on. The noise was terrific, and I was told to play as loud as possible so that the listeners — most of them in air-raid shelters — could not hear the falling bombs and the anti-aircraft fire. Early next morning I had to pass through London on my way back to Somerset. A terrible scene hung over the city, over its ruins and smouldering buildings, and high above, the sky was blue and clear with the sun shining down on these sad scenes of devastation and human folly."

"Luckily Cleveland Lodge and its organs survived the war. We returned to our house in 1945 and found that the organs were not very much worse for their long neglect and for standing in cold and damp rooms. We wondered how we could get the house going again after the long period of army occupation. It was almost impossible to get skilled labour and domestic help and I was very busy looking after our young family of three: the boys now had a little sister, Katharine, who was born in Somerset. James was working hard to finish his "History of Science"; he had to keep quiet because he had only recently recovered from a serious attack of coronary thrombosis. However, kind friends and neighbours came to our rescue and helped me to scrub, decorate and paint. One of the show pieces in James's music room was and still is the mantelpiece over the fireplace, painted by our friend Dr. C.H. Moody, then organist at Ripon Cathedral.

House and garden began to look nice again and at last we found more time for organ playing and music, when on 16 September 1946 James died of another heart attack. He died in the same room where we first met, where Dea and I had given that little concert eleven years before. At his funeral I played on the small village organ Bach's chorale prelude "Sleepers, Wake".

GUNTER RAMIN AND FAMILY

Susi had befriended her organ-teacher, Gunter Ramin, organist at the Thomaskirche during her time in Leipzig (1933–1935).

The Ramin Family and Susi in Leipzig.

Frau Ramin and her son, Peter, having tea at Cleveland Lodge in October 1938. Gunter Ramin had a BBC radio broadcast on the 15th of October.

Susi and her three children, Michael, Christopher and Katharine, Cleveland Lodge, summer 1947.

Leon Goossens, the famous oboist, with the Jeans family, summer 1951.

Above: Visit of the Organ Club to Cleveland Lodge, 3rd June 1939.

Below: Visit of the International Congress of Organists, summer 1957.

We both had agreed years before that this was the piece we should like to have played at our funerals.

The next years were very difficult. I tried to find whatever consolation I could in my children and in my music. At one stage I thought I would have to give up Cleveland Lodge, and when Oxford University offered to buy James's organ for St. Mary's Church, I nearly sold it, but then at the last moment I could not face the empty organ chamber. So I kept both organs and Cleveland Lodge." [308, p. 8, 35.]

In her numerous concerts and radio broadcasts from the mid 30s onwards, Susi had significantly raised the level of the organ performing arts in the UK. She was a consummate interpreter of the works of Bach and his predecessors as well as modern works of Austrian organ composers. After the war her interests extended to old English music. She promoted the music not only of the three most famous early English composers William Byrd, John Bull and Orlando Gibbons (16th–17th centuries), written mainly for the virginal (the predecessor of the harpsichord) but also initiated the first modern performances of works by British composers such as John Dunstable (15th century), Thomas Preston, John Dowland, Thomas Campion, Jan Sweelinck, Henry Lawes (16th century), John Lugge, John Robinson and Henry Purcell (17th century). With that repertoire, which included not only little known, but also unpublished works, she performed in the UK, and toured Europe, America and Australia.

From 1951 Susi held annual music festivals and summer schools in Cleveland Lodge for organists and performers with master-classes on keyboard instruments — organs, harpsichords, clavichords, virginals and others (see pp.215–217). These instruments were part of a large collection which James had started with Susi's new organ in 1936 and later, in 1939, a two-manual pedal harpsichord by Maendler-Schramm of Munich. Susi was also involved in research work and published articles on musical instruments, the music of the Renaissance and the Baroque, and on English church organ music. She edited works of forgotten English composers: Robinson, Gerber, Lugge and others. Among her students are such famous musicians as Peter Hurford, David Lumsden, David Sanger, George Guest, Christopher Kent, and Peter Dickinson.

Susi was often invited as a jury member at various organ competitions. On several occasions in Leipzig in 1970 she sat on the jury together with the Professor of the Moscow Conservatory, Leonid Roizman, an outstanding organist and researcher of organ music. They appreciated each other's professional and human qualities and he held Susi to be one of the greatest representatives and founder of authentic musical performance — now such an important trend.

Susi among the judges and contestants at the 1970 International Bach Organ Competition in Leipzig. Leonid Roizman (Moscow Conservatory) is immediately to her left. Susi was the first woman to be on the jury, just as she had been the first lady organist to play at York Minster and at Kings College Chapel in Cambridge some thirty-five years before.

In 1966 Susi was elected an Honorary Fellow of the Royal College of Organists. Since 1959 she had been much involved in trying to protect historic organs from wanton modernisation that had befallen many instruments in England (see p.219). She was not successful in this, and even today they have no legal protection. However her vigorous campaign combined with a growing appreciation of the historical aspects of the performance of old music among organ builders and players led to the establishment of the British Institute Of Organ Studies in 1976. Her last public performance took place in June 1989 in Leeds at a symposium devoted to the 50th anniversary of the death of Franz Schmidt, and to his music and the theme of the Apocalypse in the Austrian and German music of the 1930s.

Despite her commitment to music and her family Susi managed to maintain her hobbies of climbing and skiing, and twice she climbed the Matterhorn. A wonderful oil painting of this spectacular snow-covered peak hung in her music room. In this room she died on January the 7th, 1993 — the very room where she had first met James in 1935 and where he had died in 1946. Seven years after Susi's death on the 15th of September 2000 two Commemorative Plaques on Cleveland Lodge were unveiled, one for her contribution to Music, the other for James's contribution to Science.

SUSI AND THE EUROPEAN ALPS

A love of mountains whether for walking, climbing or skiing was Susi's abiding passion until her last days. It was a passion passed on from her father Oscar Hock who was an accomplished alpinist at the turn of the century. Susi was a member of the Ladies Alpine Club with many 4000 metres peaks to her credit. In later years hung above the fireplace in her music room was a fine oil painting of the Matterhorn, a peak that Susi had climbed twice. Her attempts to instil in her children a love of the mountains met with only varying degrees of success.

Pontresina 1939 climbing expedition, Piz Palü, March 1939

Left to right:
Führer Koller, Miss Betty Crow, Michael Jeans, Susi Jeans, Hermione Blandy, Führer Hans Melchior

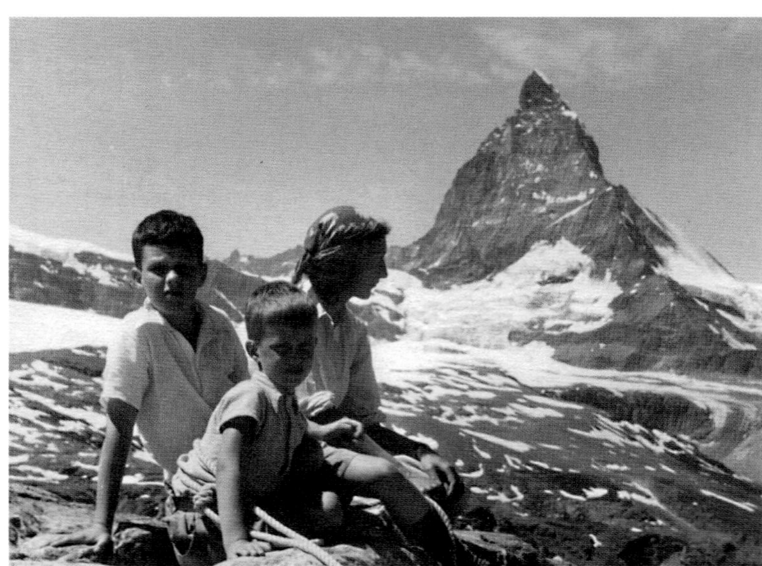

Zermatt, Switzerland, July–August 1946. Susi Jeans and her two sons (Michael and Pandi) on the Riffelhorn (2928 m) with the Matterhorn in the background. James accompanied his family to Switzerland but because of his health stayed in the lowlands at Montreux (390 m) on Lake Geneva.

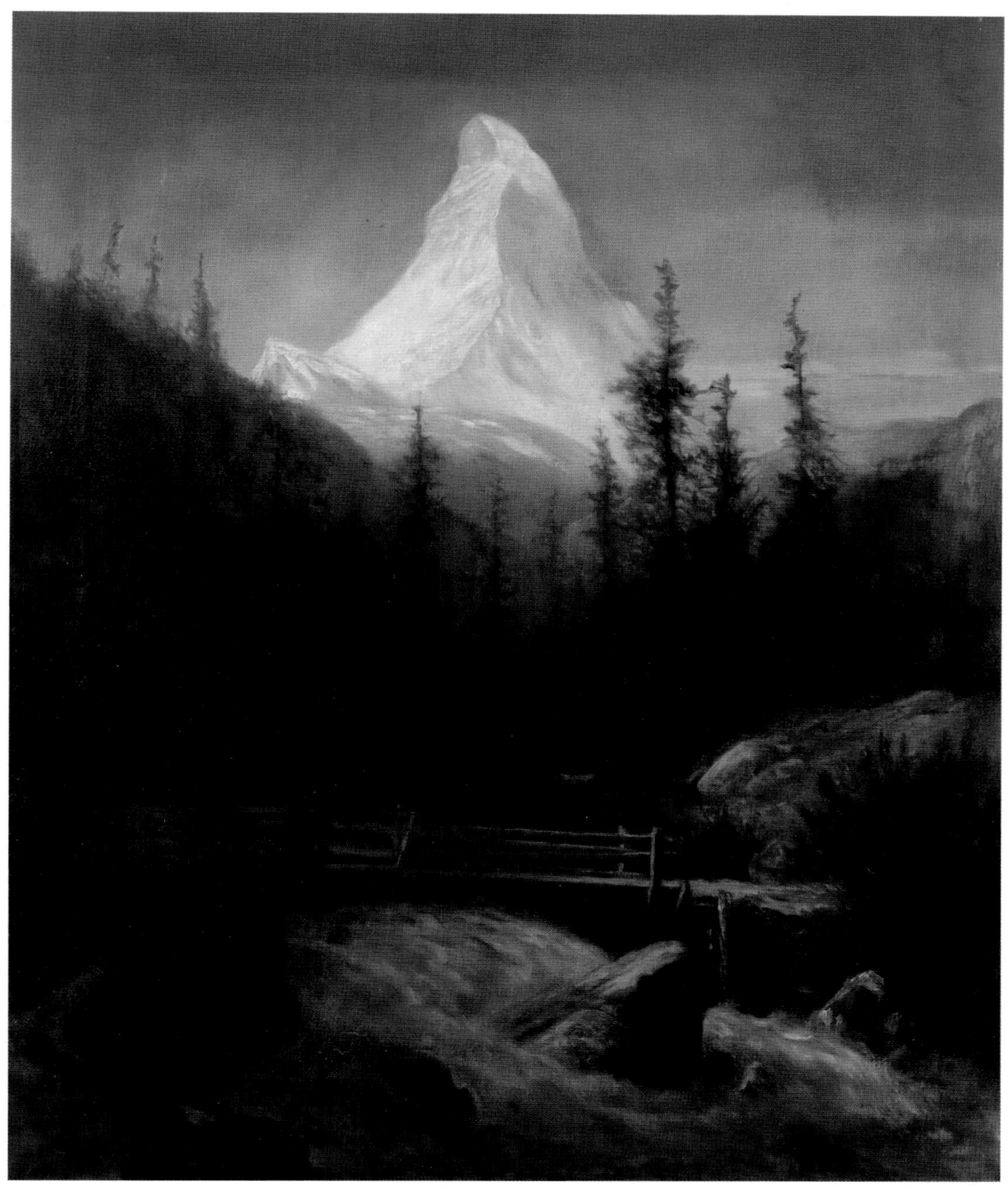

Painting of the Matterhorn that hung above the mantle piece in Susi's music room in later years.

REUNION OF THE JEANS AND HOCK FAMILIES IN 1952

Susi's siblings and her parents were a sociable outward looking and prosperous family in the relatively relaxed society of Vienna. Skiing, mountaineering, walking, and swimming and the comradeship of their friends and neighbours were an important part of the children's life. The Hock children seemed to have had limited respect for school. At times adverse school reports were extracted from the letterbox at the front gate of their newly built home and were fed to their Alsatian dog. Susi was so bad at school that she would have had to repeat the year or leave the school at the end of the year. She left and entered the Academie für Musik und Darstellende Kunst at the age of 14 years where she flourished.

A variety of circumstances led to Susi and her three siblings — Peter, Lisl and Nicki — leaving Austria before the start of the 2nd World War. Peter settled in England, Lisl in Eire, and Niki in the USA. Their parents stayed in Vienna and survived the war. Their father died in 1948. In spite of the geographical spread of the family they did their best to keep in contact. Their common love of skiing and the Alps helped bring them together. The last of these family reunions was in spring 1952 at Gaschurn, Montafon in the Vorarlberg, Austria. A page from the family photo album shows the party was made of up of their mother (Jekatarina Hock), Susi and her three siblings (Peter, Lisl and Niki), Maxi Hilber (a family friend and a ski mountaineer of unrivalled experience), and Susi's children — Michael, Katharine (Bubi), and Christopher (Pandi).

The Hock-Jeans families in Gaschurn, Montafon, Austria. 1952.

Michael
Peter
Maxi
Niki

BOXHILL MUSIC FESTIVAL

James's death in 1946 must have been a turning point in Susi's musical life. The financial strictures were severe and there was no way she could continue her prewar lifestyle. Downsizing and leaving Cleveland Lodge was the easy way out. She considered a number of properties in the general vicinity of Oxford. But her heart was not in such a "sensible" solution and her attachment to Cleveland Lodge ran deep. The idea of leaving Cleveland Lodge was not completely novel. When she had first married James he was toying with the idea. Perhaps he thought his new bride needed to set up her own household, or realised that to continue running a relatively large staff on his income without the support of Tiffany funds would be difficult. His new bride would have nothing of this and Susi slotted into Charlotte's Cleveland Lodge without trouble.

Susi was a very resourceful and feminine woman but by no means also easy to get on with. Her character is perhaps best summed up by the organ builder Henry Willis IV in an obituary. He had known Susi since she first came to England in the mid 1930s — "Your busy, untidy, vivacious, sincere, knowledgeable, musical, infuriatingly adorable, idiosyncratic personality". She was never frightened of using her talents, following her instinct and taking opportunities often in unexpected ways. Soon she set about organizing Cleveland Lodge, its garden, arable lands and cottages. Her use of a medley of barter, semi barter, market gardening and farming arrangements not only brought her children into contact with a wide selection of local people of different talents but always meant that very little money had to change hands. Cleveland Lodge and its estate carried on in this way until her death.

The success of the annual music festivals (1951–1993) was based on four factors — firstly Susi's reputation as an exceptionally talented and original musician well known to the public through radio broadcasts and recitals; secondly Cleveland Lodge was already a known centre of musical interest in the organ world before the war; thirdly it was still very much of a family home with a garden that set off wonderful views of Boxhill; and fourthly Susi managed to dragoon friends, neighbours, and her children to make sure there were no disasters leading up to or during the various festivals !

The first public concert that took place at Cleveland Lodge was the Festival of Britain Concert on the 22nd of September 1951. This was so successful that it was decided to found an annual music festival. Stephen Manton, who lived at that time at Westhumble and was the head of the Intimate Opera, joined the venture. Thus the Mickleham and Westhumble Festival was founded (1954–1966). The concerts were given with the support of the Arts Council of Great Britain and from 1964 onwards a grant was received from the Dorking Urban District Council (now the Mole Valley District Council). Concerts of the Mickleham and Westhumble Festival took place at Cleveland Lodge, at the Parish Church of Mickleham, while performances of the Intimate Opera at Mickleham Village Hall. Among the artists who have performed were Thurston Dart, Leon Goossens, Matyas Seiber, Antony Hopkins and Julian Bream: the policy of these concerts was to give performances by the best available professional musicians of early and contemporary music. In 1966 the festival was renamed the Boxhill Music Festival with two or three concerts at Cleveland Lodge arranged usually on consecutive weekends in late May or early June when the rhododendrons were in bloom. It was supported by the South-East Arts Association as well as by private donors and commercial companies.

The festival was one of the very first in England. Whether the idea had already been in the back of Susi's mind before the war is unknown. Certainly she was acquainted with John Christie of Glyndebourne who not only had built a large organ in his house in Sussex but initiated the Glyndebourne Opera Festival in 1934 that still continues today.

Susi's musical interests were wide, her musical friends numerous, and her address book extensive. She never seemed to be short of either persuading well known musicians to play for what must have been very modest fees, or finding the future generations of talent all too willing to be allowed to perform, or musical topics associated with the district, or all three — as can be appreciated from the selection of programmes shown.

Right: Various programmes from the Boxhill Festival.

Boxhill Music Festival 1972

Cleveland Lodge, Dorking

CONCERT

Alfred Deller
Counter Tenor

Susi Jeans
Organ, Harpsichord and Virginal

Friday 9th June at 8

This concert is given with financial assistance from the Dorking Urban District Council and the Arts Council of Great Britain

---

Boxhill Music Festival 1968

Cleveland Lodge, Dorking

Harpsichord Recital

by

Zuzana Ruzickova
(PRAGUE)

J. S. BACH

Goldberg Variations

Aria with 30 Variations for the Harpsichord with Two Manuals

Saturday 15th June at 8

This concert is given with the support of the Arts Council of Great Britain and of the Dorking Urban District Council.

Boxhill Music Festival 1972

Cleveland Lodge, Dorking

Harpsichord Recital

by

GILLIAN WEIR

Saturday 3rd June at 8

This concert is given with financial assistance from the Dorking Urban District Council and the Arts Council of Great Britain

---

MICKLEHAM AND WESTHUMBLE
MUSIC FESTIVAL 1962

A Concert

by

LÉON GOOSSENS

and

SUSI JEANS

at Cleveland Lodge, Westhumble

on Saturday, May 19th at 2.30 p.m.

This Concert is given with the support of the Arts Council of Great Britain

President:
H. M. Gordon Clark, Esq., J.P.

Chairman:
Lady Jeans

Hon. Treasurer: J. C. Howard, Esq.

Hon. Secretary: Mrs. Kay McLeod

Committee:
Mrs. H. M. Gordon Clark, Mrs. Cornell
Mrs. Hellyar, Mrs. Jennings, Mrs. McComish
Mrs. Statham, Mrs. Thorne, J. S. B. Buller, Esq.
Rev. J. Cornell, Stephen Manton-Bradbury, Esq.

Programme: One Shilling

Boxhill Music Festival

CLEVELAND LODGE, DORKING.

Music from Vauxhall Gardens

in honour of JONATHAN TYERS, founder, who lived at Denbies on Ranmore Common.

Sylvia Eaves	*Soprano*
Angus Smith	*Tenor*
Davitt Moroney	*Harpsichord*
Susi Jeans	*Organ*
David Jewel	*Flageolet*
David Jones	*Oboe*
Gerard McDonald	*Oboe and Flute*
Paul Carroll	*Bassoon*
String Ensemble	
Keith Gurry	*First Violin*
Michael Schofield	*Second Violin*
Gerald Manning	*Viola*
Charles Martin	*Cello*

SUNDAY, 17th. JUNE 1984 at 8 p.m.

This Concert is given with financial assistance from the South-East Arts, Boehringer Ingelheim International GmbH, National Employers Life Assurance Co. Ltd., Barclays Bank PLC., & Lloyds Bank PLC.

Rhododendrons in flower during the festival period. The brilliant yellow tree is a Turkish oak.

SUMMER SCHOOL FOR ORGANISTS & KEYBOARD PLAYERS

31st July - 5th August 1989 at Cleveland Lodge, Dorking, Surrey

DIRECTOR: Lady Jeans

****

Monday, 31st July

0900-0930	Registration	
0930-1045	GUY OLDHAM	Tuning and Temperament
1115-1230	ROBERT JUDD	Claudio Merulo & the Italian Stile antico tradition
1400-1515	ANN BOND	Mozart Church Sonatas
1545-1630	SUSI JEANS	My teachers & their methods: Franz Schütz, Franz Schmidt, Carl Straube and Charles-Marie Widor

Tuesday, 1st August

0930-1045	Prof. MICHAEL SCHNEIDER	Master Class on Max Reger and Johann Nepomuk David
1115-1230	" " "	" " " " " "
1400-1515	SUSI JEANS	Organ & Clavichord music by Walter Pach
1545-1630	(To be advised)	

Wednesday, 2nd August

0930-1045	BETTY MATTHEWS	James Hook
1115-1230	Dom L. BEVENOT, O.S.B.	Plainsong (with audience participation)
1400-1515	Dr. HARRY DIACK JOHNSTONE	The Performance of English 18th-century Music (T. Arne & W. Boyce)
1545-1630	" " "	" " " " "

Thursday, 3rd August

0930-1045	Prof. MICHAEL SCHNEIDER	The Straube tradition at Leipzig
1115-1230	Dr. DAVITT MORONEY	Master Class: C.P.E. Bach and contemporaries
1400-1515	" " "	" " " " " "
1545-1645	PETRONELLA DITTMER	Motet singing

Friday, 4th August

0930-1045	PETRONELLA DITTMER	Ideas from Violin Music of Fontana and Tartini for the Keyboard Player
1115-1230	Dr. DAVITT MORONEY	Preludes & Fugues by J.G. Albrechtsberger
1400-1515	HENRY WILLIS IV	Pipe-scaling and Voicing
1545-1630	GUY OLDHAM	Barrel Organs

Saturday, 5th August

0930-1045	TIMOTHY RISHTON	Problems of Complete Works of J.S. Bach
1115-1215	SUSI JEANS	Paul Hofhaimer (1459-1537), Organist to the Emperor Maximilian I

************************ F A R E W E L L L U N C H E O N *****************

(all are invited)

Tick if you wish to play in the Master Classes (see over) .....

APPLICATION FOR ADMISSION 31 July-5 August 1989

SUMMER SCHOOL FOR ORGANISTS & KEYBOARD PLAYERS

Name: .... Address: ....

....

Remittance enclosed for £ (payable to "CLEVELAND LODGE SUMMER SCHOOL")
(see over for details)

If not attending the whole course, please indicate below on which days you wish to attend:

....

SUMMER SCHOOL

About 1980 Susi started a weeklong summer school at Cleveland Lodge for organists and keyboard players that continued until her death in 1993.

The programme for the 1989 Summer School

MUSIC INSTRUMENTS AT CLEVELAND LODGE

Neither James nor Susi collected musical instruments in spite of the fact that at Susi's death there was a considerable number of keyboard instruments at Cleveland Lodge. These had been saved from destruction or were part of Susi's professional interest, not to mention the organ of a musical colleague and friend who could not fit it into his flat. There was James's organ built into his music room, and three other organs. The 'Manchester' organ had arrived in summer 1961 in a furniture removal van as a mass of collapsed pipes from the demolished chapel of a stately home near Manchester. It was accompanied by the Samuel Greene organ, and Guy Oldham's William Ayrton organ — as well as the Kirkman harpischord. In Susi's music room there was her neo-baroque organ, her pedal harpsichord, a Goff clavichord, and in the adjacent library was the Red Italian Virginals. The drawing room housed a grand piano, a mutilated historic organ and a variety of square pianos. In her bedroom there was her favourite Goff Clavichord. Scattered around the house were a range of smaller instruments including barrel organs, a water organ, monochords, etc..

Katherine, Susi's daughter and the only one of her three children who inherited her parents' musical talents, had her own woodwind instruments as well as a lute.

CLAVICHORDS

Susi 's relationship with her two clavichords made by T.R.C. Goff and J.C.Cobby was an intensely personal one — "such instruments should never fall into the hands of people who don't deserve them". Susi had a passionate conviction that the clavichord was the best training for any musician, Goff, a slightly eccentric aristocrat, only made instruments (harpsichords, lutes as well) for particular people where he could guarantee their appreciation. Susi was a very close friend. His clavichords were the most beautiful and sensitive of instruments. Each had its robust case that allowed them to accompany Susi not only on her long trip to the US but also on skiing holidays in the Alps. Her sons' responsibilities were to ensure that the robust case and its delicate contents came to no harm by being safely stowed away on a Transatlantic liner at Southampton or on the top of a Postbus on its way to a small village high in the Austrian Alps.

Susi Jeans playing one of her two clavichords by T. R. C. Gough and J. C. Cobby, 1964.

PEDAL HARPSICHORD

Purchased in August 1939, at cost of 5250 Reich-marks. Its payment got caught up in the 2nd World War — and there was much embarrassment when in 1947 the Custodian of Enemy Property seemed to have pocketed the money!

LUTE

Susi was keen that her daughter Katherine should play the lute. Initially one was borrowed from Guy Oldham but as a result of an unfortunate accident between a broom, her brother Christopher, and the instrument it was decided she had to have one of her own! Tom

Top left: Susi Jeans on the Maendler-Schramm (of Munich) Pedal Harpsichord (photo Varvara, late 1949).

Katherine playing the Goff lute in the drawing room at Cleveland Lodge with the portrait of her father in the background (Gerti Deutsch in the Tatler & Bystander of 17th June 1959).

Left: Susi Jeans playing her 16th century "red Italian Virginals" (photo John Sharp, September 1978).

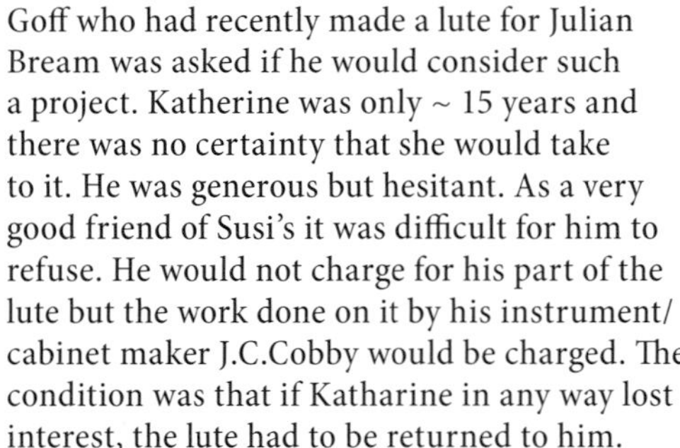

Goff who had recently made a lute for Julian Bream was asked if he would consider such a project. Katherine was only ~ 15 years and there was no certainty that she would take to it. He was generous but hesitant. As a very good friend of Susi's it was difficult for him to refuse. He would not charge for his part of the lute but the work done on it by his instrument/ cabinet maker J.C.Cobby would be charged. The condition was that if Katharine in any way lost interest, the lute had to be returned to him.

WATER ORGANS

In the 1950s Susi developed a particular interest in mechanical organs that were driven by water power, which not only turned the barrel with its keys but also provided sufficient air pressure for the pipes. Such instruments were described in historical accounts but there was doubt about whether they actually worked in practice (Jeans, S and Oldham, G. 1959. Water blown organs in the seventeenth century. The Organ, vol. 38, pp153–156). On a large scale such organs were probably part of the 16th and 17th water gardens of the Villa d'Este in Tivoli, near Rome. To prove that such a system was workable Susi's eldest son Michael — then an apprentice at Rolls Royce — was persuaded to build a working model using a small 16th mechanical organ that had been used for training birds to sing. By adjusting the water flow sufficient air pressure was built up in the chamber to sound the pipes, turn the water wheel that drove the barrel.

TUNES ON TAP

Calman

VISITORS to Box Hill, the famous Surrey beauty spot near Dorking, are likely to be startled by hearing the stirring tune of Rob Roy. This does not signify another Scottish invasion. It is merely **Lady Jeans**, 51-year-old widow of astronomer Sir James Jeans, playing a sixteenth-century water organ in the grounds of her eighteenth-century home.

Lady Jeans, a distinguished organist, delights in playing the instrument as loudly as possible to drown the noise of trippers who picnic on the hill above her estate. She simply inserts a tune reel, turns on a tap in the kitchen, and out rolls the music.

Lady Jeans told me: "Some of the reels inside have a few notches missing and the tunes are sometimes difficult to recognise. But they do silence the trippers."

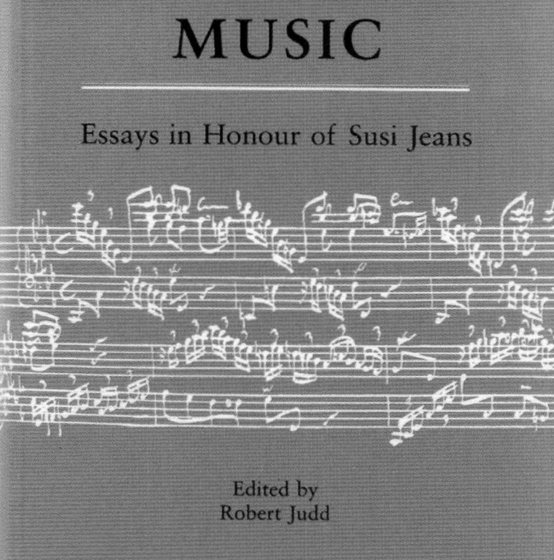

ASPECTS OF KEYBOARD MUSIC
Essays in Honour of Susi Jeans
Edited by
Robert Judd

Top left: Comments from the Daily Express (1962)

The bird organ with its water driven mechanism built by Michael Jeans.

The festschrift by her colleagues presented to Susi Jeans on her 75th birthday in 1986.

SUSI'S MUSIC ROOM

This was James's original music room where his first organ built by WM. Hill & Son and Norman & Beard was installed in 1925. With the construction of his new music room, the removal of his organ to its new home, and the installation of Susi's new neo-baroque organ in 1937 this room became the centre of Susi's life. It was so from the time of her marriage until her death in January 1993. It was in this room that she had first met James. He had died there, and so did she some 46 years later — as it was her wish. A room full of light it had fine views over the front lawns and Boxhill beyond. Within a short time it became the home of other instruments — a pedal harpsichord, the red Italian virginals, two clavichords and a bird organ. Susi is shown at one of her clavichords discussing a composition with Matyas Seiber the well-known Hungarian musician and composer who was killed in South Africa in a car crash in 1960. These scenes are from the 1950's and the 1960's before Susi's Matterhorn painting (see page 215) — acquired in the local auction house in Dorking — was hung over her fire place. Later her music room became increasingly cluttered with her books and research papers.

GREAT PACKINGTON AND THE BATTLE TO PRESERVE HISTORIC ORGANS

In the mid 1950s the last remaining organ closely associated with George Frideric Handel, his famous organ concertos, and England his adopted country was the instrument in the parish church at Great Packington, Leicestershire. The church is in the estate of the Earls of Aylesford. The organ was built in 1759 for a relative of the Aylesfords, Charles Jennens (1700–1773), a close friend and colleague of Handel. It had survived essentially unaltered, in good working order, still blown by hand, with its pipes tuned to the lower baroque pitch. It was an instrument that Susi knew well, she had played a recital on it on the 24th of November 1956, and in the following year had recorded a programme on the 25th and 26th of April. Around the same time Thurston Dart had recorded a programme for the BBC including various Handel's organ concertos using an orchestra with instruments of modern pitch. He got round the problem of the different pitches by transposing the organ part to match the higher pitch of the orchestral instruments. In July 1958 to mark the bicentenary of Handel's death Columbia Records recorded Handel's organ concertos on the Great Packington organ with an orchestra under Adrian Boult. Instead of using orchestral instruments tuned to the old pitch to match the organ, or transposing the organ part the pipes were cut and fitted with tuning slides to bring them up to modern pitch. This launched Susi on an extended battle for the preservation of historic organs with the hope of them gaining some legal protection as was widespread in Continental Europe or which protects historic houses in England. A flavour of this battle has been described in an article by Nicholas Thistlethwaite (Journal of the British Institute of Organ Studies 2016) dealing with the events leading up to the founding of the British Institute of Organ Studies in 1976:

"In 1968 Lady Susi Jeans wrote to the Musical Times as follows: "I would like to draw attention to the fact that we are in dire need in this country of an official body to look after the preservation and restoration of old organs. By 'old' I refer not only to the 17th- and 18th-century organs, but also those from the Victorian and Romantic periods; these instruments should not be 'baroquized' but left in their original state."

She went on to complain about the fitting of tuning slides and the replacement of mechanical with electric actions. Jeans, who was a distinguished player and teacher, had the advantage (arising from her Austrian background) of familiarity with the legislation that protected historic organs in many parts of mainland Europe, but her views were not welcomed by British organ-builders. Noel Mander — who should have been an ally — was incensed (and probably embarrassed) by her criticism of him for having fitted tuning slides to the Thomas Parker organ in Great Packington (1749) so that E. Power Biggs could record Handel organ concertos at modern orchestral pitch, and Cecil Clutton was infuriated by her equally outspoken criticism of the Organs Advisory Committee, of which he was joint secretary, for its pusillanimous approach, as Jeans saw it, to protecting historic instruments.

Jeans was not diplomatic but she had hit the nail on the head and had extended the debate to include the Victorian and Edwardian organs that many builders and organists regarded as ripe for modernisation."

Unfortunately even today historic organs still have no legal protection from ignorant or unscrupulous modification. Susi would have "turned in her grave" after her death in 1993 had she known that her early C19 "Manchester Organ", rescued in 1961 from a house demolition in the North and carefully restored by Fritz Abend, would have its pipes cut down and fitted with tuning slides in its new home at Lacock Abbey.

PHYSICS AND PHILOSOPHY

During his final years Jeans never stopped being interested in philosophical aspects of science. Many of his works touch upon philosophical problems, but Jeans's main opus devoted to this topic was definitely the monograph *Physics and Philosophy* (1942) [157]. This book presents a sum-total, as it were, of his views on the philosophical aspects of physics and astronomy and an outline of his worldview. In 1947, Jeans's fundamental monograph *The Growth of Physical Science* was published posthumously. In this he discusses not only the philosophical problems of physics, but also its history. However, the book's main philosophical ideas can be found in Jeans's earlier publications.

In literature on science Jeans's philosophical views are generally described as 'mentalism' — a variety of physical idealism. The philosophers V.V. Kazyutinsky and V.G. Torosyan note that the philosophical concept of 'mentalism' was heavily influenced by the ideas of Neo-Platonism, Neo-Positivism and Neo-Thomism [227; 271].

Jeans's philosophical views, like those of many other natural scientists of his time, contain certain inconsistencies and contradictions. For Jeans the philosopher, it is impossible to discuss his worldview and its foundations without mentioning God — the creator of all existence. However Jeans the natural scientist, in his discussions of specific scientific matters, often thinks as a materialist — it would probably have been impossible for him to successfully practice natural science otherwise. Jeans's statements are one thing but there is the question of his methodology: indeed, the important thing is not how a natural scientist defines themselves, but how they deal with the philosophical problems of science in practice.

Firstly Jeans's ideas about how philosophy relates to a concrete scientific discipline, namely physics. Whilst the answer to the basic question of philosophy is of the utmost importance. The correctness of the methodology of scientific analysis also depends on correct correlation between the philosophical and the scientific aspects of the problem discussed. That is the question Jeans raises in the first chapter of his *Physics and Philosophy*: the chapter is called 'What are Physics and Philosophy?' In it he discusses the nature of physical knowledge: 'The study of science provides us with such new knowledge because it is based on exact measurements. A physicist may announce, for instance, that the density of gold is 19·32, by which he means that the ratio of the weight of any piece of gold to that of a volume of water of equal size is 19·32; or that the wave length of the line Hα in the spectrum of atomic hydrogen is 0·000065628 centimetre, by which he means that the ratio of the length of a wave of Hα light to that of a centimetre is 0·000065628, a centimetre being defined as a certain fraction of the diameter of the earth, or of the length of a specified bar of platinum, or as a certain multiple of the wave-length of a line in the spectrum of cadmium.

These statements import real knowledge since each identifies a specific number, the idea of which is already in our minds, with the value of a ratio which has existence in the world outside; this idea of a ratio is again something with which our minds are familiar. Thus the statements tell us something new in a language we can understand.

Each ratio expresses a relation between two things neither of which we understand separately, such as gold and water. Our minds can never step out of their prison walls to investigate the real nature of the things — gold, water, atomic hydrogen, centimetres or wave-lengths — which inhabit that mysterious world out beyond our sense-organs. We are acquainted with such things only through the messages we receive from them through our senses, and these tell us nothing as to the essential nature of their origins. But our minds can understand and know ratios — which are pure numbers — even of quantities which are themselves incomprehensible. We can, then, acquire real knowledge of the external world of physics, but this must always consist of ratios, or, in other words, of numbers' [157, p. 7–8].

Here Jeans appears to be rather close to Berkeley (1685–1753) — he even uses the term 'idea' in its purely Berkeleian sense: 'It is evident to anyone who takes a survey of the objects of human knowledge, that they are either ideas actually imprinted on the senses, or else such as are perceived by attending to the passions and operations of the mind, or lastly ideas formed by help of memory and imagination, either compounding, dividing, or barely representing those originally perceived in the aforesaid ways' [204, p. 171].

'That neither our thoughts, nor passions, nor ideas formed by the imagination, exist without the mind, is what everybody will allow. And to me it is no less evident that the various sensations, or ideas imprinted on the sense, however blended or combined together (that is, whatever objects they compose), cannot exist otherwise than in a mind perceiving them' [204, p. 172].

'But, say you, though the ideas themselves do not exist without the mind, yet there may be things like them, whereof they are copies or resemblances, which things exist without the mind in an unthinking substance. I answer, an idea can be like nothing but an idea; a colour or figure can be like nothing but another colour or figure. If we look but never so little into our own thoughts, we shall find it impossible for us to conceive a likeness except only between our ideas' [204, p. 174].

All this was stated by the bishop George Berkeley in his main philosophical work, *A Treatise Concerning the Principles of Human*

Geo. Berkeley S.T.P.
Dec. Derensis.

Knowledge, Wherein the Chief Causes of Error and Difficulty in the Sciences, with the Grounds of Scepticism, Atheism, and Irreligion, Are Inquired Into, in 1710.

However, Jeans is aware of the limitations of Berkeleianism and raises some deep methodological questions regarding the gnoseological process; at the same time, his critique of subjective idealism usually only concerns particularities. For example, Jeans criticises Arthur Eddington's statement that it is possible to epistemologically demonstrate that the mass of the proton is 1837 times larger than the mass of the electron, saying that in the same way it would be possible to demonstrate that the mass of an apple is 1837 times larger than the mass of an orange [157, p. 76]. He gives numerous examples of differences in understanding by the physicists and the philosophers of, for example, the word 'red' and so forth. He concludes that the concepts the philosophers speak and think of are subjective, whereas those of the physicists are objective — which means it is as if they spoke different languages. In fact, there is no 'objective' red or blue colour in the sense of a sensation of red or blue without the perceiving subject; but there objectively exists such a thing as electromagnetic oscillations with certain wave lengths, that cause the subject to perceive red or blue. Jeans asserts, rather boldly, that the philosophers think only in qualitative concepts, whereas the physicists only in quantitative; he illustrates it with an old anecdote of an argument between two people who find a room either warm or cold depending on where they entered the room from. He notes, justly, that one's sensations are not indicative of heat or cold as such.

'We do not judge that an object is hot or cold, so much as that it is hotter or colder than something else' [157, p. 91].

Following Berkeley, Jeans criticises the distinction between the so-called primary qualities (solidity and extension) and secondary qualities (colour, warmth), since all of them are to do with the physics of a phenomenon. That is yet another point where the scientists and the philosophers had been focusing on different aspects of a phenomenon.

The problem of understanding the essence of a phenomenon requires an analysis of the concept of 'understanding' as such. It appears, especially in modern physics, to be closely related with the problem of demonstrability and modelling. In a section on pictorial representations of scientific concepts, Jeans observes: 'If we are to explain the workings of an organization or a machine in a comprehensible way, we must speak to our listeners in a language they understand, and in terms of ideas with which they are familiar — otherwise our explanation will mean nothing to them' [157, p. 10]. Visual ideas are the most helpful in this respect, and in classical physics such visual images satisfied the needs of science. Modern physics, however, requires highly abstract conceptions which do not have demonstrable analogues

Anglo-Irish philosopher Bishop George Berkeley (1685–1753) by John Smybert. Jeans's philosophic views on science were rather close to those of Berkeley.

or visual images that can be used for their interpretation. As was noted by Norwood Hanson, '[t]he price paid for this intellectual gain is unpicturability' [303, p. 122].

In *Physics and Philosophy* Jeans discusses the attempts at geometrical and mechanical explanations of nature made at different stages of the development of science, from antiquity to the recent decades; as none of them were successful, he pessimistically concludes: 'We see that we can never understand the true nature of reality' [157, p. 15].

Jeans considers mathematical descriptions of nature to be the most adequate: it is much discussed in his philosophical and popular works. He believes that the development of science leads towards a positivistic concept of physics, which to him means a refusal to try and uncover the essence of phenomena and limiting oneself to descriptions of their schemes through mathematical concepts — which are not even descriptions of nature, but descriptions of one's observations of nature. In this Jeans is a true supporter of positivism, according to which, 'a truly positive spirit mainly consists in replacing the study of the first and the final causes of phenomena with the study of their immutable laws; in other words, in replacing "why?" with "how?" [262, p. 81]. Likewise, his thoughts on the problem of exact measurements in physics and the importance of numbers discussed above are close to Auguste Comte's definition of mathematics as the science of indirect measurement that determines some quantities through other quantities, which can be measured directly, by means of exact relations that exist between them.

Jeans touches here upon a number of profound issues. Indeed, how does one explain, for example, 'the unreasonable effectiveness of mathematics in the natural sciences'? [208, p. 182]. And, although Eugene Wigner, in an attempt to answer this question, believes that there is 'something bordering on the mysterious and that there is no rational explanation for it', he also admits later on that 'the concepts of elementary mathematics and particularly elementary geometry were formulated to describe entities which are directly suggested by the actual world' [208, p. 184]. He then writes: 'Surely to the unpreoccupied mind, complex numbers are far from natural or simple and they cannot be suggested by physical observations. Furthermore, the use of complex numbers in quantum mechanics is not a calculational trick of applied mathematics but comes close to being a necessity in the formulation of its laws' [208, p. 189]. And concludes: 'This shows that the mathematical language has more to commend it than being the only language which we can speak; it shows that it is, in a very real sense, the correct language' [208, p. 190]. Indeed, our practice of cognition leads to the conclusion that nature speaks the language of mathematics. Richard Feynman, one of the creators of quantum electrodynamics, believes that 'physicists cannot make a conversion to any other language. If you want to learn about nature to appreciate nature, it is necessary to understand the language it speaks in. She offers her information only in one form; we are not so unhumble as to demand that she change before we pay any attention.

All the intellectual arguments that you can make will not communicate to deaf ears what the experience of music really is. In the same way all the intellectual arguments in the world will not convey an understanding of nature to those "of the other culture" [as C. P. Snow referred to representatives of the humanities in his 1959 Rede Lecture 'The Two Cultures' — A.K.]. Philosophers may try to teach you by telling you qualitatively about nature, I am trying to describe her. But it is not getting across because it is impossible. Perhaps it is because their horizons are limited in this way that some people are able to imagine that the centre of the universe is man' [277, p. 58–9].

Werner Heisenberg stated rather strongly that one should only study what can be measured — which is quite close to some thoughts expressed by Jeans. For Jeans, however, as in the philosophy of Benedict Spinoza, 'mathematics does not help us uncover the truth, it is the truth; it has an ontological meaning, it is not a method of cognition, but an object of cognition, the system of nature, that which makes nature a whole embracing all existence' [237, p. 233]. To Spinoza nature equals God; created nature equals creative nature and, as such, is God. Thus we can see the influence of Spinoza's philosophy on Jeans in the latter's famous conclusion that 'the Architect of the Universe' must be a mathematician. He first expressed this idea in 'The Mysterious Universe' — a popular essay that became hugely successful: 'We have already considered with disfavour the possibility of the universe having been planned by a biologist or an engineer; from the intrinsic evidence of this creation, clearly the Great Architect of the Universe now begins to appear as a pure mathematician' [122].

Let us now turn to the most characteristic excerpts of this work.

Jeans finds a fitting image to compare the expanding universe and the spacetime structure in the theory of general relativity: 'a soap-bubble, with irregularities and corrugations on its surface, is perhaps the best representation … of the new universe revealed to us by the theory of relativity' [He points out two main kinds of these irregularities, which he interprets as matter and radiation. — A.K.]

'We may think of the surface of the bubble as a tapestry whose threads are the world lines of atoms … As we move timewards along the tapestry, its various threads for ever shift about in space and so change their places relative to one another. The loom has been set so that they are compelled to do this according to definite rules which we call "laws of nature"…

Your consciousness touches the picture only along your world line, mine along my world line, and so on. The effect produced by this contact is primarily one of the passage of time … It may be that time, from its beginning to the end of eternity, is spread before us in the picture, but we are in contact with only one instant, just as the bicycle-wheel is in contact with only one point of the road. Then, as Weyl puts it, events do not happen; we merely come across them … ‘ [193, p. 62].

According to Jeans, waves that were once believed to spread in ‘ether’ are but an abstraction: ‘This quality of abstractedness in what were at one time regarded as material “ether-waves” recurs in a far more acute form when we turn to the system of waves which make up an electron. The “ether” in terms of which we find it convenient to explain ordinary radiation … has three dimensions in space in addition to its one dimension of time. So also has the ether in which we describe a single electron isolated in space, [though] this may not be the same ether as before. But a single electron isolated in space provides a perfectly eventless universe, the simplest conceivable event occurring when two electrons meet one another. To describe [this] …, wave-mechanics asks for a system of waves in an ether which is of seven dimensions … Most physicists would agree that the seven-dimensional space … of two electrons is purely fictitious, in which case the waves which accompany the electrons must also be regarded as fictitious … Yet it is hard to see how one can attribute a lower degree of reality to the one set of waves than to the other: it is absurd to say that the waves of one electron are real, while those of two electrons are fictitious’ [193, p. 63].

Jeans then goes on to interpret them as waves of probability and mentions Heisenberg’s uncertainty principle, according to which it is ‘impossible ever to say: an electron is just here’ [193, p. 63]. He also states that, since the idea of waves is a symbolic expression of our knowledge of the probable state and position of an electron, ‘they change as our knowledge changes, and so become largely subjective. Thus we need hardly to think of the waves as being located in space and time at all; they are mere visualizations of a mathematical formula of an undulatory, but purely abstract, nature’ [193, p. 63]. Then he states that it is necessary to go even further and deny the possibility of atomic phenomena occurring in space and time.

Kaziutinsky points out in his work [227] that there is an echo of neo-Platonic ideas in Jeans’s views: ‘According to Jeans, the material world is rather an appearance than a reality. He illustrates his thought referring to Plato’s analogy of the cave. We are like prisoners of an underground cave, says the Greek philosopher. The fire burning in the cave projects shadows of people and things behind them onto the wall. These shadows are all the prisoners can observe, and they inevitably think they are something real. However, they have no idea of what the actual things are that they see the shadows of. Jeans tries to connect the allegory of the cave with modern physics: ‘Thus the walls of the cave in which we are imprisoned are space and time; the shadows of reality which we see projected on the walls by the sunshine outside are the material particles which we see moving against a background of space and time, while the reality outside the cave which produces these shadows is outside space and time' [157, p. 193–4]. 'The meaning of this comparison is that the material world does not cover "all existence". Moreover, it is the world of appearances. The real reality, generating physical phenomena, is outside the "cave" — out of space and out of time' [227, p. 53–4].

'Just as the shadows on a wall form the projection of a three-dimensional reality into two-dimensional, so the phenomena of the space-time continuum are four-dimensional projections of realities which occupy more than four dimensions, so that events in time and space become

No other than a moving row
Of Magical Shadow-shapes that come and go.

... The essential fact is simply that all the pictures which science now draws of nature, and which alone seem capable of according with observational facts, are mathematical pictures' [193, p. 64].

Jeans insists we should abandon the discussions, which he considers fruitless, of whether it is possible to uncover the nature of reality, because we have nothing but appearances to compare it with. He believed that 'the true essence of things' could never be known. Only the laws that govern the changes in things can be discussed and compared with abstractions created by our own mind.

Jeans did realise that this thesis could be criticised. First of all, there is a possibility of ascribing a certain structure to nature according to our own preconceptions. Thus, a musician might think of the world as a giant musical instrument, while a Cubist painter might see it as a pile of cubes. History teaches us, he says, that it is not possible to achieve a comprehensive description in this way: as an example, he tells the story of our distant ancestors who tried to interpret nature in anthropomorphic terms, as well as of our more recent predecessors and their unsuccessful attempts to understand all nature through mechanical concepts.

Secondly, Jeans's statements could be challenged based on a lack of a clear boundary between pure and applied mathematics: a lot of concepts of pure mathematics are in fact based on natural phenomena, although such origins are disguised by abstract formulae. Jeans thinks that regardless of whether the laws of nature impact our thinking or our thinking is projected on the laws of nature, there is enough evidence that the creator of the universe is a mathematician.

Jeans believes that modern science has come, albeit via a different path, to the same kind of idealism as professed by Berkeley centuries earlier: the 'objectivity [of objects] arises from their subsisting "in the mind of some eternal spirit"' [193, p. 66]. Contradicting himself, however, Jeans says that that does not detract from the substantiality of things or the reality of the external world. He quotes the phrase of Chalmers Mitchell: 'the element of surprise is sufficient warrant for external reality ... a second warrant being permanence with change — permanence in your own memory, change in externality' [193, p. 66]. Jeans uses this witty remark as an argument against solipsism. 'We go beyond the mathematical formula at our own risk', he said — a risk, however, Jeans never tired of taking [193, p. 67].

Jeans raised a complex question of models of physical phenomena, which is still at the centre of attention of philosophers and natural scientists alike.

'The making of models or pictures to explain mathematical formulae and the phenomena they describe is not a step towards, but a step away from, reality; it is like making graven images of a spirit. And it is unreasonable to expect these various models to be consistent with one another as it would be to expect all the statues of Hermes, representing the god in all his varied activities — as messenger, herald, musician, thief and so on — to look alike. Some say that Hermes is the wind; if so, all his attributes are wrapped up in his mathematical description, which is neither more nor less than the equation of motion of a compressible fluid. The mathematician will know how to pick out the different aspects of the equation which represent the conveying and announcing of messages, the creation of musical tones, the blowing away of our papers, and so forth. He will hardly need statues of Hermes to remind him of them, although, if he is to rely on statues, nothing less than a whole row, all different will suffice' [193, p. 67–8]. After which Jeans sarcastically remarks: 'all the same, the mathematical physicist is still busily at work making graven images of the concepts of wave-mechanics' [193, p. 68].

It is clear today that the properties of the microcosm are reflected in the properties of formal-logical models, and that the idea of 'model' is becoming more and more abstract.

Jeans admits that metaphysics [as an idea of reality lying outside our consciousness — A.K.] is connected to physics, but they both have their own, distinct and independent, areas. However, Jeans lacks his own, original understanding of philosophy: 'For then we must agree with Comte that the task of physics is to discover and formulate laws, while that of philosophy is to interpret and discuss' [157, p. 17]. And again: 'The métier of the philosopher is to synthesize and explain facts already known; that of the scientist is in large part to discover new facts' [157, p. 96]. However, he is in doubt: 'But the physicist can warn the philosopher in advance that no intelligible interpretation of the workings of nature is to be expected' [157, p. 17]. The latter statement contradicts what he states later on: 'Because we are human beings and not mere animals, we try to discover as much as we can about the world in which our lives are cast. We have seen that there is only one method of gaining such knowledge — the method of science, which consists in a direct questioning of nature by observation and experiment.

The first thing we learn from such questioning is that the world is rational; its happenings are not determined by caprice but by law. There exists what we have called a 'pattern of events', and the primary aim of physical science is the discovery of this pattern. This, as we have seen, will be capable of description only in mathematical terms' [157, p. 174]. Thus, we can see Jeans agreeing with a positivist definition of philosophy and concluding that the external world is real and rational.

Jeans writes: 'But we not only wish to predict phenomena, but also to understand them' [157, p. 174]. However, quite pessimistically, he continues: '[W]e could never be sure that any model corresponded to reality. In brief, we can never have certain knowledge as to the nature of reality' [157, p. 175]. And later: 'The true object of scientific study can never be the realities of nature, but only our observations of nature' [157, p. 175–6]. Here we approach the question of the relationships between philosophy and natural science. We have already seen how keen Jeans was to find an answer to this question.

Jeans was not satisfied with what science had achieved in its explanation of phenomena; his inquisitive mind of a scientist needed to understand the 'first cause' of things. It should be noted that he was not alone in his endeavours. Such great scientific minds as Albert Einstein, Niels Bohr, Werner Heisenberg and Erwin Schrödinger were all highly interested in philosophy and tried to interpret the revolutionary changes in scientific worldview. Dissatisfied with the increasingly formal spirit of science, Schrödinger wrote that science that only describes the world, but does not answer the question, why it works this way and not some other way is but empty theory. But what does this help us understand? A distinguished physicist and one of the creators of the theory of electroweak unification, Steven Weinberg, said in his Nobel lecture in 1979 that the important methods were 'not mathematical methods which can make sense of an infinite variety of physically irrelevant theories, but methods which carry constraints, because these constraints may point the way toward the one true theory. In particular, I was impressed by the fact that quantum electrodynamics could in a sense be derived from symmetry principles and the constraints of renormalizability' [207, p. 205]. In the same lecture he said: 'Our job in physics is to see things simply, to understand a great many complicated phenomena in a unified way, in terms of a few simple principles. At times, our efforts are illuminated by a brilliant experiment, such as the 1973 discovery of neutral current neutrino reactions. But even in the dark times between experimental breakthroughs, there always continues a steady evolution of theoretical ideas, leading almost imperceptibly to changes in previous beliefs' [207, p. 201].

Indeed, the worldview physics has arrived at is subject to constant re-examination and concretisation; fundamental changes in physical theories bring about more abstract and deeper concepts, and older concepts turn out to be just extreme cases thereof. Philosophical ideas about the world, however, arise as an abstraction from the analysis of the whole cultural system of a given era throughout the entire history of philosophy. In the words of Werner Heisenberg, '[O]ne can scarcely say that one gains much by expressing modern knowledge in an old language. The philosophic systems of the past were formed from the bulk of knowledge available at their time and from the lines of thought to which such knowledge had led. Certainly one should not expect the philosophers of many hundreds of years ago to have foreseen the development of modern physics of the theory of relativity. Therefore, the concepts to which the philosophers were led in the process of intellectual clarification a long time ago cannot possibly be adapted to phenomena that can only be observed by the elaborate technical tools of our time' [210, p. 93]. Therefore, we often face objective difficulties when searching for a philosophical interpretation of discoveries that break the boundaries of earlier conceptual systems.

We are approaching a problem raised by Jeans which is still actively discussed: the problem of the boundaries between philosophy and natural science. These boundaries are needed in order to provide a mutual understanding, without which a fruitful cooperation of the philosophers and the natural scientists is impossible. The forms of interaction between natural science and philosophy changed through history. In the past, natural philosophy was a great influence on the development of natural science. For example, it put forward the idea of atomism. However, mid-nineteenth century marks 'the end of natural philosophy'. This meant a significant change in the relationships between natural science and philosophy. The role of philosophy as logic, methodology and epistemology of natural science comes to the foreground (see [228]).

A methodological work of the distinguished physicist and Nobel laureate Vitaly Ginzburg contains a section entitled 'Philosophy and Natural Science: Where does the boundary lie?' [213, p. 25]. In it, Ginzburg emphasises that philosophy should not replace specific sciences in solving concrete problems: it cannot answer questions that arise in the course of development of natural sciences. However, it is known to have happened sometimes. What was the reason?

Ginzburg gives a very clear answer: 'The general reason is that in the past philosophers not only accumulated, but also absolutised the views formed by natural sciences in the preceding era'. And concludes: 'Hence the attempts to deny new ideas, attempts which seem especially justified to those who think they have finally found the philosopher's stone' [211, p. 97].

It is for these precise reasons that Jeans's cosmogonic hypothesis was criticised in Soviet literature from a philosophical viewpoint. It should be made clear that we are not talking here about Jeans's philosophical views in general, but about a concrete natural-scientific hypothesis, whose strengths and weaknesses should only be discussed from the point of view of scientific facts and physical concepts.

Does the extreme rarity of two stars coming close to one another in our Galaxy, which, according to Jeans, is necessary for the formation of new planetary systems, make his hypothesis weak — as some authors thought [267]? From the point of view of modern science it does not.

First of all, the probability of stars coming close together was calculated based on average distances between the stars in the Galaxy around the Sun. However, there is reason to believe that when a planetary system was being formed around the Sun — that is, no less than 5 billion years ago (and other such systems may have been formed much earlier) — the average distance between stars was significantly smaller. This idea underlies modern catastrophic cosmogonic hypotheses, like that of Michael Woolfson [328; 327; 298]. Besides, the distances between stars in star clusters, especially globular clusters, and in the central regions of the Galaxy appear to be much smaller.

Secondly, is the low probability of formation of planetary systems really that unacceptable? It is important, however, that even an abundance of planetary systems does not disprove the catastrophic hypothesis in principle.

A cosmogonic theory in particular cannot be disproved based on conclusions that can be made about the prevalence of life in the universe. Such prominent scientist as Otto Yulievich Schmidt, of course, realised it: 'What constituted, in the eyes of astronomers, a flaw of Jeans's theory — the low probability, that is, rarity of the process of formation of planets — became its main virtue in the eyes of non-specialists unwilling to break up with religion. Jeans's hypothesis was the most suitable compromise. The rarity of planet formation on Jeans's scheme is, of course, not idealism in itself — there are rare phenomena in nature — but it opened the gates for idealism in cosmogony' [239, p. 22–3].

Of course, the connection between a methodological approach and the validity of a particular scientific theory is a delicate matter, and not always unambiguous. Jeans's cosmogonic theory as such is unrelated to philosophy, and most of the criticism arises, as we just saw, from an incorrect understanding of the 'boundary' between philosophy and natural science. Philosophy is not meant to solve problems that are within the subject of natural science; and a truly scientific philosophy will never impose its postulates, like a dictator, on concrete sciences.

Jeans begins the final chapter of his main philosophical work with a recapitulation of the problems discussed earlier. He points out the nontriviality of the fact that the world we live in is rational — that is, everything that happens in it is defined by laws as opposed to being random. He also insists that the mechanical pictures of the world are bound to fail. In the next section, dedicated to the particle-picture and the wave-picture, he makes a subjectivist conclusion that quantum mechanical determinism does not control events, but our knowledge of events.

In the section 'New Philosophical Principles' Jeans lays out the views of modern positivism, sharing the view that many philosophical difficulties can in fact be reduced to linguistic problems. '[He who is] content with a positivist conception of the aims of science will feel that he is in an entirely satisfactory position; he has discovered the pattern of events, and so can predict accurately, what more can he want?' [157, p. 180]. Jeans speaks about the probabilistic nature of knowledge: 'In real science also a hypothesis can never be proved true. If it is negated by future observations we shall know it is wrong, but if future observations confirm it we shall never be able to say it is right, since it will always be at the mercy of still further observations' [157, p. 181]. As Kazyutinsky noticed, Jeans anticipates here Karl Popper's concept of 'falsifiability': 'A theory should be considered scientific if, and only if, it is falsifiable'.

Jeans also promotes the principle of simplicity: according to it, out of two possible hypotheses the one should be favoured which is more simple. As physicists say, a true physical theory should be beautiful. This idea was expressed as early as Philo of Alexandria: 'What is not rational is ugly'. It plays a prominent role in modern views as well. As Steven Weinberg said in his Nobel lecture: 'Symmetry principles made their appearance in twentieth century physics in 1905 with Einstein's identification of the invariance group of space and time. With this as a precedent, symmetries took on a character in physicists' minds as a priori principles of universal validity, expressions of the simplicity of nature at its deepest level' [207, p. 201].

In the section 'The New Picture of Modern Physics' Jeans approaches philosophical interpretations of such essential physical concepts as space and time. He concludes: 'This leads us to postulate the existence of a world of photons and matter, existing in ordinary space; it is what the plain man describes as the material world.

So far this material world has been nothing more than a mental construct private to ourselves; the space is our perceptual space, and may have no existence outside our own consciousness' [157, p. 191].

Here Jeans definitely is, once again, close to Berkeley, who states that 'the philosophic consideration of motion does not imply the being of an absolute Space, distinct from that which is perceived by sense and related bodies; which that it cannot exist without the mind is clear upon the same principles that demonstrate the like of all other objects of sense' [204, p. 116].

Like Berkeley, Jeans declares space a non-existent essence. They both do it based on their critique of Newton's idea of absolute space. One should note Berkeley's insightfulness when he points out relativity of space and time — something which for Jeans was an established physical fact (special theory of relativity was shaped in 1905 and general theory of relativity in 1916). He wrote: 'Thus, we conclude, with a high degree of probability that the space-time unity and the objects which figure in it cannot be mere structures of our individual minds, but must have existences of their own, although we know that space and time separately are abstractions of our individual minds from the space-time unity' [157, p. 192].

Another strong influence on Jeans in the formation of his philosophical interpretation of space was Ernst Mach, who was not only a prominent physicist, but also a philosopher. Einstein wrote that he had been much influenced, directly or indirectly, by the works of Hume and Mach [287, p. 29]. Mach undertook a deep critical analysis of Newton's ideas of absolute time and space that form the foundation of classical physics and approached a relativist understanding of time and space. He wrote: 'This absolute time can be measured by comparison with no motion; it has therefore neither a practical nor a scientific value; and no one is justified in saying that he knows aught about it. It is an idle metaphysical conception' [245, p. 49].

In his discussion of cosmological models of the universe, Jeans talks about its being finite or infinite in time and space depending on concrete astronomical findings. This view was heavily criticised: 'Jeans's agnosticism is also expressed in his determination to establish temporal and spatial limitedness of the world' [281, p. 9]. This question, however, is not a philosophical one and cannot, therefore, be solved by philosophical methods. Vitaly Ginzburg writes in this regard: 'The question of finiteness or infinity of the volume of three-dimensional space is thus made into some a priori category. The vast majority of physicists and astronomers do not see any grounds for such an implication and consider the question of the volume of the universe to be a natural-scientific one and one to be solved on the basis of observation' [213, p. 27].

Even in his popular works Jeans tries to explain to the reader that there are no reasons that might make it difficult to recognise the limitedness of space. He also believes that time is limited, too, at least in the sense that it had a beginning. He wrote that there must have been a time before which the universe did not exist. And although Jeans used scientific arguments, he had a bias towards the transcendental act which he called 'creation' of the universe at a time that is not infinitely distant from ours. The universe in its present form could not have existed forever; but it should be noted that cosmological models with 'finite' time do not lead to religious conclusions. Here is what one of the creators of the 'Big Bang' theory and the President of the Papal Academy in Vatican, Monseigneur Georges Lemaître, said about interpretations of the Big Bang theory at the XI Solvay Congress on cosmology in 1958: 'As far as I can see, such a theory remains entirely outside any metaphysical or religious question. It leaves the materialist free to deny any transcendental Being. He may keep, for the bottom of space-time, the same attitude of mind he has been able to adopt for events occurring in nonsingular places in space-time' [213, p. 28].

At the same time, Jeans's concept of finite time of existence of the universe and 'heat death' as its final and fixed state is something to be criticised. His conclusion stemmed from an inadmissible extrapolation of the second law of classical thermodynamics — which is only true for closed systems — onto the whole universe. The expanding universe must be studied on the basis of relativistic thermodynamics. This issue was analysed rigorously for the first time by Richard Tolman in 1934. He comes to the conclusion: 'At the very least it would seem wisest, if we no longer dogmatically assert that the principles of thermodynamics necessarily require a universe which was created at a finite time in the past and which is fated for stagnation and death in the future'. [270, p. 458].

Jeans's approach to the problem of the correlation between determinism and freedom of will is also interesting. He criticised causality in the form in which it was understood by Kant and Bertrand Russell. He wrote that according to modern scientific views there is no reason to believe that events happening in the world could be divided, as it were, into separate phenomena and 'they are strung in pairs, as a row of dominoes, each being the cause of the event which follows and at the same time the effect of that which precedes' [157, p. 103]. On the whole, however, Jeans was inclined towards determinism, although not of the mechanistic kind. He gives multiple examples illustrating the fact that a human being's idea of their own will is but an illusion. He, therefore, insists that those who promote the concept of free will should define exactly what they mean by it and how it is different from unconscious determinism. At the same time, he wrote: 'The old physics showed us a universe which looked more like a prison than a dwelling-place. New physics shows us a universe, which looks as though it might conceivably form a suitable dwelling-place for free man, and not a mere shelter for brutes — a home in which it may at least be possible for us to mould events to our desires and live lives of endeavour and achievement' [157, p. 216].

Although, as we saw above, Jeans shared many of Berkeley's views, he did not accept the argument about the existence of primary and secondary qualities, as well as one of Berkeley's central arguments that all existence is ideas of the mind, because thoughts of the mind cannot affect matter. However, Jeans blurs the line between the scientific and the metaphysical approach and attempts to use scientific data for his idealistic philosophical conclusions. The questions posed by Jeans are global ones: what is more fundamental — thought or matter? Can we, along with Berkeley, assume that the duration of an object's existence is the duration of the existence of the thought in which it exists — a thought of God? What is the absolute thought which comprises all our individual thoughts? These questions, which one could call theological, Jeans tries to answer from within the study of physical reality, thus trying to breathe new life into the old dualism in the style of Descartes, that of thought and matter. He believes that they cannot remain antagonistic, mutually exclusive — instead, they become complementary. However, one controls the other: in the same way as waves (of matter) control a corpuscle, thought controls matter. This is closely connected to Jeans's idea of the creator of the universe being a mathematician. In fact, theologians strongly criticised Jeans precisely because his idea of God was limited to mathematics and did not contain any idea of him as the judge etc.

But is it even possible to reflect objective reality by means of mathematics alone? This idea implies that the creator has a mind which creates the world according to mathematical laws.

Jeans's idea of a creator-mathematician led him to suggest the existence of new laws of physics in the universe. As was noted earlier, Jeans was a representative of the 'optimistic' trend which insists that the data of astronomical observations can lead to discovering new laws of physics.

In another important worldview issue, however, Jeans can rather be regarded as a 'pessimist'. The issue in question is the prevalence of life in the universe. Jeans said that, although nineteenth-century astronomers had asserted that there are millions of stars surrounded by planets which may support life, this cannot be corroborated by modern cosmogonic and general astrophysical data. He writes: 'The three centuries and more which have elapsed since Giordano Bruno expressed his belief in an infinite number of worlds have changed our conception of the universe almost beyond description, but they have not brought us appreciably nearer to understanding the relation of life to the universe. We can still only guess as to the meaning of this life which, to all appearances, is so rare. Is it the final climax towards which the whole creation moves, for which the thousands of millions of years of transformation of matter in uninhabited stars and nebulae, and of waste of radiation in desert space, have been only an incredibly extravagant preparation? Or is it a mere accidental and possibly quite important by-product of natural processes, which have some other and more stupendous end in view? Or, to glance at a still more modest line of thought, must we regard it as something of the nature of a disease, which affects matter when it has lost the high temperature with which most of the matter in the universe would at once destroy life? Or, throwing humility aside, shall we venture to imagine that it is the only reality, which creates, instead of being created by, the colossal masses of the stars and nebulae and the almost inconceivably long vistas of astronomical time?

Again it is not for the astronomer to select between these alternative guesses; his task is done when he has delivered the message of astronomy' [170, p. 391–3].

While this is not the place to discuss the problem of Communication with Extraterrestrial Intelligence (CETI) in any detail, let us just note that there is more and more research that leads to the same conclusion as Jeans's about life being an extremely rare phenomenon in the universe. For example, such was the conclusion of Iosif Shklovsky, once one of the most ardent champions of the idea of multiple inhabited worlds in the universe: 'Thus, it seems that the conclusion that we are alone, if not in the Universe, then at least in our Galaxy or even in the local system of galaxies, can presently be proven no less solidly, and even much more solidly, than the traditional concept of the multiplicity of inhabited worlds. And we think that this conclusion (or even a mere possibility thereof) has extreme philosophical importance' [283, p. 273].

Jeans also understood that the position of man in the complex hierarchy of cosmic formations as the intelligent being is far from being accidental. These ideas later found a brilliant confirmation in the research of life from the viewpoint of physics [285]. Later discoveries showed that it is no accident that humanity exists at this exact stage of the development of our universe, the expanding universe. It is possible that the evolution of the universe is such that it inevitably had to lead to the emergence of intelligent life. Here is what Yakov Borisovich Zeldovich writes about it: 'The idea of spontaneous birth of multiple, or even an infinite number of, worlds is anything but new. The assumption that our universe is special because of the possibility of intelligent life in it has also been discussed for a long time. This idea has received a name — the Anthropic Principle.' He continues: 'For a prolonged expansion, the initial perturbations of the quantum born universe have to be small, for it is strong perturbations that lead to the birth of real particles .... The condition of smallness of perturbations may be due to the anthropic principle: perturbed worlds live for too short a time .... The author is also aware of the arbitrariness and obscurity of the concept of "birth" itself. Does the birth occur out of nothing, or in the space of a larger number of perturbations of measurement, or as a topological separation from the initially specified Minkowski space? Can one compare the probability of the birth of different worlds?' [221, p. 579–81].

We can see how complex the relations between biological, physical and astronomical problems are, including such a global problem as the birth and evolution of our universe, as well as the problem of the existence of life and particularly its highest form — intelligent life.

To conclude this section, it seems appropriate to cite Albert Einstein who, in his discussion with Murphy, said with regard to Jeans's philosophical views — as well as those of other natural scientists who attached themselves to certain 'fashionable' philosophical systems without any particular grounds: 'No physicist believes that the outer world is a derivative of consciousness. Otherwise he wouldn't be a physicist. Neither did the physicists you have mentioned. You must distinguish between what is a literary fashion and what is a scientific pronouncement. These men are genuine scientists and their literary formulations must not be taken as expressive of their scientific convictions' [287, p. 163].

Olivia Jeans, by Pearl Freeman, Piccadilly, London. Possibly for her engagement to Gordon Smith. Early 1930's

JBILEE.

SS, CALCUTTA, 1938.

3. M. Sen—Local Secretary.

. The Hon. Mr. Justice Costello. Dr. F. W. Aston. Prof. A. H. R. Buller. Mrs. Simonsen. Sir P. C. Ray. Prof. J. L. Simonsen.
General President. Prof. Winifred Cullis. Sir J. B. Henderson. Prof. W. Straub. Sir U. N. Brahmachari, President Medical
dent, Geology Section. Dr. A. L. du Toit. Mr. J. M. Caie. Dr. W. G. Ogg. Mr. J. Mc Farlane. Mr. T. S. Dymond. Mrs. Howarth.

R. Ruggles Gates. Mr. R. H. Kinvig. Mrs. Tattersall. Prof. Ernest Barker. Prof. W. T. Gordon. Dr. Baini Prasad.
rof. M. N. Saha. Prof. J. C. Ghosh. Prof. J. E. Lennard-Jones. Sir Lewis L. Fermor. Mrs. Arbour Stephens. Prof. W. Bothe.

P. Ghosh. .... Mr. J. Bose. Dr. A. L. Narayan. Rao Ramswami Iyyengar Bahadur. Dr. B. B. Sarkar.
Prof. G. D. Hale Carpenter. Miss Blackman. Prof. V. H. Blackman.
rak Roy Chowdhury. Dr. P. C. Biswas.

Photo by Mukherjee Studio, 186, Bowbazar St., Calcutta, India

J. H. Jeans, colleagues and research students from the Chemical Laboratories at Benares Hindu University, India, 28th December 1937.

(photo: Chakraverty Studio)

Left to right
1st Row, Sitting —
K.R. Rao; V.T.S. Rao; Subbayya; M.A. Siva Ram; N.B.V.K. Rao; Chandrakanth; V.J. Caldwell; K.S. Venket Raman, M.Sc.

2nd Row —
Prof. Lennard Jones, FRS;
Mrs Simonsen; Prof. Simonsen, FRS;
Sir James H. Jeans, FRS;
Prof. Baly, FRS; Mrs Baly; Mrs Joshi.

3rd Row —
Miss L. Kamalamma; Miss K.M. Yesoda;
Mrs Annapurna S. Rao;
Sarju Prasad, M.A., M.Sc;
Prof. P.S. Varma; S.P. Rao.

Standing —
Gopalachar; S.S. Rao; V.A.C. Menon;
D.N. Solanki, M.Sc; S.S. Joshi, D.Sc (London);
T.D. Bhaskar; K. Srinivasan; N.P. Parekh;
Miss S. Visalakshi; Gopikrishna Das;
S.M. Sastri; K.S. Visvanathan, M.Sc;
G.K. Nair; G.R. Phansalkar, M.Sc;
K. Subramanian; R.J. Hari Rao, M.Sc;
V. Narasimham; J.D. Kochar.

Absentees —
A. Purushotham, M.Sc;
S.R. Bagheswar, M.Sc;
R.R. Gorey, M.Sc;
G.P. Misra; G.S. Deshmukh;
R.N. Mukati; P.D. Swami;
R.K. Govindachar; A.N. Roy;
S. Mukherjee; S. Tandon; G. Tripathi.

A panegyric on the two world-renowned astronomers,

SIR JAMES JEANS, Sc. D., PH. D., LL. D., F. R. S.,

Secretary, Royal Society, London and

SIR ARTHUR STANLEY EDDINGTON, Sc. D.,

PH. D., LL. D., F. R. S., Plumian Professor of Astronomy, Cambridge University.

1. The greatest of the great are triumphant all over the world because their fame is pure in consequence of their erudition.

2. Just as the rays of the Sun spread over the whole earth so the fame of you both based upon your knowledge of the Sun itself and other luminaries has naturally pervaded the whole mankind.

3. What wonder if such intellectual luminaries as your goodselves have come to Bharatvarsha (India) where the knowledge of Astronomy and Astrology is the oldest among any living people at present.

4. With us the guests are always welcome and when these guests are endowed with erudition and connected with a subject so much loved in this country it is impossible to describe our sense of admiration and delight.

5. When you go away from this land of the Aryans may you remember there was an institute somewhere in India where the proficiency of you both in the field of Mathematics and Astronomy was highly appreciated and where homage has been done to you whole-heartedly.

May the knowledge of your subject spread over the whole world.

6/2, RAM BANERJEE LANE,
Calcutta, the 5th January, 1938.

Jyotish Parishad.

Chowringhee Art Press, 172, Bowbazar Street, Calcutta.

Above:
A panegyric on the world-renowned astronomers by Ivotish Parishad.

Next page:
Banquet of the Silver Jubilee Indian Science Congress, grounds of the University College of Science, Calcutta. Early January, 1938.

the outward tour it included seven corridor coaches with compartments affording very comfortable living and sleeping accommodation for two persons each, two dining cars, a brake, a servant's car and a commissariat car. At times, for local travel the party transferred to narrow-gauge trains or road transport. The party was much fêted and entertained by local dignitaries and governments and some members gave public lectures and received honorary degrees — Jeans and Eddington among others — W. Aston, E.C.C. Baly, V.H. Blackman, C.G. Jung, F.A.E. Crew — from the Benares Hindu University.

The Silver Jubilee Session of the Indian Science Congress was opened on the 3rd of January 1938 by the Viceroy of India, the Marquis of Linlithgow, in a marquee set in the grounds of the University College of Science in Calcutta. Many thousands attended the opening. Jeans delivered his own brief welcoming introduction followed by reading a considerable part of Rutherford's original address. A great range of scientific sessions filled the next six days including the Presidential address "The Depth of Space", public lectures and broadcasts. The sixth of January was a 'rest day' devoted to excursions and Jeans took part in the 150-year celebration of the Botanical Gardens. Honorary degrees were conferred on the 7th of January on some of the delegates including Eddington and Jeans by the University of Calcutta.

Numbers for the tour of south India were reduced to about 50 persons. The train left Calcutta in the evening of Sunday the 9th of January on the 1000 mile-trip to Madras. They arrived on Tuesday morning and spent a relaxing day. Between the 12th and 13th they were in Mysore City as guests of the State of Mysore. On Friday 14th in Bangalore, the industrial centre of Mysore, they were entertained by the Prime minister and members of his cabinet. They arrived in Bombay on the 15th January. On the 16th, before the party embarked on the *S.S. Straithaid* to return home, Jeans released to the press a statement on their behalf in which he said:

> "Nothing has more deeply impressed us than the interest shown in science by the community at large and the eagerness with which students are following and practising the most recent advances in research. India has achieved self-sufficiency in many directions, but there is an acknowledged need for influences which shall further bind together her varied races. Her achievements in the realm of thought and her progress in the development of industry lead us to hope that Science, which transcends all national and racial frontiers, may provide such a unifying influence. Long may Science continue to help in maintaining and advancing the position of India in the community of civilised nations."

It would be unfair to say that Jeans was neither interested in politics nor thought about the problems of social development and social progress.

In 1938 the Cambridge University Conservative Association suggested that Jeans should stand for Parliament at the next general election. The Association's representative wrote to Jeans: "As I said yesterday, I do think it would be of national value to have you a Member of Parliament, provided you were not just an ordinary member of a party there to obey the Party Whip and to be present on all sorts of dull occasions. I am very strongly of the opinion that University representation means nothing at all if the Member is expected to act and behave exactly as a Member of an ordinary constituency. If, however, a University representative were expected only to intervene when his detached advice would be of real value on important questions, then I think it is worthwhile being such a representative, and I think you yourself could have an immediate influence and you would not have to wait five years to acquire it. So for my part I do hope you will consider the suggestion very seriously. A lot of people seem to be keen on persuading you."

At first, Jeans accepted the offer: "At the Invitation of the Cambridge University Graduates Conservative Association I offer myself as a Candidate for the University Seat in Parliament recently held by Sir John Withers." He also supplemented his reply with some political observations:

> "In party politics I am a National Conservative. In the past my modest political activities have always been exercised on behalf of the Conservative Party and later for the National Government, and my vote has always been cast for a Conservative or National candidate. In general terms I am in agreement with the present policy of the Prime Minister and his National Government. For some years to come it seems to me that re-armaments must, and will, dominate our national activities; in an armed world we must ourselves be armed. We want peace and so must prepare for war. In the abstract I feel no sympathy with either Fascism or Socialism since both involve infringements of the liberty which we all hold dear. Yet I conceive it may be possible that, in times of crisis, as in times of actual war, we may have to surrender some of our liberties as an insurance against the loss of the whole."
>
> "But I do not offer myself as a strict Party man pledged to vote with the Government in all circumstances. If you do me the honour to elect me, I shall hope primarily to be of service to the Country, and so also to my University, by expressing independent, and perhaps sometimes critical, views on such questions as affect the interests of the Universities, of education (although here I can claim no great

academic knowledge or experience), of learning in general, of science in particular, and, even more particularly, on the application of science to industry and the life of the nation. For I feel that, more than any other nation, we — who must either export or starve — must infuse more scientific knowledge and technique into industry if we are to retain our position in the world. And the need for infusing as much scientific knowledge and technique as possible into our defence and social services is too obvious to call for comment I should hope to be of some service in helping to keep these and similar matters before Parliament. Although my own specialist knowledge of science is not exactly of the kind which is directly applicable in public life, I can claim some experience of, and contacts with, other departments of scientific life; I served for ten years as Secretary of the Royal Society, and also for ten years as a member of the Advisory Council of the Department of Scientific and Industrial Research of the Government. During the last seven of these 1 have been Chairman of the Scientific Grants Committee of the Department."

"Should I be chosen as one of your burgesses I shall claim that although a general supporter of the National Government, I ought to have the freedom usually accorded to a University Member, and a wide measure of independence, particularly in the directions I have already indicated, and this independence I should feel at liberty to exercise on all occasions not vital to the existence of the Government. I should not consider myself bound to be present, or to vote, on ordinary party occasions, as I feel that I could best justify my presence in Parliament in fields not very closely connected with Party politics."

However, Jeans's plans were not to be realized. With the Munich policy of appeasement and the outbreak of war he later refused to take part in the elections. Maybe there were second thoughts as well — he was in his sixties and not in the best of health, and was perfectly aware that while science was an art of working with intelligent people, politics was an art of working with fools in the first place. Jeans set out his reflections on the social progress of human society and on the economical, demographical and political problems of England and Europe on the verge of the World War II in 1930 in an essay published in *More Points of View* [124, p. 53–71]. He wrote: "Quite frankly, my point of view is that of a scientist — an astronomer. In brief, this means two things. First, because I am a scientist, I am apt to see human life as a chain of causes and effects; the life of to-morrow will be what we make it to-day; as we sow, so shall we reap. Second, because I am an astronomer, I am apt to see the problems of to-day set against a background of time in which the whole of human history shrinks to the twinkling of an eye, and to think

MUSIC AND SCIENCE, A BANQUET

Science & Music was published in October 1937. The Musicians Union held a dinner on the 23rd January 1939 at the Wharncliffe Rooms, Landmark Hotel, Marylebone, London. It was entitled “Music and Science” and was presided over by Dr Malcolm Sargent.

J.H. Jeans was the guest of honour and spoke on “Illusion”. Other guests were Lady Jeans, Mrs Sargent, Mr & Mrs Arthur Bliss, and Sir Robert and Lady Mayr.

Next page:
The event was reported in a February issue of Picture Post.

SIR JAMES JEANS, "PUBLICITY AGEN

"Scientists Envy Musicians Their Illusions"

Sir James Hopwood Jeans is one of England's—and the world's—most distinguished men of science. He is both mathematician and astronomer. His books have given ordinary men and women some idea of our universe.

"You Musicians Make Life More Happy"

A great deal of his life has been devoted to investigating and revealing to the public exactly how the matter of the universe has split up into separate and distinct bodies—the stars, the planets and the satellites.

The Man Who Has Probed the Mysteries of the Universe lights a Cigarette

Sir James Jeans has, in his time, shattered many illusions about scientific things. Recently he also gave the Music Teachers' Association something to think about. He refuted the idea that "the pianist can put any emotion he pleases into a note by the way he strikes the key . . . ."

OR THE STARS," GOES TO A BANQUET

"We Scientists Have To Tear Away Life's Illusions"

In his time Sir James Jeans has held many of the positions to which young scientists aspire. He was Secretary of the Royal Society, 1919-1929; was President of the British Association, 1934.

"Musicians Have Something Which Scientists Have Not"

These pictures were taken at a dinner of the Musicians' Club where he was present as a guest of honour, but also as a musician. He is an excellent organist, and his wife was a well-known musician in Vienna.

"Music Is Some People's Mystery"

"Yet," said Sir James, "these waves could be exactly matched down to the minutest detail by dropping weights on the keys." He suggested that the tone quality would be the same if the key were struck by an umbrella.

"But The Universe Is Mysterious, Too"

Some scientists devote themselves to the analysis of minute details and objects; he has taken the Universe as his province. He has estimated the weight of the Sun, and set a term to the life of our own earth.

of these problems specially in relation to man's past history on earth."

"... life, it seems, followed many dead-ends before finding its final road which led to man. Also we know that man is an absolutely new arrival on earth; he has possessed and governed it for less than a thousandth part of its existence."

"Most of us still think of ourselves as the final triumph of biological evolution; we are convinced we have come to stay as rulers of the earth. I wonder why. A being watching us from another planet might see things very differently. Gigantic reptiles, dinosaurs, ruled the earth for millions of years, but failed to retain their supremacy. Then huge mammals, terrible in their weight and strength, but almost brainless, governed for many million years more. Man has ruled only for a fraction of one million years. Why should he suppose that he has come to stay? Rather it seems to me he must still establish his claim to be the permanent governor of the earth. His own acts will decide whether he is fit to rule in perpetuity or not. We must maintain our position by fighting for it."

"... They could not have escaped their fate. We can. We face the future with a weapon in our hands that was not given to earlier rulers of the world — I mean scientific knowledge, and the capacity for increasing it indefinitely by scientific research."

"It is a new weapon. No doubt the men who first discovered the uses of fire, who first replaced stone weapons by bronze, or bronze by iron, were scientists in their own way. So also were those shepherds and herdsmen who first noticed that a healthy, vigorous offspring came from healthy and vigorous parents, and vice versa. Yet in those early days science entered life in such small doses as to be negligible. To-day, thanks to science, we advance more in a few years than our ancestors did through the whole duration of the Stone Age."

"It is our use of this weapon that will mould the future of our race for good or for ill. We no longer believe that human destiny is a plaything for spirits, good and evil, or for the machinations of the Devil. There is nothing to prevent our making the earth a paradise again — except ourselves. The scientific age has dawned, and we recognise that man himself is the master of his fate, the captain of his soul. He controls the course of his ship and so, of course, is free to navigate it into fair waters or foul, or even to run it on the rocks."

"It is important to choose the course with care, for we know that we have embarked on a very long voyage. The early Christians believed that the world would end in their lifetime; their Founder had said so. Quite rightly, then, they devoted their whole attention to the living generation. To-day, few, even of our religious teachers, expect the world to end in our time. The earth was in existence millions of years ago, and in all probability will still be in existence millions of years hence. For more time than we can imagine, it is likely to remain in much the same physical condition as now, and so will provide a suitable home for the human race. Whatever our views on a future life in another world, we recapture the old Jewish concept of an immortality in this world — or something which is effectively as good as immortality — enjoyed not by us but through us, by our posterity. Our problem is no longer merely to muddle through for a few more generations. We see ourselves as the architects of a tremendous future, with science giving us the power to build for good or evil, to make or to mar."

"We have hardly yet realised how grave a responsibility this casts upon us. Amongst other things, I think we shall in time come to see that we must recast a large part of our code of social morality. Virtues and vices have frequently changed places as life moved on through the ages. Witch-burning used to be a virtue, and lending money at interest a vice."

"... It is now known, as a scientific fact, that both physical and mental qualities are inherited. For this reason, I do not believe that we shall get a happy and successful nation unless we replenish our stock mainly from the more happy and more successful members of the community. Good education, good physical conditions, good environment are all valuable and necessary, but they will never make a "born-tired" or moral weakling pull his weight in the world. Neither will they give him a happy life. We want something more than good environment — we want good raw material in the form of children born from the best possible stock."

"Our unsentimental ancestors achieved this in a very simple way: they just allowed the weaker and less successful to go to the wall. Two hundred years ago three-quarters of the babies born in London died in infancy — three out of every four. Those few who survived must, on the whole, have been abnormally strong, or else born of successful parents, who were able to give them every care. Thus, it was natural for the English race to become strong and successful; the process was almost automatic."

"To-day we are heading in precisely the opposite direction. There is no weeding out of the unfit, we save nearly all our babies indiscriminately — good and bad, strong and weak, healthy and diseased. It would not be so bad if this meant that all types contribute equally to the future population of England. Unhappily it does not mean this: in actual fact the largest contribution comes from the most miserable and least successful classes. In the professional and other successful classes late marriages and small families are almost the rule; many of their men spend the important parts of their lives in India or the colonies, abroad or at sea. The result is that these classes are not even maintaining their present numbers; they are on the road to extinction. The same is true of the skilled artisans. Thus it is the most valuable elements of the nation, and not the unfit, that are now being "weeded out," to use an inappropriate word. Meanwhile our present system of doles, grants and subsidies makes marriage easier, and parenthood less of a responsibility, in the least successful classes of the community. In this way, it increases the population in precisely those classes which are even now overpopulated and unable to find employment. It is in these classes that the birth-rate is highest to-day; it is from these classes that the majority of our criminals, paupers and ne'er-do-wells come."

"... I think, reverse our present policy."

"... Yet if I am a democrat, I confess it is mainly because I cannot find anything else to be. The actual achievement of democracy is that it gives a tolerably good time to the underdog. Or, at least, it honestly tries; and it is, I think, for this reason that most of us accept it as our political creed. My objection to it is that, as I think, it forms a barrier to further upward progress. True progress — to better things — must be based on thought and knowledge. As I see it, democracy encourages the nimble charlatan at the expense of the thinker, and prefers the plausible wizard with quack remedies to the true statesman. Democracy is ever eager for rapid progress, and the only progress which can be rapid is progress downhill. For this reason I suspect that all democracies carry within them the seeds of their own destruction, and I cannot believe that democracy is to be our final form of government. And indeed, there is little enough of it left in Europe to-day."

"We are still at the very beginning of civilisation. Ordered government has a past of some thousands of years behind it, but a future of millions of years before it — at least, we hope so. The historians of the remote future will, I imagine, see democracy merely as one of the early experiments tried in that age of repeated upheavals — our own — in which mankind was still groping its way to a rational mode of life. It may be that democracy — like teething — is a state through which we have to pass on our way to higher things. Anyhow, it is a restless, feverish state, and I hope it will soon give place to something better. I wonder what. Possibly, in future ages, the power to vote and govern will not be regarded as a right, but as a distinction, to be acquired by service or merit. This may suggest that I have but little respect for the sacred principle of equality. Perhaps so. If I had to choose a one-word motto I do not think it would be "Equality." I might choose "Excelsior" — let us get on to higher things. And a traveller will not get far towards higher things if he is ever afraid of putting one foot in front of the other."

"For similar reasons, I feel very little sympathy with socialism. If I think of democracy as a juvenile ailment, I think of socialism as a definite disease. The cause of this complaint seems to me to be poverty and hard times. I am not thinking of the abstract academic socialism of Karl Marx, or of our own intelligentsia; this no longer seems to me to have much practical interest or importance. I have in mind the real, live socialism of the man who finds times hard, employment scarce and wages low, and so wants to levy toll on the wealth of his more successful neighbours, the type of socialism which flourishes in the poorest and most miserable parts of England, and in the most backward and hard-hit countries of Europe. By discouraging thrift, hard work and enterprise, this socialism lessens the wealth of a country, and so makes the poor still poorer. But experience shows that it can get no foothold in a prosperous country, so that the cure for it is better trade, better times, and, I think, better education."

"If not cured, it kills. Our socialist orators tell us much in glowing terms about the hypothetical socialist future, or at least about their dreamy visions of the socialist future. Why do they tell us so little about the socialist and communist experiments of the past, in which their theories were really tested? It is, I think, because these experiments all ended in failure. The truth seems to be that no socialist state ever endures for long — as such. Thus I do not picture the future government of the world as either socialistic or democratic."

"... The last century has seen science progress enormously on its physical side — it has ushered in the electrical and mechanical age, and has produced so many new scientific devices and inventions that we have, I think, got a bit drunk with them. I do not believe this condition is permanent. One hears frequent reference to the disintegrating effect of telephones and motor-cars on our lives. I agree as to the present, but I think we shall soon learn to make the telephone and motor-car our servants and not our masters. I have often thought that, just as the mechanical side of science has advanced in the past century, so the next century may see a similar rapid and sensational development on the biological side. And this may change the state of society more than we can imagine."

"... And, unless human nature changes vastly in the meantime, we may be sure they will regret the "good old days" in which we are now living. They will think of our age as the Golden Age, the glorious morning of the world. And I, for one, do not regret that fate has cast my life in it." [151, p. 107–19]

It is amazing how relevant Jeans's thoughts appear today. He seems to have foreseen the fate of totalitarian regimes and their ideologies, their inevitable and dramatic end, and the problems which humanity was facing then and which are becoming even more urgent today as they become a threat to the very future of life on our planet. He understood that neither social nor cultural progress was possible without freedom. Creative freedom was for him the main condition for the flourishing of both art and science — the two things without which Jeans could not imagine his life. However in the first days of the war his physical freedom — if not his creative freedom — was somewhat restricted. Cleveland Lodge was requisitioned by the military authorities and anti-tank trenches were dug across the grounds as it would have been situated in the main line of enemy advance on London. In June 1940 the Jeans family moved to Wanstrow, near Shepton Mallet in Somerset, and in August 1942 to Westbury-sub-Mendip near Wells. Meanwhile, the family grew bigger: following the first son Michael Antony born in 1936, the second son Christopher Vincent was born on the last day of 1939, and the daughter Katherine Anne was born in 1944. Jeans was an attentive father. He introduced his older son to stamp collecting and taught him to play the xylophone when he was still very young. However, only Jeans's daughter developed a substantial musical talent. During the World War II he had to devote a lot of his time to the upbringing of the children and certain mundane aspects of family life which he was not used to in times of peace. Despite their considerable fortune, the Jeanses, like everyone else, whether rich or poor, lived on rationed goods, for Great Britain was the only country where there was no substantial or socially disruptive 'black market'. How could it be any different in a country where the Royal Family lived on the same ration as the rest of the citizens?

Two letters of Jeans to his sister Gertrude shed light on his life during the war:

> Westbury-sub-Mendip, Somerset.
> April 22nd, 1944.
> My dear Gertie, I wonder whether you are still in Cornwall, or if you have gone back to London again now that the raids are less troublesome. I am glad you got out of the worst, but it is difficult to know what to do. We moved away from Dorking rather early, thinking we would get the family away before things got really bad, and the raids stopped the very day we left.
>
> If you are in London, I wonder whether you would care to have dinner with me on Friday evening the 28th. It is the first time I have been up, except for one flying visit, since we were in Dorking. I have to lecture at the Royal Institution at 5, and could give you dinner at the Ivy or the Aperitif, which is nearer at 7.30 if you liked (if so, could you reserve a table for me?). If you cared to come to the lecture, I can of course send you a ticket, and if you liked we could go for a few minutes to the private view of the Royal Academy between the lecture and dinner.
>
> We keep well here, but are very busy with household jobs, as we have very little service now. Katharine is flourishing, and full of vigour and life, but she does not put on weight at a great rate — this worries Susi, but not me. She has got nasty open blisters on her face at the moment, as Pandi turned her pram round into the sun, but it is not serious.

James Jeans and his eldest son, Michael (3 years) at Cleveland Lodge. Winter of 1939/1940. It was the coldest winter since 1881 — even the River Thames froze over — and may have resulted from the exceptional disturbance of the temperature profile in the North Sea caused by the extensive use of underwater explosives against alien shipping and submarines.

I hope you are keeping well — please let me know as soon as you can whether you will come on Friday.
Affectionately,

However, as we can see from the other letter, Jeans never managed to meet with his sister:

Westbury-sub-Mendip, Somerset.
May 4th, 1944.
My dear Gertrude,
I wrote you on April 21st, the day before you wrote to me, and wonder whether you ever got my letter. I did not know where you were, and so addressed it to 11 Cornwall Gardens — especially as it contained an invitation which I did not expect you to accept unless you were in London, namely to go with me to the private view of the Academy on the 28th, and dine with me afterwards. I marked the envelope "Please forward if away". I did not like to write to Cornwall, as if you were in London, too much time would be wasted in its going to Cornwall and back.

Susi is away for a day or two — she left this morning, taking the baby with her, as she is still feeding it. The main object is to see her gynaecologist to see if all has settled down properly after the baby, but she is also going for a night or two to Cleveland, to see if all is right there.

Park House, Shepton Mallet. Christopher Jeans ("Pandi", age 1½) being fed a half orange by his father. Summer 1940.

Park House, Wanstrow, Shepton Mallet, Somerset. The Military Authorities took over Cleveland Lodge on the 18th July 1940, its small estate occupied a strategic area in the Mole Gap in the North Downs for the planned advancement by the German Army on London. A tank trap trench was dug across the grounds. The Jeans family left on the 17th June 1940 for Park House where they stayed for two years.

Park House, Shepton Mallet. Susi teaching her younger son ("Pandi" age 2) how to ski.

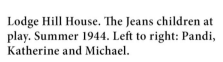

Lodge Hill House, Westbury-sub-Mendip, nr Wells, Somerset. The Jeans family moved here on the 15th August, 1942 and stayed until the end of the War.

Lodge Hill House. A Jeans family portrait, 1944. Left to right: Michael (age 7 years), Susi, Katherine Anne (born 29th Jan 1944) held by James, Pandi (age 4 years).

Lodge Hill House. The Jeans children at play. Summer 1944. Left to right: Pandi, Katherine and Michael.

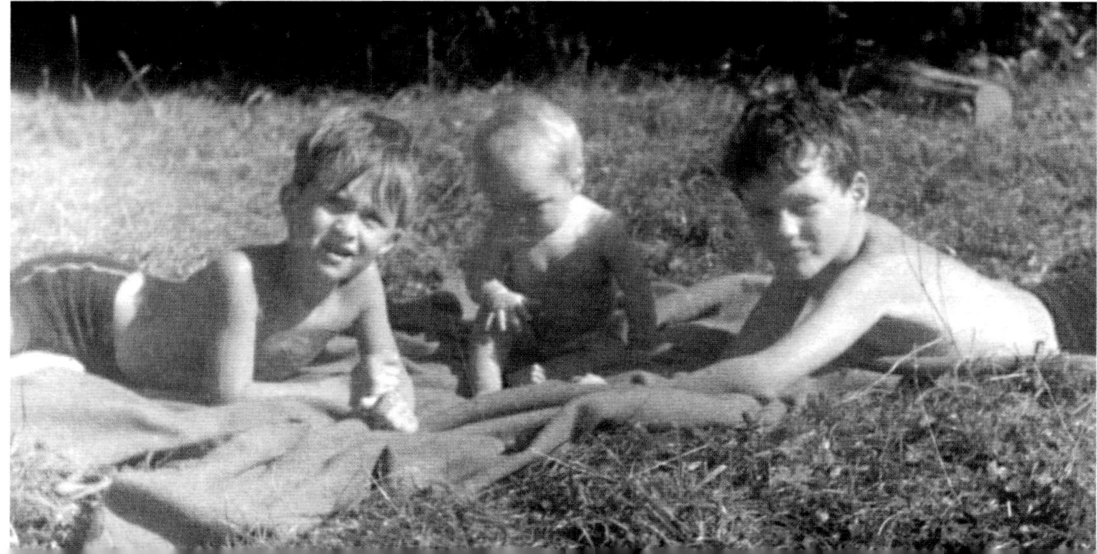

MERCHANT TAYLORS' COMPANY

Extract from the Minutes of a Court of Assistants held at Merchant Taylors' Hall on Thursday, 18th May 1944.

PURSUANT to Notice given, the Master moved:–

IT having been the custom of the Company from time whereof there is no memory to elect Members of the Royal Family and men of distinction to the Honorary Freedom of the Company, having regard to his distinguished career and more especially in recognition of his valuable services to Science, that Sir James Hopwood Jeans, O.M. be invited to accept the Honorary Freedom of the Company."

WHEN IT WAS RESOLVED that this resolution be approved and adopted.

Clerk of the Company.

BE IT REMEMBERED that on the twenty-second day of November in the year nineteen hundred and forty four, Sir James Hopwood Jeans, O.M. was admitted to the Freedom of the Company, pursuant to the above resolution.

Master

Warden

Warden

Warden

Warden

Clerk of the Company.

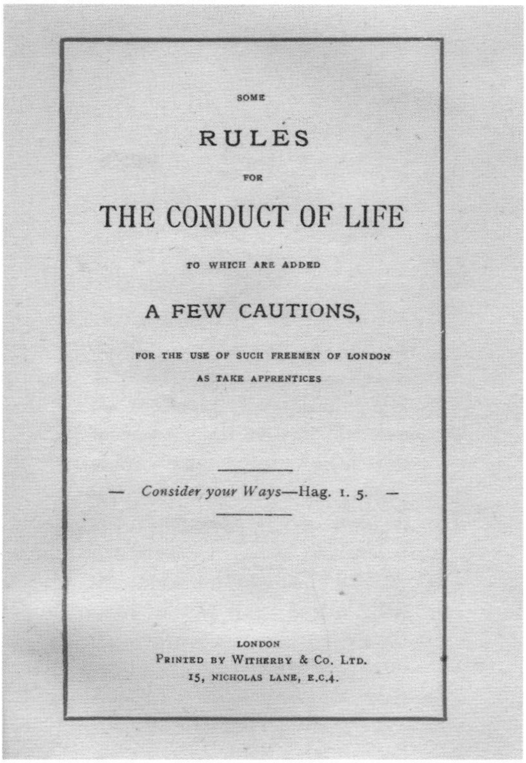

SOME

RULES

FOR

THE CONDUCT OF LIFE

TO WHICH ARE ADDED

A FEW CAUTIONS,

FOR THE USE OF SUCH FREEMEN OF LONDON
AS TAKE APPRENTICES

— *Consider your Ways*—Hag. I. 5. —

LONDON
PRINTED BY WITHERBY & CO. LTD.
15, NICHOLAS LANE, E.C.4.

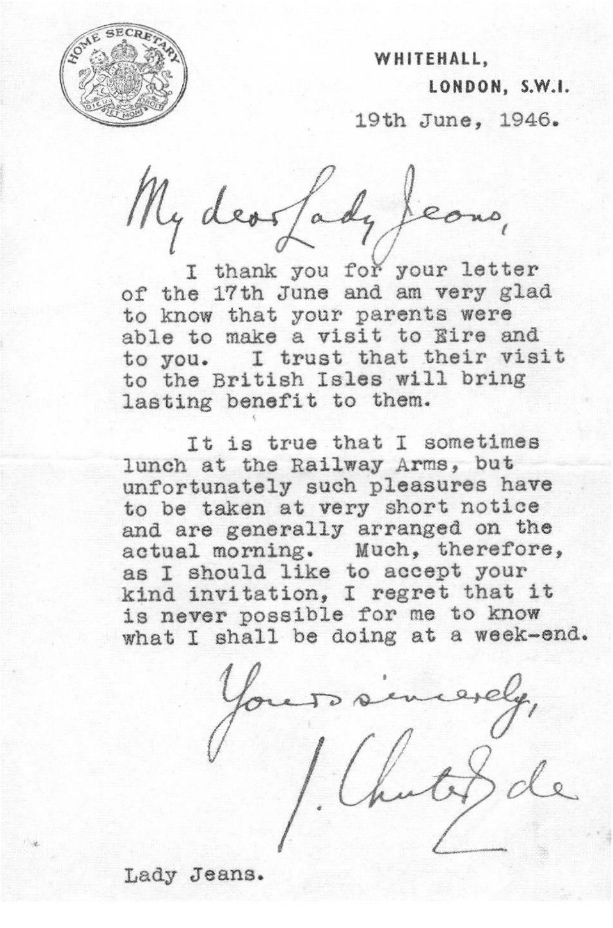

HOME SECRETARY

WHITEHALL,
LONDON, S.W.I.

19th June, 1946.

My dear Lady Jeans,

I thank you for your letter of the 17th June and am very glad to know that your parents were able to make a visit to Eire and to you. I trust that their visit to the British Isles will bring lasting benefit to them.

It is true that I sometimes lunch at the Railway Arms, but unfortunately such pleasures have to be taken at very short notice and are generally arranged on the actual morning. Much, therefore, as I should like to accept your kind invitation, I regret that it is never possible for me to know what I shall be doing at a week-end.

Yours sincerely,

J. Chuter Ede

Lady Jeans.

Above:
J. H. Jeans was granted the honorary Freedom of the City of London on the 20th May 1946. With this came a little book with some rules (35 in number) for the conduct of life, particularly how to treat apprentices.

Left:
A letter from the Home Secretary, James Chuter-Ede, suggesting that he had facilitated this visit of Susi's parents from Vienna to their children and grandchildren in England and Eire.

Opposite page:
The illuminated scroll with the Extract from the Minutes of a Council of Assistants held at Merchant Taylors Hall on the 18th May 1944 recording the granting of Sir James Jeans later in November the honorary Freedom of the Merchant Taylors' Company.

For the first time, they have refused permission for her to sleep in Cleveland, so she has to stay with friends across the road.

I was up on the 28th, to lecture at the Royal Institution, but except for that have been very little in London, and do not expect to be there again for some time.

The infant is wonderfully well, and full of energy; she looks very like Olivia did, but on a larger scale. Susi is well, but not as well as she might be, if it were not for childbearing and housekeeping. However, she keeps pretty quiet. I cook the breakfast and supper, and she cooks the mid-day dinner. We have a "Help" come in to wash up and prepare the tea. I have one or two of the boys on my hands most of the time. Michael went back to school yesterday, and now I have Pandy in my room every few minutes complaining he has no one to play with, which is true — poor child! There is no longer any school here to which we can send him.

I hope you keep well; do send me a line whenever you have anything to tell me. Affectionately,

In 1944, two years before his death, Jeans gave the Deneke Lecture in Oxford. It was entitled 'The Astronomical Horizon' [164] and it is clear that he had lost none of his ability to be both engaging, challenging and controversial. He began it thus: "The history of astronomy, it has been truly said, is a history of receding horizons. Every increase in telescopic power and — what is hardly less important — every gain in the sensitivity of photographic plates, has opened up new depths of space for exploration, and the centre of astronomical interest has tended to follow the limits of vision. Until the middle of the last century, interest was centred in the planets of the solar system; after that it shifted to the stars of the galactic system; now many astronomers find their main interest in the remote nebulae which lie at the extreme limits of vision of our largest telescopes — the astronomical horizon." [164, p. 3]. However he dealt with not only the history of astronomy and the historical development of ideas about the universe, starting from Aristarchus of Samos and up to the middle of the twentieth century, but also with philosophical discussions and insights into the future development of science — which Jeans did not live to witness.

After the war, Jeans returned with his family to Cleveland Lodge and only occasionally visited London to give lectures at the Royal Institution. In his final years, Jeans was rather ill. In January 1945, he was diagnosed with coronary thrombosis. He had to give up many of his responsibilities and restrict his activities. However, when Jeans was feeling well, he visited the Royal Astronomical Society Club to meet his colleagues and get updates on the latest news of the scientific world.

Cleveland Lodge, spring 1946. Oscar and Katharina Hock with their son-in-law, James Jeans, and their grandchildren Katherine and Christopher.

Jeans went to Montreux in Switzerland in the summer of 1946, but that was his last summer holiday trip. Soon after his return, on the evening of the 15th of September, Jeans felt unwell and after six painful hours died of a second heart attack caused by coronary thrombosis. He spent the morning of his last day listening to music. The official statement said that Sir James Jeans had died on the 16th of September 1946 in his house in Cleveland Lodge, and that science had thus lost one of its most brilliant minds. Jeans was buried in Mickleham churchyard in the presence of only the family and closest friends.

Above: The headstone of the grave of Charlotte Tiffany Jeans (1877–1934).

Above right: The headstone of the grave of James Hopwood Jeans (11 Sept 1877–16 Sept 1946) and Susi Jeans (25 Jan 1911–7 Jan 1993). The headstone was carved by Frere Laurence Bévenot of Ampleworth Abbey, York — a close musical friend of Susi's and a skilled stone carver.

Right:
St Michael of All Angels, the local part-Norman church at Mickleham, Surrey where J. H. Jeans and his first wife, Charlotte Tiffany, and his second wife, Susi, are buried. January 2015.

Below: The graveyard of St. Michaels and All Angels Church at Mickleham in high summer.

Cleveland Lodge, Dorking, Surrey in 1981.
A watercolour by John Morris.

CLEVELAND LODGE, ITS FATE

On Susi's death in January 1993 Cleveland Lodge was gifted by deed of variation of her will to the Royal School of Church Music (RSCM) so it might become their new centre of operations as they were urgently seeking to leave Addington Palace in Croydon. After major renovations and extensions involving considerable Lottery funding and collaboration from the Mole Valley District Council the RSCM took up residence in 1996. Already by 2004 they were facing financial difficulties caused by the changing requirements of its members, and in 2006 they moved to Salisbury where they now share the facilities of Sarum College. This move caused serious planning concern as Cleveland Lodge lay in the Metropolitan Green Belt in highly sensitive rural surroundings which are designated an Area of Outstanding Natural Beauty. In granting planning permission for the RSCM's use of Cleveland Lodge the Council had considered that the particular circumstances of the proposal enabled an exception to be made to the normal Green Belt policies of restraint. No appropriate alternative occupier could be found by the RSCM and it was sold to a developer and the buildings were 'converted' to residential use (see over page) — Cleveland Lodge was completely demolished and crushed, leaving only the end wall of the house with its blue plagues next to Westhumble Street — and a multiple dwelling look-alike building arose from its foot print.

THE INSTITUTE OF PHYSICS
SIR
JAMES
HOPWOOD JEANS
1877 - 1946
Physicist, Astronomer
and popularizer of Science
lived here
1918 - 1946
LADY SUSI JEANS
1911 - 1993
Organist and Scholar
lived here
1935 - 1993

Cleveland Lodge . RSCM
2002-3

The Remains of Cleveland Lodge, Summer
Searching the huge pile of crushed brick and concr
memento I could find was a fragment of a green

The Jeans home from 1918 to 1993.
against the background of Boxhill, the only
tile from my Mother's fireplace.

KOZENKO'S SCHOLARLY BIOGRAPHY

Shortly before Alexander Kozenko joined 'the majority' — he died on the 3rd October 2015 in Moscow — he wrote an account of how during the 1980s and 1990s in the USSR he managed to realize his plans to publish a biography of J.H.Jeans and the consequences of his subsequent visit to England. This extract emphasizes the importance of whom you know or chance to meet that underpins scientific cooperation even under adverse conditions. The full account is with the Jeans papers in the archives of Trinity College, Cambridge.

"My interest in astronomy developed as early as age ten, so the name of the prominent British physicist and astronomer James Jeans was known to me since I was a child. There was a copy of the 1932 edition of *The Universe Around Us* in my mother's library beautifully translated by Professor N. Idelson. And Jeans's portrait was in G.A. Gurev's popular book *The Universe*, which was given to my mother by her father in 1935. However, a serious acquaintance with Jeans's work did not begin until I was working on my dissertation on the theory of figures of equilibrium of rotating, self-gravitating configurations. I was struck by Jeans's immense mathematical talent and the refined methods he applied to his work on related problems. He was the author of the idea of Gravitational Instability which is fundamental to modern cosmogony and cosmology. Later, it became clear to me that Jeans was, along with such scholars as Arthur Eddington and Karl Schwarzschild, one of the creators of a new scientific field, theoretical astrophysics."

"Without a doubt, the life and work of such an important figure deserved to be known by the general public. So I decided to write a scholarly biography of Sir James Jeans. At that time, there was a wonderful series put out by the *Nauka (Science)* publishing house entitled *Scientific Biographies*. I made an application for publication and this was accepted. I began to collect the material for the book. A decisive moment in my work, however, occurred in 1980, when at a congress in Budapest I met R.E. Pudritz, then a PhD student of Martin Rees. We were discussing our scholarly plans and I told him about my interest in Sir James Jeans's biography. He asked me if I knew that Jeans's widow, Lady Jeans, was alive and said he would contact her to ask for her permission to give me her address. Not only did he give me her contacts, but he also sent me photocopies of some of Jeans's works. When my work on the book was nearing its end, I asked Lady Jeans to send me some family photographs of her choice. She was kind enough to send me a few family portraits."

"However, I underestimated the difficulties that were awaiting me. When I submitted the manuscript to the publishers, along with all the positive reviews, I was told that they would not publish the book, because Jeans supported idealistic philosophical views. That, of course, was nonsense, especially since the book contained a chapter where I specifically focused on the analysis of Jeans's philosophical views. But to overcome this obstacle, support of a very influential member of the Academy of Sciences was needed. I decided to seek help from the Academy member and Nobel Prize winner Vitaly Lazarevich Ginzburg, who was a man of courage and strong moral principles. He was head of the Department of Theoretical Physics of the Physical Institute of the Academy of Sciences, where Andrei Dmitrievich Sakharov worked after falling from grace with the Soviet government. Ginzburg strongly supported my idea of publishing the biography. Nevertheless, I was obliged to make a few references to the classics of Marxism-Leninism in my book. In 1985, this small volume was published in an abridged form, where a lot of facts of Jeans's life as well as photographs were taken out. But I was happy even with that. Of course, I sent a copy of the book to Lady Jeans with an inscription expressing my gratitude. We kept in touch exchanging letters and postcards for Christmas. In one of her letters Lady Jeans mentioned that she had a friend at the Moscow Conservatory — the organist Professor Leonid Isaakovich Roisman. She remembered working with him on the panels of judges at a number of organ competitions and sent me a photograph of the two of them among the judges of an organ competition in Leipzig [page 205]. I made a copy of the photograph and presented it to Roisman with a copy of my book. That awakened a lot of interest and a lot of questions about my contact with Lady Jeans. He thought very highly of her as an organist and had an idea of inviting her to Moscow for a series of master classes and possibly a concert. I, in turn, came up with an idea of making a joint application to the *Muzyka (Music)* Publishing House to publish a translation of Jeans's book *Science and Music* written in 1937 and dedicated to his wife. I had known of Roisman for a long time and sometimes went to his organ concerts, and now he began to send me invitations to them. Once Lady Jeans tried to telephone me but I was not at home: however, she spoke to my mother, who had learnt German from when she was a child and spoke it fluently. Apparently, Lady Jeans was so impressed by this that she decided to invite me over. Soon afterwards she sent me a letter of invitation. However, that caused more difficulties. For the Soviet authorities at the time a private letter without any stamps and seals had no meaning whatsoever — it was impossible for a USSR citizen to go abroad without an official invitation. But I got lucky again. Ernest André Gellner (9.12.1925—05.11.1995), a prominent English philosopher and social anthropologist and Professor at the University of Cambridge, was working in Moscow at the time. He was interested in the problems of syncretism in religious beliefs of different peoples and my mother, a well-known ethnologist and anthropologist studying the ethnic groups of the Western Pamir, was consulting him on syncretism in their religious views. Gellner was a fluent speaker of several languages, among them Russian. Once, when he was dining at our house, I showed him Lady Jeans's letter. He said there was no problem. He took the letter from me and took it to the British Ambassador in Moscow, who put the round stamp of the Embassy on it. That was enough to solve my problem: in 1989, at the time of ever-increasing liberalisation, I was granted permission to go to the United Kingdom. Unfortunately, as I was about to share the good news with Professor Roisman, I heard of his sudden death."

"I arrived to London at the end of April and went from Victoria train station to Westhumble — Box Hill. Despite it being rather late in the evening, Lady Jeans herself met me at the station. She was 77 at the time; tall and sporty-looking, with white hair, and wearing a very simple jacket and trousers. 'Susi', she introduced herself. 'And you must be Alexander.' It took no longer than five minutes to walk from the station to the Cleveland Lodge. Susi showed me my rooms on the first floor and invited me to dinner, which was already served. At that point, in darkness, I could not fully appreciate the size of that enormous mansion which had, as it later turned out, tens of rooms. The next day Susi took me on a guided tour of Cleveland Lodge, showing me Sir James Jeans's study, her music room, lots of antique musical instruments, among them eleven organs. Despite her being slightly disappointed with my rather poor command of spoken English, Susi told me a lot about Sir James and showed me some materials from the family archive. Cleveland Lodge was a very beautiful estate. Purple and white rhododendrons were blooming everywhere, and from the windows overviewing the garden one could see a vast perfectly groomed lawn bordered by a tall hedge."

"While I was staying at Cleveland Lodge, Susi had a visit from her daughter Katharine, also a musician, who was then living in the North of England, quite far away from her mother. A few prominent musicians and musicologists came to see Lady Jeans during my visit. Sometimes she played for me on her favourite small clavichord. Lady Jeans was hugely respected in London's scholarly and musical circles. She arranged for me to visit the archive of the London Royal Society and to have access to yet unsorted archives of Sir James Jeans and Sir Arthur Eddington, whose biography and works I was also interested in. I attended an annual meeting of the Royal

Astronomical Society in London and was invited by Professor Michael M. Woolfson, who was developing Jeans's theory on the origins of planets, and Professor Runcorn to visit the University of York and Newcastle University respectively. I also made a short visit to Durham University. I gave talks on the results of my latest research on the time of the formation of Jupiter and its impact on the formation of terrestrial planets. "

"Meeting Susi's second son, Christopher, allowed me to visit Cambridge. There I met Lady Jeffreys, whose husband Sir Harold Jeffreys had passed away only two months before. I gave her a copy of my book about James Jeans, because she could read Russian. Lady Jeffreys' reaction to it was very positive. She asked me to write something similar about her late husband — a prominent 20th-century geophysicist. At the University of Cambridge Institute of Astronomy I had a conversation with Martin Rees (later Sir Martin) who at the time occupied the same position of Plumian Professor of Astronomy as Harold Jeffreys had before him. I also visited St. John's and Trinity Colleges. About a year later, in August 1990, I came to Cambridge on the invitation of Lady Jeffreys. Lady Jeffreys (née Bertha Swirles) was herself a brilliant mathematician and knew her husband's work fairly well. Particularly, she was the editor of the six volume edition of his collected works published by Gordon and Breach. She was, therefore, able to provide me with the most relevant materials for his scholarly biography, as well as with photocopies and copies of the photographs that I needed. During that visit to Cambridge, I had regular meetings with Christopher Jeans and his wife Friederike, as I was gathering the material for a second improved edition of Jeans's biography. On my way back I visited Lady Jeans in Cleveland Lodge."

"In April 1991 I came to Cambridge again to participate in the events marking the centenary of Sir Harold Jeffreys. Another participant from Russia was Professor N.V. Kondorskaya, who collaborated with Sir Harold on The International Seismological Summary. The celebratory proceedings were concluded by a banquet at the Athenaeum Club on Pall Mall in London. That year I saw Lady Jeans for the last time. She was already unwell then. In the beginning of 1993 I got a letter from Christopher Jeans saying that his mother had passed away on 7 January 1993. My wife and I visited the United Kingdom several times after that invited by Christopher Jeans. We stayed at his welcoming and friendly house in Cambridge and we are very grateful to him and his wife Friederike for their hospitality. "

"I decided to prepare a second edition of Jeans's biography when, in the 1990s, the Gordon and Breach publishing house started a project which involved publishing translations of this kind of books into English. I was reluctant to submit the original version of the book because of all the references to the classics of Marxism-Leninism. Besides, I was now in possession of the new expanded material, which I wanted to include in the second edition and have *that* version translated. However, while I was working on the second version of the book, Gordon and Breach's project was discontinued. However, I had scholarly biographies of Arthur Eddington, Harold Jeffreys, and the new extended version of the biography of James Jeans published in Russian. These books acquaint the Russian readers with the life and work of these outstanding English scholars and their contribution to the development of science."

BIBLIOGRAPHY

WORKS OF J.H. JEANS

1900

1. The striated electrical discharge // Phil. Mag. Vol. 49. P. 245–262. Vol. 1. P. 521–529.

1901

2. The distribution of molecular energy // Phil. Trans. Roy. Soc. London, A. Vol. 196. P. 397–430.
3. The theoretical evaluation of γ // Phil. Mag. Vol. 2. P. 638–651.
4. The mechanism of radiation // Phil. Mag. Vol. 2. P. 421–455.

1902

5. The equilibrium of rotating liquid cylinders // Phil. Trans. Roy. Soc. London, A. Vol. 200. P. 67–104.
6. Conditions necessary for equipartition of energy // Phil. Mag. Vol. 4. P. 585–596.
7. The stability of a spherical nebula // Phil. Trans. Roy. Soc. London, A. Vol. 198. P. 1–53.

1903

8. The vibrations and stability of a gravitating planet // Phil. Trans. Roy. Soc. London, A. Vol. 201. P. 157–184.
9. The kinetic theory of gases developed from a new standpoint // Phil. Mag. Vol. 5. P. 597–620.
10. On the vibrations set up by molecular collisions // Phil. Mag. Vol. 6. P. 279–286.

1904

11. The Dynamical Theory of Gases. Cambridge: Cambridge Univ. Press. 352 pp.
12. The kinetic theory of gases // Phil. Mag. Vol. 6. P. 720–722. Vol. 7. P. 468–469.
13. A suggested explanation of radioactivity // Nature Vol. 70. P. 101.
14. The determination of the size of molecules from the kinetic theory of gases // Phil. Mag. Vol. 8. P. 692–699.
15. The persistence of molecular velocities in the kinetic theory of gases // Phil. Mag. Vol. 8. P. 700–703.

1905

16. Gas-theory and radiation // Nature. Vol. 72. P. 101–102.
17. The partition of energy between matter and ether // Phil. Mag. Vol. 10. P. 91–98.
18. A comparison between two theories of radiation // Nature. Vol. 72. P. 293–294.
19. Statistical mechanics applied to ether and matter // Proc. Roy. Soc. London, A. Vol. 76. P. 296–311.
20. On the density of Algol variables // Astrophys. J. Vol. XXII. No. 2. P. 93–102.
21. On the law of radiation // Proc. Roy. Soc. London, A. Vol. 76. P. 545–552.

1906

22. The constitution of the atom // Phil. Mag. Vol. 11. P. 604–607.
23. The thermodynamic theory of radiation // Phil. Mag. Vol. 12. P. 57–60.
24. The H–theorem and the dynamical theory of gases // Phil. Mag. Vol. 12. P. 80–82.
25. The stability of submarines // Nature. Vol. 74. P. 270.
26. The deduction of Wien's law // Phys. Ztschr. Bd. 7. S. 667. Bd. 8. S. 91–92.

1907

27. An Elementary Treatise on Theoretical Mechanics. Boston, New York, [etc.]: Ginn & Co. 364 pp.

1908

28. The Mathematical Theory of Electricity and Magnetism. Cambridge: Cambridge Univ. Press. 536 pp.
29. Radiation theory // Phys. Ztschr. Bd. 8. S. 853–855.

1909

30. The temperature of radiation and the partition of energy // Phil. Mag. Vol. 17. P. 229–254.
31. The motion of electrons in solids, Part I and II // Phil. Mag. Vol. 17. P. 773–794. Vol. 18. P. 204–226.

1910

32. The motion of a particle about a doublet // Phil. Mag. Vol. 20. P. 380–382.
33. The radiation from electron orbits // Phil. Mag. Vol. 20. P. 642–651.
34. On non-Newtonian mechanical systems and Planck's theory of radiation // Phil. Mag. Vol. 20. P. 943–954.

1911

35. The Mathematical Theory of Electricity and Magnetism. 2nd ed. Cambridge: Cambridge Univ. Press. 584 pp.

1913

36. On the "kinetic theory" of star-clusters // Mon. Not. Roy. Astr. Soc. Vol. LXXIV. P. 109–112.

1914

37. Report on Radiation and the Quantum Theory. Physical Society Report. London: The Electrician Publishing Co. 90 pp.
38. Gravitational instability and the nebular hypothesis // Phil. Trans. Roy. Soc. London, A. Vol. 213. P. 457–485.
39. Radiation and free electrons // Phil. Mag. Vol. 27. P. 14–22.

1915

40. On the potential of ellipsoidal bodies and the figures of equilibrium of rotating liquid masses // Phil. Trans. Roy. Soc. London, A. Vol. 215. P. 27–78.
41. On the theory of star-streaming and the structure of the universe // Month. Notic. Roy. Astron. Soc. Vol. 76. P. 70–84.
42. The Mathematical Theory of Electricity and Magnetism. 3rd ed. Cambridge: Cambridge Univ. Press. 587 pp.

1916

43. On the theory of star-streaming, and the structure of the universe (2nd Paper) // Mon. Not. Roy. Astron. Soc. Vol. 76. P. 552–567.
44. On the law of distribution in star-clusters // Mon. Not. Roy. Astron. Soc. Vol. 76. P. 567–572.
45. On the instability of the pear-shaped figure of equilibrium of a rotating mass of liquid // Phil. Trans. Roy. Soc. London, A. Vol. 217. P. 1–34.
46. The Dynamical Theory of Gases. 2nd ed. Cambridge: Cambridge Univ. Press. 436 pp.

1917

47. Rotation as a factor in cosmic evolution // Mon. Not. Roy. Astron. Soc. Vol. 77. P. 186–199.
48. Gravitational instability and the figure of the Earth // Proc. Roy. Soc. London, A. Vol. 93. P. 413–417.
49. Internal motions in spiral nebulae // Observatory. Vol. 40. P. 60–61.
50. The radiation of the stars // Nature. Vol. 99. P. 365.
51. The motion of tidally-distorted masses, with special reference to theories of cosmogony // Mem. Roy. Astron. Soc. Vol. 62. P. 1–48.
52. Note on the action of viscosity in gaseous and nebular masses // Mon. Not. Roy. Astron. Soc. Vol. 77. P. 200–204.
53. The equations of radiative transfer of energy // Mon. Not. Roy. Astron. Soc. Vol. 78. P. 28–36.
54. The evolution and radiation of gaseous stars // Mon. Not. Roy. Astron. Soc. Vol. 78. P. 36–47.
55. Recent Developments of Molecular Physics // Royal Institution of Great Britain weekly evening meeting, Friday, March 30, 1917. P. 1–11.

1918

56. The present position of the nebular hypothesis // Scientia, Bologna. Vol. 24. P. 270–281.
57. The evolution of binary systems // Mon. Not. Roy. Astron. Soc. Vol. 79. P. 100–106.

1919

58. Problems of Cosmogony and Stellar Dynamics. Adams Prize Essay, 1917. Cambridge: Cambridge Univ. Press. 293 pp.
59. The configurations of rotating compressible masses (Bakerian lecture) // Phil. Trans. Roy. Soc. London, A. Vol. 218. P. 157–210.
60. The internal constitution and radiation of gaseous stars // Mon. Not. Roy. Astron. Soc. Vol. 79. P. 319–332.
61. The origin of binary systems // Mon. Not. Roy. Astron. Soc. Vol. 79. P. 408–416.

1920

62. Discussion on the Theory of Relativity, J.H. Jeans and others. Proc. Roy. Soc., A. Vol. 97. P. 66–79.
63. The Dynamical Theory of Gases. 3rd ed. Cambridge: Cambridge Univ. Press. 442 pp.
64. The Mathematical Theory of Electricity and Magnetism. 4th ed. Cambridge: Cambridge Univ. Press. 627 pp.

1922

65. The motion of stars in a Kapteyn Universe // Mon. Not. Roy, Astron. Soc. Vol. 82. P. 122–132.
66. The dynamics of moving clusters // Mon. Not. Roy. Astron. Soc. Vol. 82. P. 132–139.
67. The origin of binary stars // Scientia, Janvier 1922. P. 11–22.

1923

68. The Nebular Hypothesis and Modern Cosmogony (Halley lecture, 23 May 1922). Oxford: Clarendon Press. 31 pp.
69. The radiation problem (8th Guthrie lecture) // Proc. Phys. Soc. Lond. Vol. 35. P. 222–224.
70. The physical significance of Van der Waals equation (Van der Waals memorial lecture) // J. Chem. Soc. Vol. 123. P. 3398–3414.
71. Theory of the scattering of α- and β-rays // Proc. Roy. Soc. London, A. Vol. 102. P. 437–453.
72. The propagation of earthquake waves.–Proc. Roy. Soc. London, A. Vol. 102. P. 554–574.
73. The motion of the stars // Scientia, Mars 1923, No. 3 P. 181–194.
74. On the tidal distortion of rotating nebulae // Mon. Not. Roy. Astron. Soc. Vol. 83. P. 453–458.
75. The mechanism and structure of planetary nebulae // Mon. Not. Roy. Astron. Soc. Vol. 83. P. 481–493. (Supplement 1923).
76. Internal motions in spiral nebulae // Mon. Not. Roy. Astron. Soc. Vol. 84. P. 60–76.
77. Cosmogony and stellar evolution. Smithsonian report for 1921. P. 153–164 (Publication 2677). Washington: Government printing office, 1923. [Lectures delivered at King's College, London, on May 3 and 10, 1921. Reprinted by permission from Nature, June 30 and July 7, 1921.]

1924

78. Cosmogonic problems associated with a secular decrease of mass // Mon. Not. Roy. Astron. Soc. Vol. 85. P. 2–11.
79. The Origin of the Solar System // Probleme der Astronomie, Festschrift für Hugo v. Seeliger. Berlin: Verlag von Julius Springer, 1924. P. 1–24.
80. The Origin of the Solar System // Royal Inst. of Gr. Br., Weekly Evening Meeting. Friday, February 15, 1924. P. 20.
81. Report on Radiation and the Quantum Theory. 2nd ed. The Physical Soc. of London: Fleetway Press, Ltd. 86 pp.
82. The Origin of the Solar System // Nature. Vol. 113. No. 2835. March. Supp. 329–340.

1925

83. Electric forces and quanta (16th Kelvin lecture) // Nature. Vol. 115. P. 361–368.
84. Electric forces and quanta (16th Kelvin lecture) // J. of Institution of Electrical Engineers Vol. 63. No. 341. May. P. 483–489.
85. On the masses, luminosities and surface temperatures of the stars // Mon. Not. Roy. Astron. Soc. Vol. 85. P. 196–211.
86. On the masses, luminosities and surface temperatures of the stars. Second paper // Mon. Not. Roy. Astron. Soc. Vol. 85. P. 394–403.

87. On the masses, luminosities and surface temperatures of the stars. Final note // Mon. Not. Roy. Astron. Soc. Vol. 85. P. 792–797.
88. On a theorem of von Zeipel on radiative equilibrium // Mon. Not. Roy. Astron. Soc. Vol. 85. P. 526–530. Supplement 1925. Vol. 85. P. 933–935.
89. Note on the distance and structure of the spiral nebulae // Mon. Not. Roy. Astron. Soc. Vol. 85. P. 531–534.
90. On Cepheid and long period variation and the formation of binary stars by fission // Mon. Not. Roy. Astron. Soc. Vol. 85. P. 797–813.
91. The effect of varying mass on a binary system // Mon. Not. Roy. Astron. Soc. Vol. 85. P. 912–914.
92. A theory of stellar evolution // Mon. Not. Roy. Astron. Soc. Vol. 85. P. 914–933.
93. The Origin of the Solar System. Smithsonian report for 1924. P. 139–159. (Publication 2796). Washington: Government printing office, 1925.
94. The New Outlook in Cosmogony // The Nineteenth Century and After. Vol. 98 (Dec. 1925). P. 813–822.
95. The Dynamical Theory of Gases. 4th ed. Cambridge: Cambridge Univ. Press. 444 pp.
96. The Mathematical Theory of Electricity and Magnetism. 5th ed. Cambridge: Cambridge Univ. Press. 652 pp.

1926

97. Atomicity and Quanta (Rouse Ball lecture, 1925). Cambridge: Cambridge Univ. Press. 64 pp.
98. The radiation from a pulsating star and from a star in process of fission // Mon. Not. Roy. Astron. Soc. Vol. 86. P. 85–93.
99. On radiative viscosity and the rotation of astronomical masses // Mon. Not. Roy. Astron. Soc. Vol. 86. P. 328–335. 2nd paper: 444–458.
100. Stellar opacity and the atomic weight of stellar matter // Mon. Not. Roy. Astron. Soc. Vol. 86. P. 561–574.
101. The exact equation of radiative equilibrium // Mon. Not. Roy. Astron. Soc. Vol. 86. P. 574–578.
102. Note on the internal densities and temperatures of the stars // Mon. Not. Roy. Astron. Soc. Vol. 87. P. 36–43.
103. The President's address on presenting the Gold Medal of the Society to Professor Albert Einstein, for his researches on Relativity and the Theory of Gravitation // MNRAS. Vol. 86. No. 4. P. 262–269.
104. Recent Development of Cosmical Physics // Supplement to Nature. No. 2979 (Dec. 4, 1926). P. 29–40.

1927

105. On liquid stars and the liberation of stellar energy // Mon. Not. Roy. Astron. Soc. Vol. 87. P. 400–414.
106. On liquid stars — configurations of stability, long-period variables and stellar evolution // Mon. Not. Roy. Astron. Soc. Vol. 84. P. 720–739. (Supplement 1927).
107. The genesis of the great nebulae // Nature. February 26, 1927.
108. The survey of the stars // Nature. March 12, 1927. (Address on Feb. 11, referring to the award of the Gold Medal of the Society to Prof. Frank Schlesinger for his work on stellar parallax and astronomical photography).
109. Isaac Newton // Nature. March 26, 1927. (Opening address delivered on March 19, in the Old School, King's School, Grantham, at the commemoration of the two-hundredth anniversary of the death of Sir Isaac Newton).

110. The Birth of the World // Harmsworth's Universal History of the World / Ed. by Sir J.A. Hammerton. Vol. 1. London: The Amalgamated Press Ltd.

1928

111. Astronomy and Cosmogony. Cambridge: Cambridge Univ. Press. 420 pp.
112. The wider aspects of cosmogony // Nature. Vol. 121. No. 3047. Supplement. P. 463–470.
113. The wider aspects of cosmogony // J. of the Royal Soc. of Arts. Proceedings of the Society. (15-th ordinary meeting. Trueman Wood lecture, March, 1928) — Discussion, April 27, 1928. Vol. 76. P. 611–626.
114. The physics of the universe (H.H. Wills memorial lecture. Bristol) // Nature. Vol. 122. No. 3079. Supplement. P. 689–700.
115. Liquid stars — a correction // Mon. Not. Roy. Astron. Soc. Vol. 88. P. 393–395.
116. Liquid stars // Nature. Feb. 4, 1928.
117. Recent developments of cosmical physics. The Smithsonian report for 1927. P. 167–189. (Publication 2929). US Gov. Pr. of Wash.: 1928.

1929

118. The Universe Around Us. New York: Macmillan; Cambridge: Cambridge Univ. Press. 352 pp.
119. The wider aspects of cosmogony. The Smithsonian report for 1928. P. 165–178 (Publication 2982). US Gov. Pr. of Wash.: 1929.
120. Astronomy and Cosmogony. 2nd ed. Cambridge: Cambridge Univ. Press. 428 pp.

1930

121. Eos, or the Wider Aspects of Cosmogony. London: Kegan Paul. 88 p.
122. The Mysterious Universe. (Rede lecture, 1930). Cambridge: Cambridge Univ. Press. 154 pp.
123. The physics of the universe. The Smithsonian report for 1929. P. 161–181. (Publication 3035). Smithsonian institution, Washington: 1930.
124. Point of view // More Points of View / Ed. G. Lowes Dickinson. London: George Allen and Unwin Ltd. P. 53–71.
125. The Universe Around Us. 2nd ed. Cambridge: Cambridge Univ. Press. 363 pp.

1931

126. The Stars in their Courses. Cambridge: Cambridge Univ. Press; New York: Macmillan. 200 pp.
127. The annihilation of matter // Nature. Vol. 128. No. 3220 (Supplement). P. 103–110.
128. Beyond the Milky Way // Nature. Vol. 128. No. 3237 (Supplement). P. 825–832.
129. The origin of the solar system // J. Franklin Inst. Vol. 212 (August, 1931). P. 135–145.
130. The origin of the solar system // Nature. Vol. 128. Sept. 12, 1931. P. 432–435.
131. The evolution of the universe // Nature. Oct. 24, 1931.
132. An Evolving Universe // Carnegie Institution of Washington, News service bulletin. School edition. Vol. II. No. 23, 24. P. 153–160.
133. Man and the Stars, or the Wider Aspects of Cosmogony. New York: Dutton. 88 pp.

1932

134. What is radiation? (14th Silvanus Thompson memorial lecture, December 2, 1931) // Brit. J. Radiology. Vol. V, New Series, No. 49. P. 21–37.
135. An Evolving Universe. The Smithsonian report for 1931. P. 229–238 (Publication 3146). Smithsonian institution, Washington, 1932.

1933

136. The New Background of Science. Cambridge: Cambridge Univ. Press. 303 pp.
137. The Expansion of the Universe. Birmingham and Midland Institute. 21 pp.
138. The Universe Around Us. 3rd ed. Cambridge: Cambridge Univ. Press. 380 pp.

1934

139. Through Space and Time. Cambridge: Cambridge Univ. Press. 224 pp.
140. The New World-Picture of Modern Physics. The Presidential Address. British Association for the Advancement of Science. Aberdeen, 1934. 18 pp.
141. The New Background of Science. 2nd ed. Cambridge: Cambridge Univ. Press. 326 pp.

1935

142. The New World-picture of Modern Physics. The Smithsonian report for 1934. P. 81–98 (Publication 3306). Smithsonian institution, Washington, 1935.
143. The size and age of the universe. Royal Institution of Great Britain, Weekly evening meeting, Friday, November 29, 1935. 24 pp.

1936

144. The size and age of the universe // Not. Proc. Roy. Instn. Vol. 29. No. 1. P. 65–86.
145. The size and age of the universe // Nature Vol. 137. No. 3453 (Supplement). P. 17–24.
146. Some problems of present-day astronomy (lecture — April 1936). Vienna.
147. Gegenwartsprobleme der Astronomie. Achtzehnter Gastvortrag, gehalten am 29. April 1936, Wien, Komitee zur Veranstaltung von Gastvorträgen ausländischer Gelehrten der exakten Wissenschaften // Monatshefte für Mathematik und Physik. Vol. 45. No. 1. P. 105–119.
148. The World: Whence and How? // Encyclopedia of Modern Knowledge / Ed. by Sir J.A. Hammerton. London : Amalgamated Press. P. 3–14.
149. Man and the Universe (Sir Halley Steward Lecture, 1935) // Scientific Progress. London: George Allen and Unwin. P. 13–38.

1937

150. Science and Music. Cambridge: Cambridge Univ. Press; New York, Macmillan. 258 pp.
151. Point of view // Living Philosophies / Albert Einstein, John Dewey, Sir James Jeans et al. New York: Simeon and Shuster. P. 107–119.

1938

152. The Depths of Space. The Lorimer lecture. Publication of the Astronomical Society of Edinburgh. No. 1, 1938. 22 pp.

1939

153. The Expanding Universe and the origin of the Great Nebulae // Nature. Jan. 28, 1939.

1940

154. An Introduction to the Kinetic Theory of Gases. Cambridge: Cambridge Univ. Press; New York: Macmillan. 311 pp.

1941

155. The Philosophy of Physical Science // Nature. August 2, 1941. Vol. 148. P. 140.
156. The Physical Condition of the Planets. Roy. Inst. of Gr. Br., Special Afternoon Lecture, March 25, 1941 // Proc. Roy. Inst. Vol. 31. Part II. 23 pp.

1942

157. Physics and Philosophy. Cambridge: Cambridge Univ. Press. 222 pp.

1943

158. The evolution of the solar system // Endeavour. Vol. 2. No. 5. 9 pp.
159. Astronomical problems of to-day [Abstract] // Royal Institution of Great Britain. Weekly evening meeting, Friday, March 26, 1943. 7 pp.
160. Is there life on the other Worlds? Smithsonian report for 1942. P. 145–150. US Gov. Pr., Washington.
161. Newton and the science of to-day // Proc. Roy. Soc. of London, A. Vol. 181. P. 251–262.
162. The New Physics and Metaphysical Materialism: Symposium with L.S. Stebbing, R.B. Braithwaite and E.T. Whittaker. Joint Meeting of the Institute of Physics, the Mind Association, and the Aristotelian Society, on May 19, 1943 // Proceedings of the Aristotelian Society. Vol. 43. P. 185–202.

1944

163. The Universe Around Us. 4th ed. rev. and reset. Cambridge: Cambridge Univ. Press; New York: Macmillan. 297 pp.

1945

164. The astronomical horizon. (The Philip Maurice Deneke lecture, 1944). Oxford: Oxford University Press. 23 pp.

1947

165. The Growth of Physical Science. Cambridge: Cambridge Univ. Press. 864 pp.

WORKS OF JEANS PUBLISHED IN RUSSIAN

166. Гипотеза Лапласа и современное учение о происхождении мира. (The Nebular Hypothesis and Modern Cosmogony) // Новейшее учение о происхождении мира. М.: Гостехтеориздат, 1923. С. 40–50.
167. Происхождение Солнечной системы. (The Origin of the Solar System) // Успехи физических наук. 1924. Т. 4. С. 217–239.
168. Современное развитие космической физики. (Recent Development of Cosmical Physics) // Новейшие течения научной мысли. 5 / Пер. с англ. С.И. Вавилова. М.: Гостехтеориздат, 1928. С. 7–46.
169. Физика Вселенной (The Physics of the Universe) // Под знаменем марксизма. 1929. № 1. С. 163–178.

170. Вселенная вокруг нас. (The Universe Around Us) / Пер. с англ. Н.И. Идельсона. М.: Гостехтеориздат, 1932. 403 с.
171. Происхождение Солнечной системы. (The Origin of the Solar System) // Мироведение. 1932. Т. 21. № 1–2. С. 50–57.
172. Движение миров. (The Stars in their Courses) / Пер. с англ. под ред. проф. А.А. Михайлова. М.: Гостехтеориздат, 1933. 183 с.
173. Астрономическая картина мира. (Astronomy and Cosmogony, selected chapters) // Основные проблемы космической физики / Под ред. М.П. Бронштейна. Харьков; Киев: Гос. науч.-техн. изд-во Украины, 1934. С. 9–33.
174. Джинс Дж., Эддингтон А., Милн Е. Дискуссия о возрасте Вселенной. (A Discussion on the Age of the Universe, with A. Eddington and E. Milne) // Мироведение. 1935. Т. 24. № 5. С. 295–300.
175. Движение миров. (The Stars in their Courses). М.: Детгиз, 1937. 152 с.

LITERATURE ABOUT J. JEANS

176. Бронштейн М.П. Джеймс Джинс // Творцы науки о звездах. Л.: Красная газ., 1930. С. 75–88.
177. Еремеева А.И. Выдающиеся астрономы мира. Рекомендательный указатель. М.: Книга, 1966. 382 с.
178. Колчинский И.Г., Корсунь А.А., Родригес М.Г. Астрономы: Биографический справочник. Киев: Наук. думка, 1977. С. 89–91.
179. Храмов Ю.А. Физики: биогр. справ. Киев: Наук. думка, 1977. С. 124–125.
180. Chapman, S. Jeans, Sir James Hopwood // Dictionary of National Biography, 1941–1950 / Ed. by L. G. Wickham Legg and E. T. Williams. Oxford: Oxford University Press, 1959. P. 430–432.
181. Commemoration of the birth centenary of Sir James Jeans // Quart. J. Boy. Astron. Soc., 1978. Vol. 19. P. 158–159.
182. Hudson, R. James Jeans and Radiative Theory // J. Studies in history and philosophy of science. 1989, March. Vol. 20. No. 1. P. 57–76.
183. Growther, I.G. British Scientists of the Twentieth Century. London: Routledge & Kegan Paul, 1952. P. 93–139.
184. McCrea, W.H. The Writing and Cosmology of Sir James Jeans // Irish Astron. J. 1956. Vol. 4. No. 1. P. 23–28.
185. McCrea, W.H. Jeans centenary talk (Sir James Hopwood Jeans, OM, FRS, 1877–1946) // Quart. J. Roy. Astron. Soc. 1978. Vol. 19. P. 160–166.
186. McCrea, W.H. Sir James Hopwood Jeans (Pioneer of Modern Astrophysics) // Phys. Bull. 1978. Vol. 29. P. 257–259.
187. Milne, E.A. Sir James Jeans, O.M., F.R.S. // Nature. October 19, 1946. Vol. 158. P. 542–546.
188. Milne, E.A. Obituary. James Hopwood Jeans // Journal of the London Mathematical Society. 1946. Vol. 21. P. 310–320.
189. Milne, E.A. Sir James Jeans, O.M., F.R.S. // Cambridge Review — 1, 2.
190. Milne, E.A. Sir James Jeans // Obituary Notices of Fellows of the Royal Society. Vol. 5. March 1947. P. 572–589.
191. Milne, E.A. Sir James Hopwood Jeans. Obituary Notice // Monthly Notices of the Royal Astronomical Society. 1947. Vol. 107. No. 1. P. 46–53.
192. Milne, E.A. Obituary Notice: Sir James Jeans, O.M., F.R.S. // Proceedings of the Physical Society. 1947. Vol. 59. P. 503–506.

193. Milne, E.A. Sir James Jeans: A Biography. Cambridge: Cambridge University Press, 1952. 176 pp.
194. Oldham, G. Sir James Jeans, OM, FRS. Centenary concert — New Quartet specially composed // Quart. J. Roy. Astron. Soc. 1978. Vol. 19. P. 175–176.
195. Rees, M. Jeans centenary (Lecture). London, 1977.
196. Sir James Jeans, "Publicity Agent for the Stars", goes to a banquet // Picture Post, Feb. 18, 1939.
197. Smith, R.W. Sir James Hopwood Jeans, 1877–1946 // J. Brit. Astron. Assoc. 1977. Vol. 88. No. 1. P. 8–18.
198. Stebbing, L.S. The Parables of Sir James Jeans. Adult Education // The Quarterly Journal of the British Institute of Adult Education. 1934. Vol. VII. No. 2. P. 100–108.
199. Wilson, D.B. On the Importance of Eliminating Science and Religion from the History of Science and Religion: The Cases of J.H. Jeans and A.S. Eddington // Bulletin of A.A.S. 1993. Vol. 25. No. 3. P. 1243.
200. Woodruff, A.E. James Jeans // Dictionary of scientific biography. 1973. Vol. 5. P. 84–86.

LITERATURE BY OTHER AUTHORS

201. Антонов В.А., Фридман А.М. Равновесие и устойчивость гравитирующих систем. М.: ВИНИТИ, 1975. Т. 10. 160 с. (Итоги науки и техники. Сер. Астрономия).
202. Белые карлики / Под ред. В.С. Имшенника. М.: Мир, 1975. 256 с.
203. Бесконечность и Вселенная / Под ред. В. В. Казютинского и др. М.: Мысль, 1969.
204. Беркли Дж. Сочинения. М.: Мысль, 1978. 556 с.
205. Биографии великих химиков / Под ред. К. Хейнинга. М.: Мир, 1981. 388 с.
206. Блинников С.И. К вопросу о законе вращения политропных конфигураций // Астрон. журн. 1972. Т. 49. Вып. 3. С. 654–657.
207. Вайнберг С. Идейные основы единой теории слабых и электромагнитных взаимодействий // Успехи физ. наук. 1980. Т. 132. Вып. 2. С. 201–217.
208. Вигнер Е. Этюды о симметрии. М.: Мир, 1971. 318 с.
209. Витязев А.В., Козенко А.В. Происхождение Солнечной системы // Земля и Вселенная. 1988. № 2. с. 25–32.
210. Гейзенберг В. Физика и философия. М.: Изд-во иностр. лит., 1963. 203 с.
211. Гинзбург В.Л. Современная астрофизика. М.: Наука, 1970. 192 с.
212. Гинзбург В.Л. О физике и астрофизике. М.: Наука, 1974. 120 с.
213. Гинзбург В.Л. Замечание о методологии и развитии физики и астрономии // Вопр. философии. 1980. № 12. С. 24–26.
214. Голсуорси Дж. Собр. соч. в 16 т. М., 1962. Т. 2.
215. Голсуорси Дж. Собр. соч. в 16 т. М., 1962. Т. 3.
216. Горбацкий В.Г. Космическая газодинамика. М.: Наука, 1977. 360 с.
217. Дарвин Дж.Г. Приливы и родственные им явления в Солнечной системе. М.: Наука. 1965. 2-е изд. 252 с.
218. Дибай Э.А., Каплан С.А. Размерности и подобие астрофизических величин. М.: Наука, 1976. 399 с.
219. Дубинин Н.П. Диалектика происхождения жизни и происхождения человека // Вопр. философии. 1979. № 11. С. 32.

220. Жарков В.Н., Паньков В.А., Калачников А.А., Оснач А.И. Введение в физику Луны. М.: Наука, 1969. 312 с.
221. Зельдович Я.Б. Рождение закрытой Вселенной и антропогенный принцип // Письма в "Астрон. журн.". 1981. Т. 7. № 10. С. 579–581.
222. Зельдович Я.Б., Блинников С.И., Шакура Н. Я. Физические основы строения и эволюции звезд. М.: Изд-во МГУ, 1981. 159 с.
223. Зельдович Я.Б., Новиков И.Д. Строение и эволюция Вселенной. М.: Наука, 1975. 736 с.
224. Зельдович Я.Б., Новиков И.Д. Физика и космология // Астрономия. Методология. Мировоззрение. М.: Наука, 1979. С. 121–136.
225. Идлис Г.М. Основные черты наблюдаемой астрономической Вселенной как характерные свойства обитаемой космической системы // Изв. Астрофиз. Ин-та КазССР. 1958. Т. 7. С. 38–54.
226. История XIX века / Под ред. Лависса и Рамбо. Т. 7. М., 1939.
227. Казютинский В.В. Вселенная, астрономия, философия. М.: Знание, 1972. 64 с.
228. Козенко А.В. Гравитационное поле политропы единичного индекса со слабодифференциальным вращением // Астрон. журн. 1975. Т. 52. С. 887–890.
229. Козенко А.В. Джеймс Хопвуд Джинс. М.: Наука, 1985. 145 с.
230. Козенко А.В. О периодизации истории астрофизики // Вопр. истории естествознания и техники. 1993. № 3. С. 100.
231. Козенко А.В. Артур Стенли Эддингтон. М.: Наука. 1997. 145 с.
232. Козенко А.В. Философия науки Артура Эддингтона // Вопросы философии. 1997. № 9. С. 118–126.
233. Козенко А.В. Гарольд Джеффрис. М.: Наука. 2008. 248 с.
234. Козенко А.В., Потапова Л.В. 250 лет теории фигуры Земли: Периодизация развития теории фигуры сжимаемой гравитирующей медленновращающейся жидкости // На рубежах познания Вселенной. М.: ТОО "Янус", 1994. С. 13–31. (Ист.-астрон. исслед. XXIV).
235. Конт О. Курс положительной философии. СПб., 1899. 302 с.
236. Крат В.А. Фигуры равновесия небесных тел. М.: Гостехтеориздат, 1950. 239 с.
237. Кузнецов Б.Г. История философии для физиков и математиков. М.: Наука, 1974, с. 233.
238. Лаплас П. Изложение системы мира. СПб., 1861.
239. Левин Б.Ю. Происхождение Земли и планет. М.: Физматгиз, 1959. 84 с.
240. Лекторский В.А. От позитивизма к неопозитивизму // Буржуазная философия XX века. М.: Политиздат, 1974. С. 336.
241. Лившиц Е.М. О гравитационной неустойчивости расширяющегося мира // ЖЭТФ. 1946. Т. 16. С. 587–597.
242. Литтлвуд Дж. Математическая смесь. М.: Наука, 1978. 143 с.
243. Лоренц Г.А. Старые и новые проблемы физики. М.: Наука, 1970. 278 с.
244. Планк М., 1858–1958 / Под ред. А.Ф. Иоффе, А.Т. Григорьяна. М.: Изд–во АН СССР, 1958. 278 с.
245. Мах Э. Механика // В кн.: Альберт Эйнштейн и теория гравитации. М.: Мир, 1979. С. 49–72.
246. Нильс Бор. Жизнь и творчество / Под ред. Б.Г. Кузнецова. М.: Наука, 1967. 344 с.
247. Парийский Н.Н. Новые попытки объяснения происхождения Солнечной системы // Астрон. журн. 1939. Т. 16, Вып. 1. С. 77–83.

248. Парийский Н. Н. К вопросу о происхождении Солнечной системы // Астрон, журн. 1943. Т. 20. Вып. 2. С. 9–28.
249. Пиппард А.Б. Традиции Кавендиша // Образованный ученый. М.: Наука, 1979. 160 с.
250. Поляченко В.Л., Фридман А.М. Колебания и неустойчивости многокомпонентной гравитирующей среды // ЖЭТФ. 1981. Т. 81. С. 13–21.
251. Проблемы современной космогонии / Под ред. В.А. Амбарцумяна. М.: Наука, 1972. 450 с.
252. Проблема СЕТI / Под ред. С.А. Каплана. М.: Мир, 1975. 315 с.
253. Происхождение и эволюция галактик и звезд / Под ред. С.Б. Пикельнера. М.: Наука, 1976. 408 с.
254. Происхождение и эволюция звезд / Под ред. А.Г. Масевич. М.: Изд-во иностр. лит., 1962. 366 с.
255. Промышленность и техника. СПб., 1904. Т. 3. Электричество. 644 с.
256. Пуанкаре А. Избранные труды. М.: Наука, 1974. Т. 3. 771 с.
257. Резерфорд — ученый и учитель / Под ред. П.Л. Капицы. М.: Наука, 1973. 216 с.
258. Рейн Н.Ф. Методический анализ космогонической теории Джинса. Происхождение Солнечной системы // Тр. ГАИШ. 1936. Т. 7. Вып. 2. С. 5–67.
259. Рейн Н.Ф., Парийский Н.Н. Катастрофические гипотезы происхождения Солнечной системы // Успехи астрон. наук. 1941. Т. 2. С. 137–156.
260. Реклю Э. Британские острова. СПб., 1899. 424 с.
261. Рессел Г.Н. Солнечная система и ее происхождение. М.: ОГИЗ, 1944. 104 с.
262. Родоначальники позитивизма. Спб., 1912. Вып. 4. 139 с.
263. Рожанский И.Д. Античная наука. М.: Наука, 1980. 199 с.
264. Сноу Ч.П. Две культуры. М.: Прогресс, 1973. 142 с.
265. Степин В.С. Эволюционный стиль мышления в современной астрофизике // Астрономия. Методология. Мировоззрение. М.: Наука, 1979. С. 107–120.
266. Строение звездных систем / Под ред. П.Н. Холопова. М.: Изд-во иностр. лит., 1962. 664 с.
267. Сытинская Н.Н. Современная наука о происхождении Солнечной системы. М.: Изд-во АПН РСФСР, 1956. 95 с.
268. Тассуль Ж.-Л. Теория вращающихся звезд. М.: Мир. 1982. 472 с.
269. Тимирязев А.К. Жизнь и труды Дж.Дж. Томсона (1856–1940) // Успехи химии. 1941. Т. 10. № 1. С. 109–110.
270. Толмен Р. Относительность, термодинамика, космология. М.: Наука, 1974. 520 с.
271. Торосян В.Г. Теория и реальность в астрофизике. Автореф. дис. ... канд. филос. наук. М., 1977. 24 с.
272. Тревельян Дж.М. История Англии от Чосера до королевы Виктории. Смоленск: "Русич", 2002. 620 с.
273. Тугушува М.П. Джон Голсуорси. М.: Терра, 2000. 384 с.
274. Уайтхед А.Н. Избранные работы по философии. М.: Прогресс, 1990.
275. Уилсон М. Встреча на далеком меридиане. М.: Изд-во иностр. лит., 1961. 430 с.
276. Уитни Ч. Открытие нашей Галактики. М.: Мир, 1975. 237 с.
277. Фейнман Р. Характер физических законов. М.: Мир, 1968. 232 с.
278. Цвейг С. Вчерашний мир (воспоминания европейца) М.: Вагриус, 2004. 348 с. С.18–19.
279. Чандрасекхар С. Эллипсоидальные фигуры равновесия. М.: Мир, 1973, 288 с.
280. Шепли Х. Звезды и люди. М.: Изд-во иностр. лит., 1962. 152 с.

281. Ширвиндт Н. Предисловие // Дж. Джинс. Вселенная, вокруг нас. М.; Л., 1932. С. 5–10.
282. Шкловский И.С. Звезды, их рождение, жизнь и смерть. М.: Наука. 1975. 367 с.
283. Шкловский И.С. О возможной уникальности разумной жизни во Вселенной // Астрономия. Методология. Мировоззрение. М.: Наука, 1979. С. 252–274.
284. Шмидт О.Ю. Происхождение Земли и планет. М.: Изд-во АН СССР, 1962. 131 с.
285. Шредингер Э. Что такое жизнь? С точки зрения физика. М.: Атомиздат, 1972. 88 с.
286. Эйнштейн А. Собрание научных трудов: В 4-х т. Т.3. М.: Наука, 1966. 632 с.
287. Эйнштейн А. Собрание научных трудов: В 4-х т. Т. 4. М.: Наука, 1967. 599 с.
288. Эйнштейновский сборник, 1971. М.; Наука, 1972. 398 с.
289. Энциклопедический словарь. 7-е издание Русского библиографического института "Гранат". М., 1910–. Т. 12.
290. Babinet, M. Compte rendu // Comptes rendus des séances de l'Académie des sciences. (Paris). 1861. Vol. 52. P. 481.
291. Bingham, A.M. The Tiffany Fortune, and Other Chronicles of a Connecticut Family. Chestnut Hill, Massachusetts: Abed and Left Publishers, 1996. 420 pp.
292. Blaauw, A. History of IAU: The Birth and First Half-Century of the International Astronomical Union. Dordrecht: Kluver Acad. Publ., 1994.
293. Brush, S.G. From Bump to Clump: Theories of the Origin of the Solar System 1900–1960 // Space science comes of age: Perspectives in the history of the space sciences; Proceedings of the Symposium, Washington, DC, March 23, 24, 1981. Washington, DC, Smithsonian Institution Press, 1981. P. 78–100.
294. Brush, S.G. Poincaré and cosmic evolution // Physics today, March, 1980. 8 p.
295. Buffon, J.L. Histoire naturelle. Paris, 1749. 151 p.
296. Chamberlin, Th.C. Fundamental problems in geology // Yearbook No. 4. Carnegie Inst. of Techn. Pittsburg, 1905. P. 195–258.
297. Chandrasekhar, S. James Jeans // Science. Vol. 105. No. 2722. February 28, 1947. P. 224–226.
298. Dormand, J.R., Woolfson, M.M. The Origin of the Solar System: The Capture Theory. Chichester: Ellis Horwood, 1989.
299. Droysen, I.G. Historik. München, 1943. 362 S.
300. Eddington, A.S. The Internal Constitutional of the Stars. Cambridge: Cambridge Univ. Press, 1926.
301. Eddington, A.S. The Nature of the Physical World. Cambridge: Cambridge Univ. Press, 1928.
302. Eddington, A.S. The Philosophy of Physical Science. Cambridge: Cambridge Univ. Press, 1939.
303. Hanson, N.R. Patterns of discovery. Cambridge: Cambridge Univ. Press, 1958. 122 pp.
304. Harrison, R. Sidney and Beatrice Webb // Socialism and Intelligentsia 1880–1914 / Ed. by C. Levy. London: Routledge, 1982.
305. Hutchings G.E. The book of Box Hill. Dorking, Surrey, 1952. 48 pp.
306. James, R.A. The structure and stability of rotating gas masses // Astrophys. J. 1964. Vol. 140. P. 552–582.
307. Jeans, C.M. "Driftweed" and Later Poems. Cambridge: Cambridge Univ. Press, 1935. 132 pp.
308. Jeans, S. Lady Jeans Writes of Two Instruments in Cleveland Lodge // The Diapason, March 1, 1958.

309. Jeans, W.T. Creators of the age of steel. London: Chapman and Hall, 1884. 348 pp.
310. Jeans, W.T. Lives of the Electricians. London: Whitaker and Co, 1887. 327 pp.
311. Jardetsky, J. Theories of Figures of Celestial Bodies. London: Interscience, 1958. 221 pp.
312. Jeffreys, H. The Earth. Cambridge: Cambridge Univ. Press, 1929. 480 p.
313. Low, C., Lynden-Bell D. The minimum Jeans mass or when fragmentation must stop // Mon. Not. Roy. Astron. Soc. 1976. Vol. 176. P. 367–390.
314. Lyttleton, R.A. The theoretical basis of the fission theory of binary stars // Trans. Intern. Astron. Union. 1952. Vol. 8. P. 717–721.
315. Lyttleton, R.A. The Stability of Rotating Liquid Masses. Cambridge: Cambridge Univ. Press, 1953. 311 p.
316. Mulhern, F. "Teachers, Writers, Celebrities": Intelligentsias and Their Histories // New Left Review. 1981. No. 126
317. Morrot, H.V. The life and letters of John Galsworthy. London: William Heinemann Ltd, 1935. 750 pp.
318. Moulton, F.R. On the Evolution of the Solar system // Astrophys. J. 1905. Vol. 12. P. 165–181.
319. News Chronicle, 6 Sept. 1934.
320. The Passing Show, October 1933.
321. Rayleigh, J., Lord. Remarks upon the Law of Complete Radiation // Phil. Mag. 1900. Vol. 49. P. 539–540.
322. Roach, J. Victorian Universities and the National Intelligentsia // Victorian Studies. December 1959. Vol. 3. P. 131–150.
323. Thomson, H. The Choice of a Profession. London: Chapman and Hall, 1857.
324. Todhunter, I. A History of the Mathematical Theories of Attraction and the Figure of the Earth. London: Macmillan and Co, 1873. 381 pp.
325. Wasiutinski, J. Studies in Hydrodynamics and Structure of Stars and Planets. Oslo: Dybwad, 1946. 277 p.
326. Webb, B. My Apprenticeship. London: Longmans, Green, 1926.
327. Woolfson, M.M. Origin of the Solar System // Nature. 1960. Vol. 187. P. 47–48.
328. Woolfson, M.M. A Capture Theory of the Origin of the Solar System // Proc. Roy. Soc. London, A. 1964. Vol. 282. P. 485–507.
329. Zarkov (Zharkov), V.N. Struttura interna della Terra e dei pianeti. Editori Riuniti — Edizioni Mir, 1986. 405 pp.
330. Zharkov V.N., Leontjev V.V., Kozenko A.V. Models, figures, and gravitational moments of the Galilean satellites of Jupiter and icy satellites of Saturn // Icarus. 1985. Vol. 61. P. 92–100.